Books by Beth Brown

THE THAT'S THAT STORY
MINNIE, THE TIRED TROLLEY CAR
BLINKIE
LITTLE GIRL BLUE

Compiled by Beth Brown

THE WONDERFUL WORLD OF DOGS
THE WONDERFUL WORLD OF CATS

THE WONDERFUL WORLD
OF Horses

Compiled by

BETH BROWN

THE WONDERFUL WORLD
OF Horses

SC
B
C.1

Pictures by

LEONARD SHORTALL

HARPER & ROW, PUBLISHERS

New York, Evanston, and London

Grateful acknowledgment is made to the following for permission to reprint selections included in this book:

"Copper" by Beth Brown; copyright © 1963 by Beth Brown.

"A Miserable, Merry Christmas" from *Boy on Horseback* by Lincoln Steffens; copyright 1931, 1935 by Harcourt, Brace & World, Inc.; copyright © 1959 by Peter Steffens; reprinted by permission of the publishers.

"Stable Call" by Cornelia Meigs from *Young Americans*, published by Ginn and Company; reprinted by permission of the publishers.

"The Widow's Son" from *Fairy Tales* retold by Katharine Gibson; copyright 1940 by Whitman Publishing Company; reprinted by permission of the publishers.

"A Touch of Arab" by Vivian Breckenfeld from *American Girl*; reprinted by permission of the author and *American Girl*, a magazine for all girls published by the Girl Scouts of the U.S.A.

"The Birth of Jumper" reprinted with the permission of Charles Scribner's Sons from *Jumper*, pages 5-14, by Nicholas Kalashnikoff; copyright 1944 Charles Scribner's Sons.

"The Mudhen, V.S." by Merrit P. Allen from *Boys' Life*; reprinted by permission of Miss Vera Cline and *Boys' Life*, published by the Boy Scouts of America.

"Pony Penning Day" from *Misty of Chincoteague* by Marguerite Henry; copyright 1947 by Rand McNally & Company.

"The Pacing Mustang" is reprinted with the permission of Charles Scribner's Sons from *Wild Animals I Have Known* by Ernest Thompson Seton.

"The Kind Caliph and the Horse Thief" from *Wonder Tales of Horses and Heroes* by Frances Carpenter; copyright 1952 by Frances Carpenter Huntington; reprinted by permission of Doubleday & Company, Inc.

"First Day Finish" copyright 1944 by Jessamyn West; reprinted from her volume, *The Friendly Persuasion*, by permission of Harcourt, Brace & World, Inc.

To R. H., my editor,
for wisdom at the helm

Contents

ix

Beth Brown

Copper

HE REACHED THE pasture bars at last.

In a moment he would be going in. He would be going on. He would be riding into the Elysian fields which lay beyond.

But for some strange reason the way was barred. The gate was locked. There was no one here—not even the kindly old keeper who always tended it.

Copper whinnied. Nobody came. He neighed. Only his echo answered. He switched his tail. The bell on his junk cart sounded in the night, and then all was silent again.

The fog rolled toward him in billows. He grew

1

uneasy. Where was the old gatekeeper who had opened the gate before for his flying mane and his thundering hoofs and the burst of joy in his heart?

Then he remembered the promise.

Johnny had promised to be along, and Copper had promised to wait. But time was running out like a river. Only three minutes were left, three short minutes of life. These were given to both human and animal—three minutes of grace here at the boundary between the two worlds to look back upon the past before going on, or going back again.

If only Johnny would hurry.

Copper drew a deep breath. The swift regression began. His body dropped the solidity of its heavy old coat and its weary old bones. He stepped from the shafts of the junk cart. Once more he was young again.

Now impression followed impression as his memory gave up its storehouse. He saw his life from beginning to end—and the reason he was waiting for Johnny. Time swung him in a giant arc to a day on the ranch with its abounding freedom.

There it was again, just as he had seen it when he had first come into being—that great sweep of cerulean blue canopy high above the shimmering green pasture lands.

It all came back in a swift flood of images—the color of the great wide world into which he had been tossed, a small brown, helpless heap. He heard his feeble whinny. He felt his mother nosing him softly. He tried to stand. His awkward forelegs crumpled under him. He lay with the earth beside him and then fought free

2

of its embrace. Life called him to rise, to run, to revel.

Now there was a new sound. Human voices came to him.

"Should I give him a hand?"

"No. Leave him alone."

"Just look at him, will you? He's fighting to win."

"Yeah. And he's making it this time."

The newborn stood there, wobbling uncertainly. But he stood there just the same, regarding the two men who were surveying the odd picture he made. His brown skin lay in folds like those of an old man whose flesh was gone. His legs were long and ungainly. His bulging joints were gnarled like the knobs of an ancient oak tree. His feet were small, much too small for his frame.

One of the men was saying, "He'll fill out. You won't know him. After all, he's only twenty minutes old—"

"Look! Two teeth!"

The tall man seemed the expert. "Ten hands," he reported. "Thirty-two inches heart girth—" The voice droned on and on.

These men seemed strange to him and would always be strangers. But off in the distance he heard a cry. The sound of that voice stirred the sharp fires of memory. He knew that voice. It had called to him long before this sunny morning between the clear blue sky and the sweet green fragrance.

"He's here, isn't he?"

"Yes, Johnny. He's here!"

"Hurry up!" said one of the men.

"I'm coming as fast as I can—"

But it wasn't very fast. That much the horse could see as he watched the twisted approach of the small, crooked body. He heard the uncertain step made by the hobble of a flagging foot. Then he felt the touch of a hand, soft, cool, strong. The glowing face was coming closer. Now Copper was looking into a pair of eyes like pieces of vivid, unexpected blue sky. The eyes were regarding him with boyish wonder and warmth.

"I knew he'd be here! All the way in from town I told myself he'd be waiting for me!"

"How do you like him, Johnny?" the tall man said.

"Isn't he the most beautiful golden copper you ever saw?" bragged the short one.

"Copper," echoed Johnny softly. "He was black before —a midnight black—"

"What are you talking about?"

"Black—with a white blaze between his eyes. . . ."

"Crazy kid, that son of mine. That's what comes of having been born with a caul."

Johnny was saying, "He was a mustang then and I was the son of an Indian chief. We used to ride the hills together, didn't we?"

And then the horse remembered it too. He knew he had belonged to the boy a hundred years ago. And hundreds of years before that, they had shared the adventure of chase. A boy of dark skin was in the saddle then, his dark hair crowned by a white turban. They were riding to the wars on hoofs that were swift as lightning. It was said the Creator had taken a handful of south

5

wind and given each newborn Arabian the power of flight without wings. In those days of great horses and great horsemen the Mongol, the Hun, and the Turk had conquered China, India, and Europe. Genghis Khan became master of the world, but then Genghis Khan had a master too. His horse of fire and thunder was his exalted ruler.

Copper sighed. The past vanished. The picture faded. For a fleeting instant he felt the aching weight of the junk cart like a nudge reminding him of the chains that still bound him to life. Then he was free again, his memory floating out from him. He was back on the ranch again in those days of joyous comradeship with Johnny.

The boy fed him. He groomed him. He rode him. They shared the sky and the sun and the spring wind and the soft earth. The high hills invited them. The secret valleys received them. The gray caves sheltered them. The silver pool refreshed them. They rode till the stars pricked the sky to say it was time for supper and the sleepy sound of Johnny's voice whispered "Home" without either whip or spur.

Between them there were silences and between them there were words.

"I can hear you plain as day," Johnny would say.

"Know why?"

"No. Why?"

"You hear because you listen."

And Copper taught Johnny to listen to the rest of the world as well—to all the voices of the wind and on the

6

earth and in the trees, each with its own tone, no two alike and all rich in wisdom.

There was wisdom in Copper, too, who knew how to take Johnny's body and cradle it with care as they rode together, faster and faster with the passing of days.

The horse grew taller and the boy grew taller. The horse grew stronger and the boy grew stronger. Now and then, without warning, Copper would charge into the wind with a burst of rage in an effort to drop the weight of that haunting hobble like a bridle lost on the path.

It was only when Johnny walked that Copper was aware of that hobble. When they rode, it was no longer there. They were one, and Johnny was as straight of limb as a soaring pine tree reaching for the sky.

Even now Copper could see the sky as he saw it the day Johnny brought the news. He was looking out beyond the great double doors at the far horizon of gray hills. Then Johnny stood in the doorway, shutting out the light.

"Oh, Copper!" He stumbled toward Copper and flung both arms around his neck. "Oh, Copper!"

"What's happened?"

"Oh, Copper!"

"What is it?"

"The ranch. We've lost the ranch."

"Don't cry. Crying hurts. Tell me, Johnny. What is it?"

"I told you. We've lost the ranch."

7

"Everything?"

"Yes."

"Even me?"

"Yes, Copper. Even you. They're taking you away."

"How far away?"

"I don't know."

"Stop crying."

But Johnny could not stop crying. It wasn't easy to comfort himself or to reassure Copper. "No matter where you go, I'll find you," he declared. "I'll be along. Just you wait. Promise me you'll wait."

"I'll wait," said Copper. "I promise."

And he held to that promise.

He waited.

A new life now began for Copper. A new world now revolved around him. He saw a new creature standing before him, and as he stirred up the magic of past memories, he reached into his consciousness and lifted out another image of himself.

Copper was a race horse.

He recalled all of it so clearly. He could see his stall with the brass plate upon which his name and pedigree had been engraved. He could smell the hay piled sweet and dusty. A barn swallow twittered by an open window in the loft.

People came and went. His hours were full of people dancing attendance upon him, of schooling, of grooming until his coat shone like an old coin and his mane swept the wind like a comet.

The food was good. His bed was soft. His sleep was

sweet. He was the crown jewel of a kingdom crowded with grooms and exercise boys, betting men, dealers, owners, and jockeys—each with a jargon of his own, a goal of his own, a scheme of his own—with Copper being moved like a pawn on a chessboard.

At first Copper was confused. There were days his jockey would not let him win. There were days he was forced to win. There were times he was spurred, almost beyond his strength, to sweep under the wire a clean length in the lead.

Time raced beside him.

He was sent abroad. He came home with honors. He was sold to a syndicate of betting men. He had a dozen owners now, and thousands cheered him on to victory in the greatest race of the year and the greatest hours of his life.

They hung a huge horseshoe of vivid roses around his neck. There was a whir and click of countless cameras. He was the center of a surging sea of faces. These were the faces of strangers. Johnny was not in their midst.

Then the faces drifted off and the clamor died away. Except for the two men and their secret, Copper was alone with his pain. He had felt the stab as he crossed the finish line. And now he heard the verdict.

"Well, sir, he did it. Just as I thought he would. But he's through—"

"What do you mean? What kind of talk is that?"

"That leg is gone. It was going before he was halfway home—"

"How do you know?"

9

"I saw it go. It happened on the curve. He twisted it real bad. If you ask me, he made it on the last of his nerve."

"Will he ever race again?"

"No, sir. He's finished."

"I'm sorry. Take him away."

"Doesn't seem to want to go—"

"Maybe he's waiting for someone. Look! He keeps looking for someone, that's sure."

"Too bad he'll never race again—"

Copper wheeled about slowly. It was over. The hour of his dream had come and gone—without Johnny.

But he did ride.

He rode inside a paddock—round and round on a treadmill of monotony. He was one of the many saddle horses stabled at the Circle C Ranch.

Again he saw his past unfolding, sequence by sequence, each one linked to the last and all of them linked to Johnny.

The memory of his days at the ranch were sharp in contrast to those that had gone before. The stable was old. The food was poor. The flies were thick and troublesome. All sorts of people clambered up on his back. Some of them knew how to ride. Most of them came here to learn.

He had to learn, too. He had to be patient, gentle, obedient. He flavored the dull taste of his days with the secret spice of listening for the sounds that came up through the earth of his drafty stall, sorting out the approaching footsteps in the hope of hearing a familiar hobble.

COPPER

Sometimes, in his dreams, he heard its music and awakened with a start, only to find he had lost the sound again. The only footsteps were his own. His leg troubled him, particularly during the long, cold winter weather. He was limping badly.

And then, on a Sunday—their busy day—he fell and threw his rider.

"We were going down the hill," the riding master reported, "when he struck a stone or something—"

"Good thing Mr. Christopher didn't get killed!"

"Yeah. Only the horse got hurt."

"You should have seen the landslide. Dust a mile high. . . ."

"A funny thing happened. When he got to the bottom, he lay there like a goner. Then he lifted his head and looked up. He wouldn't get up. He just lay there, waiting for something or someone—"

"Well, we got a buyer waiting for him!"

And the day before Christmas, Copper was sold. He knew it was Christmas. As they carted him away he saw the lights go on in the giant tree at the door.

After that, there came a succession of days and of buyers, of new scenes and old stables.

The job at the junkyard was the last stop on the line. His coat was dull. His bones were tired. His eyes were full of years.

At times the junkman failed to groom him. Sometimes he failed to feed him. It did not matter. He lived in dreams. And one cold day a deep sleep drew him to its bosom and he was warm again and full of oats and hay. . . .

When he awoke, he found the familiar road. He climbed the familiar hill. Now here he was—full of life —waiting outside the pasture gate.

The fog was still rolling toward him in thick, gray, puffy billows. Off in the distance he heard a clock striking the hour of midnight. Now in the gloom he saw a light. The single eye of a lantern came closer and closer. He heard the sound of a key in the lock. The gate swung open slowly—and there was the familiar, kindly old keeper.

The old man was smiling. He swung the lantern high over his head and blinked in surprise at the sight of the early comer. A beam of light found Copper and held him.

"Why, hello, Copper!"

"Hello, Peter!"

"You're just on time this time. Come on in!"

"Do you mind if I wait?"

"Anybody special?"

"Yes, a boy named Johnny."

The old man chuckled. "Yes, boys are special. I don't blame you for waiting. I know just how you feel—"

"The feeling is mutual, Peter."

"Been waiting a long time?"

"All my life."

"I hope for your sake he comes."

"I wish I knew where to find him."

"Well, the world is smaller than you think. After all, it's not a very big planet!"

"I know—"

12

"I'd hate to get lost on the North Star!"

"Just the same, it's a wonder to me how they find this place. I'll never forget that last parade. I never saw such a turnout!"

"We expect double the number this time, Copper." He reflected. "Who would dream there were so many horses down in the world below!" He went on. "Well, they'll have a good, long, refreshing sleep and they'll rest until they're strong again. Then they'll go back to live all over again and give themselves to men. Quite a cycle, don't you think?"

"Yes," said Copper.

The old man set down the lantern thoughtfully. "I'd love to stand here and talk to you for the rest of my life, but I've got to open up shop, you know, and be ready for those that are coming. Mind if I get back to work?"

"Don't let me stop you."

"Sure you don't want to come in and be going along with the others? You can't wait forever for your Johnny. . . ."

"I promised I'd wait. I won't go without him."

"You mean you love him so much you'd even give up your chances of getting into heaven?"

"Yes."

"Well, I'm happy to hear it, Copper. Not every horse feels that way about the human race. Seems like every life is a lesson forward. Guess you merit your reward."

"Okay! Let's have that lump of sugar!"

Instead, the old man did an odd thing. He came

13

through the gate, held up the lantern, and swung it three times, back and forth, like a signal into the night.

"Well, time's running out." He pushed the gate back —all the way back. "Better stand to one side, Copper. It's three minutes past midnight. They'll be coming through in a second. They'll be here. They'll be—"

The rest of his words were lost. A surge of sound swelled in the distance, shattering the silence of the night. Then they came.

A ghostly rider on a white charger was the first to appear, plume blowing, mane flying, hoofs flashing fire. The rider waved to Peter and called aloud a greeting in a strange tongue.

Now on filed the others in a thundering cavalcade. Farm horses. Race horses. Trotters. Show horses. Red and white and black flashed before Copper's eyes, passing before him in a cloud of golden dust. Now a woman held the reins. Now a farm boy came into view, jogging on the broad, inviting back of a work horse. Now a stagecoach lumbered through the gate. Now the measured hoofbeat of an approaching cavalry brought a young smile to the old face of the keeper. A snow-white filly raced through the gate, the remains of a rawhide rope trailing behind her.

Then suddenly the procession ended. The last echo died away. The dust began to settle. The fog began to thicken. The glow of the old man's lantern reached out to Copper with a dying eye.

"Still there, are you?"

14

"Yes, Peter."

"Wonderful, wasn't it?"

"Yes," said Copper. Just yes. He was watching the old man reach for his keys. The gate was beginning to move. Soon it would be over. The gate to heaven would be closed.

"I wonder why he's late?" said the old keeper. "I sent word you were waiting for him—"

For a moment Copper was speechless. "You mean to say he may come, that Johnny may come after all?" Copper was transported with joy. "Oh, Peter—" his voice broke. "And you did this for me?"

"All I did was flash my light for a minute or two. How long did you say you have loved him?"

Then the sound of a hobble broke out in the night. And the voice of a boy began calling.

"Copper! Copper! Where are you?"

"Here, Johnny! Here!"

"Hurry," said the old keeper. "I'm locking up."

And now Copper was yelling, "You'll have to run for it, Johnny! Run for it!"

Johnny ran. He leaped. He was safe on Copper's back, clinging fast to his mane.

"How about me?" shouted Copper. "Don't I even have time to get out of this rig?"

"No," said Peter with a laugh. "Come just as you are!"

But as the horse and the boy came through the gate, the old man gave the cart a kick and it rattled down the hill and out of sight.

"Where are we going?" said Johnny.

15

The old man chortled. "What a question to ask!" Then his grin glowed with even a brighter light than his lantern. "Where else but heaven, Johnny, my boy!" He barred the gate. "Didn't you know all horses go to heaven?"

Lincoln Steffens

A Miserable,
Merry Christmas

WHAT INTERESTED me in our new neighborhood
was not the school, nor the room I was to have in the
house all to myself, but the stable which was built back
of the house. My father let me direct the making of a
stall, a little smaller than the other stalls, for my pony,
and I prayed and hoped and my sister Lou believed
that that meant that I would get the pony, perhaps for
Christmas. I pointed out to her that there were three
other stalls and no horses at all. This I said in order that
she should answer it. She could not. My father, sounded,
said that someday we might have horses and a cow;
meanwhile that stable added to the value of a house.

17

"Someday" is a pain to a boy who lives in and knows only "now." My good little sisters, to comfort me, remarked that Christmas was coming, but Christmas was always coming, and grown-ups were always talking about it, asking what you wanted and then giving you what they wanted you to have. Though everybody knew what I wanted, I told them all again. My mother knew that I told God, too, every night. I wanted a pony, and to make sure that they understood, I declared that I wanted nothing else.

"Nothing but a pony?" my father asked.

"Nothing," I said.

"Not even a pair of high boots?"

That was hard. I did want boots, but I stuck to the pony. "No, not even boots."

"Nor candy? There ought to be something to fill your stocking with, and Santa Claus can't put a pony into a stocking."

That was true, and he couldn't lead a pony down the chimney, either. But no. "All I want is a pony," I said. "If I can't have a pony, give me nothing, nothing."

Now I had been looking myself for the pony I wanted, going to sales stables, inquiring of horsemen, and I had seen several that would do. My father let me "try" them. I tried so many ponies that I was learning fast to sit on a horse. I chose several, but my father always found some fault with each one. I was in despair. When Christmas was at hand I had given up all hope of a pony, and on Christmas Eve I hung up my stocking along with my sisters, of whom, by the way, I now had

18

three. I haven't mentioned them, or their coming, because, you understand, they were girls, and girls, young girls, counted for nothing in my manly life. They did not mind me, either; they were so happy that Christmas Eve that I caught some of their merriment. I speculated on what I'd get; I hung up the biggest stocking I had, and we all went reluctantly to bed to wait till morning. Not to sleep; not right away. We were told that we must not only sleep promptly, we must not wake up till seven-thirty the next morning —or if we did, we must not go to the fireplace for our Christmas. Impossible.

We did sleep that night, but we woke up at six A.M. We lay in our beds and debated through open doors whether to obey till, say, half past six. Then we bolted. I don't know who started it, but there was a rush. We all disobeyed; we raced to get first to the fireplace in the front room downstairs. And there they were, the gifts, all sorts of wonderful things, mixed-up piles of presents; only as I disentangled the mess, I saw that my stocking was empty; it hung limp; not a thing in it; and under and around it—nothing. My sisters had knelt down each by her pile of gifts. They were squealing with delight, till they looked up and saw me standing there in my nightgown with nothing. They left their piles to come to me and look at my empty place. Nothing. They felt my stocking: nothing.

I don't remember whether I cried at that moment, but my sisters did. They ran with me back to my bed, and there we all cried till I became indignant. That

19

helped some. I got up, dressed, and driving my sisters away, I went alone out into the yard, down to the stable, and there, all by myself, I wept. My mother came out to me by and by. She found me in the pony stall, sobbing on the floor, and she tried to comfort me. But I heard my father outside; he had come part way with her, and she was having some sort of angry words with him. She tried to comfort me; besought me to come to breakfast. I could not; I wanted no comfort and no breakfast. She left me and went on into the house with more sharp words for my father.

I don't know what kind of breakfast the family had. My sisters said it was "awful." They were ashamed to enjoy their own toys. They came to me, and I was rude. I ran away from them. I went around to the front of the house, sat down on the steps, and, the crying over, I ached. I was wronged, I was hurt—I can feel now what I felt then. I am sure that if one could see the wounds upon our hearts, there would be found still upon mine a scar from that terrible Christmas morning. And my father, the practical joker, he must have been hurt, too, a little. I saw him looking out of the window. He was watching me or something for an hour or two, drawing back the curtain ever so little lest I catch him. But I saw his face, and I think I can see now the anxiety upon it, the worried impatience.

After I don't know how long—surely an hour or two— I was brought to the climax of my agony by the sight of a man riding a pony down the street, a pony and a brand-new saddle; the most beautiful saddle I ever saw,

20

and it was a boy's saddle. The man's feet were not in the stirrups; his legs were too long. The outfit was perfect; it was realization of all my dreams, the answer to all my prayers. A fine new bridle, with a light curb bit. And the pony! As he drew near, I saw that the pony was really a small horse, what we called an Indian pony, a bay, with black mane and tail, and one white foot and a white star on his forehead. For such a horse as that I would have given, I could have forgiven, anything.

But the man, a disheveled fellow with a blackened eye and a fresh-cut face, came along, reading the numbers on the houses. As my hopes—my impossible hopes—rose, he looked at our door and passed by, he and the pony, and the saddle and the bridle. Too much. I fell upon the steps, and having wept before, I broke now into such a flood of tears that I was a floating wreck when I heard a voice.

"Say, kid," it said, "do you know a boy named Lennie Steffens?"

I looked up. It was the man on the pony, back again, at our horse block.

"Yes," I spluttered through my tears. "That's me."

"Well," he said, "then this is your horse. I've been looking all over for you and your house. Why don't you put your number where it can be seen?"

"Get down," I said, running out to him.

The man went on saying something about "ought to have got here at seven o'clock; he told me to bring the nag here and tie him to your post and leave him for you..."

"Get down," I said.

He got down, and he boosted me up to the saddle. He offered to fit the stirrups to me, but I didn't want him to. I wanted to ride.

"What's the matter with you?" he said angrily. "What are you crying for? Don't you like the horse? He's a dandy, this horse; I know him of old. He's fine at cattle; he'll drive 'em alone."

I hardly heard, I could scarcely wait, but he per-

22

sisted. He adjusted the stirrups, and then, finally, off I rode, slowly, at a walk, so happy, so thrilled, that I did not know what I was doing. I did not look back at the house or the man. I rode off up the street, taking note of everything—of the reins, of the pony's long mane, of the carved leather saddle. I had never seen anything so beautiful. And mine! I was going to ride up past Miss Kay's house. But I noticed on the horn of the saddle some stains like raindrops, so I turned and trotted home, not to the house but to the stable. There was the family —father, mother, sisters—all waiting for me, all happy now. They had been putting in place the tools of my new business: blankets, currycomb, brush, pitchfork— everything, and there was hay in the loft.

"What did you come back so soon for?" somebody asked. "Why didn't you go on riding?"

I pointed to the stains. "I wasn't going to get my new saddle rained on," I said. And my father laughed. "It isn't raining," he said. "Those are not raindrops."

"They are tears," my mother gasped, and she gave my father a look which sent him off to the house. Worse still, my mother offered to wipe away the tears still running out of my eyes. I gave her such a look as she had given him, and she went off after my father, drying her own tears.

My sisters remained and we all unsaddled the pony, put on his halter, led him to his stall, tied and fed him. It began really to rain; so all the rest of that memorable day we curried and combed that pony. The girls plaited his mane, forelock, and tail, while I pitchforked hay to him and curried and brushed, curried and brushed. For a change we brought him out to drink. We led him up and down, blanketed like a race horse; we took turns at that. But the best, most inexhaustible fun was to clean him.

When we went reluctantly to our midday Christmas dinner, we smelt of horse, and my sisters had to wash their faces and hands. I was asked to, but I wouldn't, till my mother bade me look in the mirror. Then I washed up—quick. My face was caked with muddy lines of tears that had coursed over my cheeks to my mouth. Having washed away that shame, I ate my dinner, and as I ate I grew hungrier. It was my first meal that day, and as I filled up on the turkey and the stuffing, the cranberries and the pies, the fruit and the nuts —as I swelled, I could laugh. My mother said I still choked and sobbed now and then, but I laughed, too. I saw and enjoyed my sisters' presents till—I had to go out and attend to my pony, who was there, really and truly there, the promise, the beginning, of a happy double life. And—I went and looked to make sure—there was the saddle, too, and the bridle.

But that Christmas, which my father had planned so carefully, was it the best or the worst I ever knew? He often asked me that; I never could answer as a boy. I think now that it was both. It covered the whole distance from broken-hearted misery to bursting happiness —too fast. A grown-up could hardly have stood it.

Cornelia Meigs

Stable Call

IF IT HAD BEEN wartime, there would have been no place in the company for Rodman Phelps, aged fourteen and in no way enrolled in the United States Army. But this was a bold adventure of a different sort. The soldiers were sent out as a guard for a great project— the laying out of a railroad across unsettled country full of broad plains, difficult rivers, broken hills, and unfriendly Indians. In the early 1870s the Northern Pacific Railroad was only in its first beginnings. So this expedition was no matter of building roadbeds and laying rails, but merely of seeking out the best line across the unknown territory, of surveying the chosen

25

way slowly and exactly all the way from the Great
Lakes to the Missouri River and from the Missouri to
the Yellowstone. There were but six engineers who
were doing the work, but the body of troops sent
to keep them safe amounted to a small army.

It was only a month before that the news of this
march had come to the fort where Rod's father, Colonel Phelps, was in command. Every young officer, every
enlisted man of any spirit, was anxious to be one of those
chosen to go. It seemed almost too wonderful to believe
that Colonel Custer of the Seventh Cavalry, who was to
be in charge of the soldiers on the journey, should have
said, with his easy good nature, "How about my taking
the boy along, Phelps? He can go if he wants to. He
seems to me to be the kind who wouldn't make a nuisance of himself. There will be some good hunting—
buffalo and elk and antelope. And, after all, as I see it,
with such a big force there's not too much danger. We
may never even be attacked by the Sioux."

Rod had held his breath while his father thought it
over. "Why, yes, he may go," was the glorious permission finally given. "Only, as you say, he must be sure
not to be a bother to anyone in any way."

The boy could see that Custer's second in command,
Lieutenant Tracy, was none too well pleased with the
plan. "Trust a boy to get himself in the way somehow,"
Rod heard him mumble. But a horse was found for Rod,
his things were got together, and they were off.

Through all the march, which had been long and
hard, he had been careful never to make a nuisance of

26

himself, never to be in the way or to cause any delay. He was never the last in saddling up in the morning. He always got his horse tied and fed and watered as soon as any of the more experienced soldiers; he always leaped at the sound of the bugle call, no matter what its message. But he wanted to do better than that—to be of some real and active use, if only to show his bravery to that watching, doubtful Lieutenant Tracy. "This sort of journey is no place for a boy," he said aloud, more than once in Rod's presence. Rod vowed to himself that before the march was over he would prove that he had as good a right in that company as any other.

Perhaps, he thought, as he sat up in the dark one night about a month after they had started on the trip, perhaps it might be this very night. Was it the rustle of the tent flap, moving in the soft prairie wind, which had roused Rod to raise his head from the pile of army blankets and listen? Suppose he were to be the one to give warning of a Sioux attack! He held his breath but heard nothing strange. The Broad Dakota prairie was still, except for the far-off cry of a wolf; a horse whinnied and shifted its feet; the guard tramped past. That was all. Rod was very sleepy. He snuggled down between blankets again.

Then suddenly there was a terrible shouting, stamping, yelling, and a crash of guns. A dark form ran past the tent door; a half-dressed soldier came after it, and another, and another. Horses snorted, reared, broke loose, and went galloping through the camp. Shots were fired in every direction; officers roared orders, and men shouted in reply. But above everything there rose, high and terrifying, the Indian war cry.

A half-dozen Indians had ridden straight through the camp, charging down the narrow lanes between the tent rows, shouting and emptying their guns into the tents. Their object had plainly been to stampede the horses and drive them away. The plan had not succeeded, however; for only a few of the horses had broken away and nearly all of these were caught again by the soldiers.

The shooting in the dark had done little harm; for this was not meant to be a serious attack. It was mostly an act of daring on the part of the Sioux, the proof to the white man that they were close on his heels. But when morning came and men and horses were counted, it was found that Colonel Custer's best horse, Ajax, swift and big-shouldered, was gone.

"Six Indians threw us into a good deal of an uproar," one gray-haired soldier admitted. "It's sure bad luck that Custer's horse was the one to be lost. He was the best in the whole regiment. The colonel's sending a group of men to see if they can find him. But they mustn't take long, for we've got a long march ahead of us today."

The old man's words gave Rod an idea. And when the men, with an officer in command, went galloping out to look for the horse, the boy was trailing behind them. His long-legged horse was not so sturdy or so experienced as theirs. Rod had to urge it again and again to keep up with the others.

The searchers swung over one hill and then another, and at last saw a galloping animal which the officer, with a field glass, made out to be the lost horse. They quickened their speed and bore down upon him as he grazed and ran and then stopped to graze again.

"He always was a wild thing," the sergeant said. "Even the Indians couldn't catch him. I shouldn't be surprised if we fail to get him back, too."

This proved true enough. The big creature stood once for a minute on the top of the hill. Then he stretched his neck and sped away more swiftly than they could follow, swinging down the long slope and disappearing into a group of cottonwoods around a water hole. The sergeant looked back over his shoulder.

"The line's getting under way," he said. "We'll have to give the horse up and go back. Remember that we've been ordered never to forget that the Indians are always watching." He gave his command, and the men swung with their horses obediently.

But Rod, so he argued with himself, was not strictly bound to follow military orders. The horse had grazed out beyond the clump of trees, a single, lonely figure in that great empty waste. Rod had patted him often; the animal would know his voice if he could get near enough to call. The others were mounting the hill and disappearing on the other side. The boy turned his horse.

Down he rode; down the long slope into the broad basin. He was nearing the horse, which raised his head

29

and stood looking. Then his own horse whinnied, and Ajax answered, the shrill greeting of one horse friend to another.

Rod was not many yards away. He rose in his stirrups and called, "Ajax! Ajax!" For an instant the animal stood motionless. Then he swung around and was off in a thunder of hoofs. There was no hope of overtaking him.

Rod pulled up and let his own horse rest for a minute. He had been so sure; but he had been wrong. Had it been wise to lag so far behind? He took one more glance back at the fleeing Ajax. The ground the horse was mounting went up, up, to a long roll of hill; and just below the top something moved—riders, seemingly heading down toward the level. There could be no doubt that they were Indians.

The boy rode on, urging his mount to the top of its clumsy speed. When he looked back he saw that the Indians were following him.

He would not look back again, he told himself. He realized now the foolishness of what he had done. This was just what the men had always been warned against. This was the very thing for which the Indians had waited so long. Sometime, they must have reasoned, a person in that marching column would stray away from the safety that numbers brought and let himself fall into danger. Rod had thought himself so wise and responsible, and now he was the one to bring about the special thing that they had all sought to avoid.

"We don't want to have to stop to waste time and blood fighting the Indians," he had heard the colonel say more than once. "With the season so late, it's our business to get on."

Would they risk a battle to save one thoughtless boy who had got himself into danger? No! The one thing he desired now was that they should leave him behind and think no more about him. It might ruin the success of the whole journey if there was a fight and the engineers were kept from their work. How could he have been so foolish?

The Indians were close. They were still riding on the level while Rod was mounting the hill, so they gained on him rapidly. He could see them spread out like a fan, swinging their rifles into position. There was a report, and he ducked without thinking, although the ball flew high. One more effort and he would be over the hill. But the second shot was very close, and the yell that followed it and the drumming of hoofs sounded at his very heels. It was time to turn and make a stand now. His hand closed on the handle of his pistol.

But then there was a shout ahead of him, and heads rose over the edge of the hill! How good the blue uniforms looked as they swept into sight! The soldiers had been sent back to his rescue. He had hoped that they would go on without him, but how glad, how gloriously glad he was that they had not.

The group opened, and he and his stumbling horse rode into the midst of it, followed by a last scattering of bullets. The Indians swung out, circling to right and left. They did not care for a fight. They had only been enjoying themselves, chasing a foolishly bold boy. The little company of soldiers galloped away toward the column.

The immediate joy and relief in Rod's heart gave place little by little to hot shame and regret. It was just his luck, he thought unhappily, that the officer who had been sent back to get him should be Lieutenant Tracy. He did not say a word to Rod as they rode back, but the boy heard what he said to the man beside him. "This is just the kind of thing I expected from the very first. Anyone would know that the boy would make trouble."

Just before they rode even with the marching ranks, Rod pushed his horse up beside Tracy and spoke. "Couldn't—couldn't you tell the colonel that it was only because I wanted so to get back Ajax . . . that it was because Ajax was his horse—"

"That isn't my business," replied the other. "And it's yours to see that you obey orders and don't delay the column again."

Rod knew the report would be harsh. He had been foolish, but there had been a good chance that he could get the horse. "I'll make up for it yet," he found himself promising suddenly. Somehow he would prove that he was not so foolish as he had seemed.

The march went on, day after day, following the basin of a winding river. Rod took his turn with the rest at guard duty, and he watched the engineers with their instruments, marking curves, mapping, and surveying. He tried to think of the rails and the thundering trains that were to follow.

As he looked across the hills, watching for the Indians, he thought there should not be a war. There was room for both white men and Indians. Some of the tribes had sent word that they were willing to let the railroad cross their lands, but the Sioux had not given in. Had they got Ajax? Rod often wondered. He never put aside the idea that he himself would get him back. Sometimes he went with the hunters to get buffalo, elk, or bear for food. The company had come a long way from headquarters and supplies were getting low. The Indians still hung at their heels, never risking an open fight, but always a cloud of danger.

33

When the survey reached the Yellowstone River, the procession turned back. That was as far as they could hope to go before the winter blizzards. They must make haste now back to the headquarters on the Missouri. The march was difficult and discouraging. Food was scarce, the game had been frightened away, and they found little hunting on their homeward track. Horses gave out and had to be turned loose, and a number of soldiers who usually rode had to march on foot. One day the march was almost stopped because the colonel's horse had gone lame and he had no spare mount. "If we only hadn't lost Ajax!" Rod heard him say again and again.

Rod offered his own horse, but the colonel only smiled. "He's not up to my weight," he said. Certainly he was not—a sorry beast that had never been very good. Now, tired and stubborn, he was very little to offer in the way of horseflesh. The colonel thanked the boy, however, and Rod felt that for the first time he was half forgiven for his foolishness so many weeks ago.

The boy felt that he was an experienced soldier now —tough, brown, and dusty as were all the men. He could care for the horses, set up a tent, and make a bedroll as well as the rest. And he had made friends with almost everyone. One of his best comrades was the bugler, Tom Davis, a young man not much older than Rod. He taught Rod the camp calls, and there were several mornings when Tom got a few minutes of extra sleep while the camp was awakened by Rod's slightly uncertain notes calling them to rise.

34

"I can't get 'em up! I can't get 'em up!"—thus the soldiers had long ago put words to the notes which he blew, clear and loud, although a little unskilled. He could sound stable call also, when all the horses were driven up to be fed; and taps, when the camp settled down to its sleep. The Indians heard it too, he was certain, as they circled the dark hills, always watching.

At last the troops came back into the basin of the Heart River, where the first daring ride through the camp had occurred. "Watch for Ajax" was an unnecessary order, for all eyes were searching the hills and levels as the long column went crawling across the plain. Moving dots in the distance were sometimes antelope, now and then elk, more often Indians.

But one day Lieutenant Tracy, leveling his field glass, announced suddenly, "There he is! The Indians got him. There's a Sioux riding him."

Grudgingly he let Rod look. It was true. There at a distance, watching the column pass, was the tall horse with an Indian on his back.

Men were to be sent to try to get him. "You can risk a good deal to fetch him back," the colonel said to Tracy, who was to be in charge. "I never thought losing a horse could make such a difference. I'd give anything to get him."

Rod stepped up with a boldness he had not felt in many weeks. "May I go?" he asked.

He saw it in Tracy's eyes to refuse, but the colonel said, "Yes, let him go. It seems to me he wasn't so wrong in trying to get him before."

35

Rod was happier than he had been for a long time as they galloped away, Tracy in the lead and Rod and his friend Tom Davis riding together.

It was a useless attempt. The Indian on Ajax saw them coming and, as the company bore upon him, rode away. Clouds of red warriors suddenly appeared, circling and shouting, plainly hoping for a fight. Tracy drew rein; the Indians stood still also. "The colonel ordered us not to attack," he said. He turned to go back; and immediately all but a few of the Indian riders disappeared, while the rest followed the white men at a distance, their laughter and insults coming faintly down in the wind.

The men growled and muttered; it was hard to be laughed at by the enemy. But orders were orders. At the head of the bold half-dozen Indians was the man who seemed to be their leader and who was riding Ajax. The horse, after months in the wilds, seemed to have developed fear of white men. He snorted and shied. At last the soldiers turned back to their own ranks and dismounted. Their attempt to capture Ajax was a failure. Rod heard Tracy reporting to the colonel, "They are too many and too quick for us, sir," and the colonel's regretful reply, "Yes, we'll have to march on."

Suddenly the boy was seized with an idea. He rushed through the camp, found the tent of Tom Davis, snatched the bugle from its peg, and flung himself on his horse. He rode some yards out from the camp, Indians circling near but safely out of reach of the soldiers' guns. No one ordered the boy back. Everyone watched,

36

spellbound, wondering what he meant to do. Now he was almost out of rifle shot of his companions—so far away that the fire of the soldiers could scarcely protect him from attack. The Indians, accepting his challenge, advanced nearer and nearer, circling carefully. Within shot now, the leader on Ajax came closer than the rest.

Then Rod put the bugle to his lips, stood up in his stirrups, and blew. Stable call—those were the notes that sounded, the order that rang through the camp at evening when the march was over and the horses were gathered and fed. It had never been so steady or so clear.

Come all who are able,
And go to the stable...

Rod heard the rustle and tramp of the horses behind him. They were pulling at their bridles, answering naturally the signal they all knew so well. The men held them steady—watching, watching. Ajax heard; he pricked up his ears; he stood still; he snorted.

And give your horses some oats and some corn.

The big horse leaped forward. The Sioux's whip swung brutally, but it was of no use. Habit and old training were too strong. Ajax lowered his head, snorted again, and bolted. Straight toward the soldiers' ranks he shot like a flash of lighting, his rider yelling, jerking, lashing. The rude bridle was as nothing against the

37

horse's charge. Nearer and nearer they came, and the Indian at last threw himself from the horse's back, rolling in the dust, and jumping up to flee on foot, out of reach of gunfire.

A great roar went up from the watching soldiers, joined even by the laughter of the Indian's own comrades. A Sioux on foot is no warrior at all, but a creature to be despised even by his own friends. He ran, a bullet or two following him, kicking up the dust at his heels. One of his companions rode close, took him up behind, and the whole band sped away.

Rod had dismounted and caught Ajax by the rude loop of the Indian bridle under his jaw. The animal was trembling and so was the boy. The colonel strode out alone and laid his hand on the mane of his horse.

"I offer you the thanks of the regiment, Rod," he said quietly.

Retold by Katharine Gibson

The Widow's Son

ONCE UPON A TIME there was a widow who had an only son. She was so poor that day by day she had less and less until there was not a cupful of meal in the house. So she sent the lad out into the world to seek his fortune. He had not gone far when he met a man who was looking for a likely lad to serve him.

"If I'm to have a master, it might as well be this one as another," said the lad to himself. And indeed he thought he'd made a fine bargain, for all he had to do, from dawn to dark, was to keep the man company. Not a stroke of work did the lad lift his hand to.

39

One day the man had to go on a journey. "You can go all about the house," he said, "save into four rooms at the back. If you open the door of any of them, even by the smallest crack, it will cost you your life."

At first the lad was willing enough, but at the end of three days he could stand it no longer, so he unlocked the door of the first room and went in. It was quite empty save for a shelf on which was a bramble-bush rod.

"I can't see much in that," said the lad. "Surely there can be no harm in looking at it."

When the man came home, he asked at once, "Have you been near those rooms?"

"Oh, no," answered the lad, "I've been busy enough in the garden."

But the man soon found that the boy had entered the first room. Straightway he told the boy it was his last day on earth. But the lad begged so piteously that the man gave him one more chance.

Now it so happened that the master was forced to go away again, this time for a week. "If you open another of those doors, you will not escape your doom," he said.

The lad contented himself as best he could, but finally his curiosity got the best of him. He went into the second room. All he saw was an earthenware pitcher and a stone.

"Surely there can be nothing wrong in finding a pitcher and a stone. Many's the one I've seen that looked no different than these."

40

As soon as the man put his foot inside the house he asked the lad if he'd kept out of trouble.

"That I have," said the boy.

But the man was quick to find that the lad had gone into the second room. He took him by the collar and was about to strike him down, when the lad prayed so sorrowfully to be spared that at last he let him go.

Not long after, the man had to set out, this time for a fortnight. Terrible were his threats. The lad was frightened and determined not to go near the third room, but he was unable to resist. When he entered the room, it appeared quite empty, and it was not until he happened to see a trap door and opened it that he discovered a big caldron boiling away with no fire under it.

"Now, I wonder what can be cooking there," he thought, "and not a spark to warm it?" At the risk of burning himself he put one finger in the bubbling broth, and when he took it out, it was entirely gilded.

"Now, that will not be so easy to hide," he said. But then he wrapped a rag around it.

When the man came home and instantly asked what had happened, the lad told him he had hurt his finger while chopping a bit of wood. The man tore off the cloth and the lad was in for it. The man straightway cut some long willow whips, and the lad felt the sting of them for many days. But when he was well, it was over, and he and his master were as friendly as before.

Now, once more, the man rode away on a journey; this time he told the lad he would be gone for a month.

"Open that fourth door," he said, "and the breath you breathe when you see me again will be your last."

The lad was quite determined not to enter the room; but at the end of eight days he found himself in the fourth room. There he saw a fine black horse with a manger of hot coals at his head and a forkful of hay at his tail. The lad thought this all wrong, so he turned the horse about. The horse was indeed grateful and when he had finished the hay, he told the lad that his master was a troll in disguise who was plotting some cruel enchantment of the lad or, perhaps, was meaning to take his life.

"If you will do as I say," said the horse, it will help us both. First, go into the room that's over this one. There you will find suits of mail, swords, and many saddles. Do not chose the finest, those that are of silver or inlaid with gems, but of each take that one which is old and rusty." This the lad did, and quickly.

"Now," said the horse, "strip off your ragged clothes and bathe in that caldron, and when you are finished, dip into it sword, suit of mail, my saddle and bridle."

"Mayhap this will be the end of me," said the lad, but in he went. When he came out, his skin was as white as the mistletoe, his dark hair smooth as a crow's wing, his cheeks as red as a winter apple, and his black eyes bright as dew at dawn. The saddle and bridle, the mail and the sword, were all burnished with gold and alight with jewels.

"Now how do you find yourself, lad?" asked the horse. The lad stood still and he felt new strength running like fire through his veins.

"Can you lift me, lad?" Yes, the lad could easily do that; and as for his heavy sword, he played it around his head as though it had been but a flaming brand.

"Make haste," said the horse; "get the bramble-bush rod, the pitcher and the stone, and let us be off."

This the lad hurried to do. Soon he was galloping along the road on the back of the black horse.

But they had not traveled long when the horse said, "Look behind you; what do you see?"

"I see strange creatures riding, maybe a score or more."

"That is the troll and his men; they are seeking to capture us. Take the bramble-bush rod out of your wallet and throw it over your shoulder. But, mind you, do not let it touch me." The lad threw it far behind them; and at once a great thicket grew up, so the trolls had to turn back for their axes and pruning knives.

The two journeyed on safely enough, but after a time the horse said, "Look behind you; what do you see?"

"A thick cloud of dust, and out of it a great crowd coming, as many as would fill a village square."

"It's the troll with more of his crew. Take the rock from your wallet and cast it far behind you. Be sure it doesn't touch me."

When the lad had done this, a stone mountain rose up and almost hid the sun. The trolls had to go home to get their picks and shovels.

Afterward the horse and the lad went along cheerily enough, but once more the horse said, "Look behind you; what do you see?"

43

"A whole troop of queer ones, more than you'd meet on twenty Fair Days."

"Aye, that's the troll and his pack. Take the pitcher, throw the water as far behind you as you can, and do not let so much as a drop fall upon me."

This the lad did, but in his haste he spilled a single drop on the horse's flank; at once they were in a wide lake and likely to be drowned. The horse managed to swim out only just in time. As for the trolls, there was half a sea in front of them. They tried to drink it up, and for all anyone knows, they are drinking still.

By nightfall the horse and the lad came near the king's castle. The horse stopped under the shade of a great lime tree.

"Take off your suit of mail," commanded the horse; "hide it and your sword in the hollow of this tree. Put on your old rags and make yourself a wig of fir moss. Then go to the castle and ask for service with the cook. I will wait here; if you have need of me, shake my bridle three times and we shall be off."

When the lad in his fir-moss wig asked the cook if he might have a place as scullery boy, she said she'd have no such dirty-looking one about her kitchen. She sent him to the coachman. The coachman said a fine sight he'd be leading out the king's horses, and sent him to the gardener. The gardener was badly in need of a boy to do the roughest work, so he took the lad. There was no place to sleep. At last the lad noticed that in the arbor at one end was a space where the branches were so closely interwoven and the leaves so broad they

45

made a shelter quite as thick as a thatch. There, on a pallet of straw, the lad made his bed.

Now one day the princess was walking in the garden. When he first saw her, the lad was so dazzled by the golden glint of her hair, each curl like a tiny vine tendril, and by the blue of her eyes, deep like a lake on Midsummer Eve, that he could only stand still and hang his head.

When the princess saw the lad in his fir-moss wig, she called out, "Take off that ugly cap, boy."

"That I cannot do," said the lad.

"Then you must be a troll," said the princess.

"If it grows there, surely I am," answered the lad.

The princess wondered more and more if the fir-moss cap was fast to his head and if the gardener's lad was indeed a troll, so she lost no chance to watch him. At last, on a certain noon when the sun was hot, the lad lay down on his straw pallet beneath the arbor for a nap, and, to cool himself, he took off the fir-moss wig.

So it was the princess discovered him. When she looked at his white skin, his red cheeks, the shine of his black hair and the dark shadows his lashes made, she found she had no heart at all; for in that moment she gave it to the sleeping lad.

The princess went at once to her father, the king, and told him how she had lost her heart to the gardener's lad and would wed no other. When he heard this, the king could not contain his anger. Straightway he put the lad in jail and shut the princess in a tower room with none but her old nurse for company. The princess wept and

46

wept for the gardener's boy and she wept because she had now no heart of her own.

Now it so happened that before three days had gone by, the castle was guarded at every gate and not a man but took down his sword and helmet. For the king's ancient enemy, with a great press of knights, was seen riding to do battle. The gardener's lad begged to be allowed to bear arms. At last, more as a jest than for any good reason, he was given an old horse and a bit of rusty armor. He had no more than started when the horse got stuck in a bog. There sat the lad, yelling and bawling, but not able to stir an inch, while all the king's men streamed past him, laughing enough to fall off their saddles.

As soon as they were out of sight, the lad hopped over the bog, now on a dry patch, now on a log. He donned his mail, buckled his sword to his belt, shook the bridle of the black horse three times. Off they galloped, just in time to turn the battle against the king's enemy. All the countryside talked of nothing but the unknown champion. But when the army rode back to the castle, there was the lad, sitting on the old horse in the middle of the bog.

"A fine warrior, you!" they jeered.

"That's as may be," said the lad.

The next day was the same, save that the battle was fiercer and the deeds of the champion even more daring. The king ordered his most faithful nobles to look for the hero, but he was not to be found.

At evening, when the battle was over, there was the

47

lad under his fir-moss wig, astride his nag, and looking as gloomy as ten days of rain. One of the king's archers shot an arrow at him and grazed his knee.

"Fool," he cried, "that's so you'll remember men have been fighting this day."

"Yes," said the lad, "I'll remember."

But the king, seeing the lad's sad state, sent one of his butlers to bind up the lad's leg with the king's own scarlet scarf.

The third day the fighting was such as never had been seen before, and only at sundown was the lad able to capture the king's enemy. This time the nobles had no trouble in picking out the brave knight because the lad wore the red band about his knee. The lad was paid great honor and was led to the banquet hall. Such was the king's pleasure that he sent for the princess. She came from her tower arrayed in her richest gown. When she saw the champion, she cried, "Here's the gardener's lad that has my heart!"

The banquet became a wedding feast, and none were ever so joyous as the princess and the lad. The princess never missed her heart at all, now that the lad had it safe in his keeping.

Some days after the celebrations were over, the lad went to the royal stables where his black horse had a fine stall. The great animal was hanging his head, and the groom said he had eaten little or nothing since the battle.

"Ah," said the horse, "all goes well with you; but for me, the days grow worse and worse. I beg of you to slay me with your sword."

"Never," cried the lad, "for I have won all my fortune because of your help and good counsel."

The black horse reared up; flame came from his nostrils. "End my life or I will end yours," he cried, and he stamped his iron-shod hoofs upon the stones of the floor until they rang like funeral bells. The poor lad was forced to draw his blade from the scabbard. But no sooner had he killed the horse than a handsome prince stood before him.

"I was bewitched by the troll. Only you, lad, could free me. The castle where you found me was stolen by the troll, but this night I shall dine in my own hall."

Though the prince's kingdom was nearby, there was never any quarrel between him and the lad. The two met as neighbors and lived so with good cheer from that day forth, forever after.

Vivian Breckenfeld

A Touch of Arab

USUALLY THE DAY we rode into the canyon to open the ranger cabin was the happiest of the whole year. On that day my father stopped being Professor Mallory of the Geology Department and changed into Ranger Mallory of Merced Canyon—and I had Cirque to ride. After a little time in the Sierra Nevada you get used to the light, but on the day you ride in, the sun seems so near, and shines so gold-and-silver bright, that it stirs you up inside. The mountains have a sparkle on them.

Always before—and that's eleven summers, because we have been going to the Merced cabin ever since my mother died when I was three—Ranger Mallory's eyes

50

would get sort of big behind his glasses and the tip of his nose would quiver at the smell of wild azaleas in Little Yosemite. He'd crack silly jokes as we rode and call himself "Old Sourdough." But this year he looked as if he had just flunked one of his favorite students.

"Look at Cirque, Daddy," I said. "Isn't he beautiful? He's so glad to be out of pasture he wants to dance uphill." Cirque is western stock horse with just a touch of Arab. That makes him strong and dependable and brave, but a little flashy, too—he likes to prance.

But Daddy didn't seem to appreciate Cirque's polished granite coat and lovely legs. Surely, I thought, after we climb the zigzags and get to foaming water, or to where we can see the Clark Range, he will get his mountain face. The Clark Range looks like black starched fringe combed straight up against the sky. We think it's very exciting.

It was when we stopped for lunch that Daddy told me. We had built a cooking fire and were waiting for the water to boil for tea when he said, "I wish you'd stop trying to balance yourself on that branch, Meggie. I really don't want an acrobat for a daughter. Besides, I need to talk to you." He kept digging at the damp crust of pine needles on the ground as he spoke. "I'm sorry Meg, but this is going to be a mighty short summer."

"What on earth do you mean?" I asked him. "It's not even July yet."

"But this year I'm having just a two-week business-man's vacation." He put his hand on my arm. "Meg, my

51

dear," he said almost pleadingly, "I do hope you'll understand." Then he told me that he had resigned from the Forest Service to accept a job teaching at summer session, and that he wanted me to go to a girls' camp.

"I don't want you growing up one-sided," he said, "with no interest outside of your riding. You must cultivate other enthusiasms. You need friendship with boys and girls your own age. That's why I want you to go to this camp and make an honest effort to get along with the other girls and join in all their different activities."

"But Cirque!" I cried. "Darling Cirque! What will we do—"

"A professor's salary is not designed to include boarding a horse in town," Daddy answered slowly. "I'm sorry, but I think the time has come when we'll have to sell Cirque. Surely you wouldn't want to keep an educated young gentleman at pasture indefinitely. Would you, Meggie?"

I shook my head, but deep inside I knew there was more behind this selling Cirque than just money. Several times that spring I had cut school to practice for the gymkhana, and when Daddy found out about it he'd looked pretty grim.

"Education," he had said to me, his jaw particularly square, "is the bones of life. Without it you may grow up bright and pretty, but sometime life will crumble on you because you haven't the right bones underneath."

"Why do you have to be a professor all over your private life?" I'd railed. "You know I'm going to live on a

52

ranch and raise stock horses. What's analyzing the *Merchant of Venice* got to do with that?"

"Quite a lot," Daddy had said, and I knew there was no use arguing with him.

After that miserable lunch on the trail we rode the rest of the fourteen miles to our cabin, trying to talk about things that wouldn't hurt too much. But as we passed the granite slide where the Merced tumbles down in foaming sheets of water, I couldn't help remembering old Mr. Scripps.

"Did they ever find him?" I had to ask.

"Yes, they did," Daddy answered, as if rushing water were no longer beautiful. "At the bottom of Nevada Falls. There will be one advantage to our short summer, anyhow."

"How could there be?"

"I probably won't have to hunt for any lost fishermen or campers."

Usually when we arrive at the Ranger Station I want to squeal for joy. Our brown log cabin looks so welcoming under the Jeffrey pines! This year I could only wonder whose name would be tacked up on the bulletin board where the little metal sign, RANGER ARTHUR B. MALLORY, had hung for so long. Cirque was all for dashing upstream to see if the big bridge, where the Lyell Fork joins the Merced, had lasted out the winter. Since the trail gang put a concrete pier under the bridge it has never washed out, but before that, every time we had a heavy storm the melted snow, swirling down in torrents from the upper falls, had carried the

53

bridge with it. I unsaddled Cirque and turned him into the corral beside the cabin, then went inside to unpack. What I really wanted to do was bury my face in a pillow, or run across the river on my log and crawl into the underbrush, where the does hide their new fawns.

It was silly for Daddy to think that getting rid of Cirque would make me spend more time with what he calls "comrades of my own age." Those dopes! Last year he practically drove me to join a sort of dancing club. The dancing part wasn't bad—dancing is pretty good exercise. But the girls were so silly and the boys so juvenile in their conversation, I only went once. But it had never occurred to me that my not going to dances, and being bored by my schoolmates, would get mixed up in Daddy's mind with my loving Cirque so much. How could I make him understand the way I felt about my darling? My father wouldn't sell me, no matter how much I cost to keep!

Suddenly an idea hit me. Cirque looks especially beautiful standing on his hind legs or jumping. If, every day for two weeks, Daddy had to watch my horse doing extra-special, prancy tricks, perhaps—

I raced into the cabin for my lucky T-shirt—the blue-and-white striped one I wore when I won the bareback hackamore race at the gymkhana. Then I jerked the top bars off the corral gate and made Cirque jump so that every muscle showed under his glossy coat. Finally, to rest him, we practiced a kind of circus trick I have been wanting to learn. That was when Wake came along.

Right next to our cabin is a mammoth Jeffrey pine

54

with one branch overhanging the corral. I stood on Cirque's back (that isn't hard if you have grippy toes and are used to climbing over logs) and swung myself to the overhanging branch. The hard part was dropping down again on Cirque's back while he was loping by. I was riding around standing up, when I spotted something that looked like a great blue heron—all legs, with a hump on top—leaning against the corral, one of his legs wound around the other. When I rode over, the hump turned out to be a knapsack, and the heron asked, "Can I take a picture of you doing that stunt? You're a wonderful color. Like the ocean—extremely clean blue-and-white."

"I don't mind," I said, wondering whether he meant that my shirt looked like the ocean, or my face. My eyes are violently blue, and my eyebrows and hair looked mighty pale against my sun-browned skin.

While he set up a tripod Cirque and I did our trick over and over.

"What's your horse's name?" he asked.

"Cirque."

"Circ, for circus?"

"Circus nothing! He's a mountain horse. His name is C-i-r-q-u-e. Don't you know any geology? A cirque is the round place hollowed out of the granite at the head of a stream by a glacier. You ought to study geology," I told him. "It makes the mountains much more interesting."

He said he doubted if he'd ever have time.

That was Wake. His whole name was Wakefield Bender. He was seventeen, and this was his first trip into the Sierra Nevada. He had heard that the Merced, just below the Ranger cabin, was full of cascades running between granite cliffs, and he thought they would make interesting pictures.

Daddy suggested I help him choose a place to camp. It was lucky I did. Wake didn't know any more about the woods than I know about photography.

"This looks like a fine place to hang my hat," he announced at the place where the trail crossed Rafferty Creek, two minutes from our cabin. "I'd like to wake up in the morning looking at those big black rocks sticking out through the bubbles."

"You'll wake up in a puddle if it rains," I told him. "Rafferty catches a tremendous runoff. It spreads out all over the place after a shower."

As he was looking back at the foam of water he stumbled and nearly went flat. If I had known how easy it was for Wake to stumble I never would have cut through the woods on a deer trail! He laughed about his clumsiness, though, even when a rock sent him sprawling. I couldn't help laughing too. He looked so silly with his heron legs waving in the air.

"Your legs remind me of Alice and her neck," I said. "They've grown so fast you don't know how to manage them."

"Quick!" he shouted. "Find me a mushroom to nibble!"

After that we were easy together. Somehow, when people too old for fairy tales both like *Alice in Wonder-*

56

land it gives them the feeling of being old friends.

The place I had in mind for Wake's camp didn't suit him at all. "This has no character," he objected.

"But look at the firewood! And it has perfect screening from the wind."

He still shook his head. "It's just shrubbery. I want to camp where the outlook has form—composition of some kind. A picture to live with."

Finally he made camp on a granite shelf, where little crooked pines grow out of the cracks in the rock. As I watched him unpack I hoped he had food in his knapsack as well as camera stuff, because he was awfully thin. You could see his shoulderblades right through his shirt. I couldn't help liking him. He had nice brown eyes that looked straight at you—that is, when one of them wasn't covered up with the piece of rumply hair. I asked him why he didn't get a haircut before he came away.

"There wasn't time," he said. "And anyhow, I'd spent all my allowance on film."

Wake walked over to our cabin quite often to watch me jumping Cirque, and sometimes I rode past his camp to tell him about something I thought he might like to photograph. I never picked the things he wanted, though. It was the cascades that fascinated him. They were difficult to photograph because the canyon walls are so steep, and he was anxious to explore the other side of the river for a better angle, so one day I showed him where my log crosses. My log—I call it mine because I've used it so many years—is the only way over the

Merced between our cabin and the big junction bridge five miles upstream. Wake said he wished he could skitter about fallen trees the way I do. His legs reminded me of a colt's—they wouldn't quite obey him.

We had several conversations before I asked him about dancing. I wanted to know if he thought dancing was important for a girl to learn, the way Daddy seemed to think it was.

"I certainly don't think it's important," he told me. "Most girls at dances are so silly I can't find anything to talk to them about. I only go to parties myself because I don't wish to become a recluse."

If Wake felt tongue-tied at dances I decided I needn't bother with them either. Because certainly Wake had more ideas to the minute than anyone I'd ever known, except my father.

Half our businessman's vacation was gone when the first storm broke. It had been building for two days, but I couldn't make Wake believe that those cloudy afternoons meant the sky would pour down buckets of water someday soon. First the clouds grew gray, then black. Daddy looked at the barometer and put the fattest chunk of pine he could find into our stove. Big drops began to spatter against the glass, hitting slowly at first, in little spurts between the gusts of wind. Then the wind came roaring down off the Clark Range and whole sheets of water pounded the windows.

We could almost see the river rising as every crack and gully on the canyon walls filled with rain and melted snow. I knew my log would soon be under water

58

—might even be swept away. After a little the rain changed to hail—big, mountain hail, like mothballs. I thought the windowpanes would shatter.

But if the rain comes fast, it never lasts long. The minute the storm was over I went out to see how Cirque was. He looked pretty shivery, huddled against Daddy's horse in one corner of the corral. Even his beautiful tail was droopy.

"How about a good run to warm up?" I asked him.

His ears said "Let's go!"

I was wondering about Wake, too, remembering the casual way he'd anchored his pup tent to a couple of twiggy bushes. If his bedding was wet I thought it would be friendly to invite him into the cabin to dry off. I was sure Daddy wouldn't mind, though he always says we can't take in all the campers in the Sierra to dry off every time it rains.

I jumped on Cirque bareback and we galloped down the trail to where I could see Wake's tent. The granite sand was still full of puddles that splashed as we tore along, and Cirque skidded to a quick stop with his forefeet in the air. He's glorious when he does that. I wished Daddy could have seen him.

"Hi, Wake!" I shouted. "Did you get all your stuff under cover?" When nobody answered I crashed Cirque right across the dead timber to Wake's camp. He wasn't there. All his things were spread around outside the tent, soaking wet, so I knew he must have been off taking pictures when it began to rain.

Suddenly I was frightened. I don't think I ever felt

really frightened in the mountains before. Daddy never lets us get into jams, because he knows ahead of time where danger lies; but Wake was such a baby in the woods, slipping and stumbling, never paying any attention to where he was going because he was so busy thinking about his lovely pictures. I was sure he had gone to photograph the cascades, for he'd been talking about them so much, never satisfied with the shots he had already made.

My heels dug into Cirque, and he bounded straight ahead like a deer through underbrush. I headed for my log because I was positive that was where Wake had crossed the river. The Merced had risen at least ten inches, and the current was so strong that even a champion swimmer would have been dashed over the falls. It was sweeping across the top of the log now, and I dared not try to cross on it.

Then I saw his head—the rest of him was under water. I'm never going to forget the way his eyes looked. They were wide open and glinty, like a wild animal's facing a light at night. With one hand he was clinging to a branch of driftwood that had wedged against my log; with the other, he was trying to hold his camera out of the water. He saw me, too, but I knew he couldn't hear my voice. The water was so loud it drowned the sound.

There was no time to go for Daddy. Wake was on the upstream side of the log, but the driftwood he was clinging to might come loose any minute. Then the water would sweep him right under the log. If that happened he wouldn't have a chance. Not against the cascades.

I thought of old Mr. Scripps washing the whole way down to Nevada Falls. Cirque and I were going to have to get Wake out! There wasn't any other way. "Please God," I prayed, "make the driftwood stick together until we get there."

Cirque understood too, I think. He began quivering all over as I urged him right to the edge of the river. "Come on, Cirque," I whispered, wishing my bare heels were spurs. In a moment the current was swirling around his knees. He planted his forefeet on the bottom and refused to budge.

"Cirque!" I cried. "We've got to get Wake out of there quickly!"

He lowered his head, sniffling the roily brown water, then looked around at me as if he were saying, "Meg, old girl, it's too much for us. The old Merced is too strong for you and me."

A terrible gust of wind whipped the branches of a tree against my face. I realized then exactly what I would have to do. Without my weight Cirque stood a chance of crossing the river. But he would have to be driven forcibly into the water. I leaned as far forward as I could and screamed at Wake, "Catch Cirque's tail!" Then I stood up on Cirque's back and grabbed the tree branch with one hand. With one foot I whacked him across the rump with all my might and bellowed, "Go on, Cirque!" Startled, he lunged into the stream, while I swung over the water. It was hard getting my legs up on the branch, because it wasn't steady like the pine over the corral. But finally I made it.

Blessed Cirque. He understood. He waded out as far as he could toward Wake, and all I could do was to sit there, biting blood out of my lips. When the current took him he began to swim, struggling with all his brave stock-horse heart against the flood water. Wake had to let his camera go, but he caught Cirque's tail and the horse dragged him, slowly but surely, up on the other side.

I thought, of course, that Wake would jump on Cirque, ride to the junction bridge and back to the ranger cabin for Daddy. But I could see that he was too exhausted to move.

Cirque stood over him, sniffing with his velvet nose. Then he pawed the ground as if he were saying, "Come on! My mistress can't hang on that branch forever." But Wake just lay there, shivering. Cirque tossed his head and whinnied—then crashed off into the underbrush alone. It's five miles to the junction bridge and five miles back on our side of the river, so I knew I'd have to hang on a good long time. But I never supposed any time would *feel* so long. I tried to settle myself more comfortably in the crotch of the tree, and watched the mad waters swirling around the trunk.

Daddy came at last. He lassoed me with a rope, then threw another rope over the branch for me to shinny down. When I felt the ground under my feet again and Daddy's arms around me, I got silly and cried. He tossed me up in back of his saddle, and all the way back to the cabin I hugged him around the waist, tight, the way I used to ride when I was a little girl. Daddy said Cirque must have galloped every inch of the way. He'd come to the corral fence lathered with sweat, in spite of the icy wind, and Daddy had known right away, when he saw him riderless, that something had happened to me.

"Get yourself warm, Meg; then put plenty of water on to heat and fill every bottle you can lay your hands on. Make a hot drink," he called back as he dashed out the door, "and warm some blankets in front of the fire."

I was so busy carrying out his instructions that it didn't seem any time before he was back with the still-dripping Wake. Daddy took off Wake's clothes, bundled him into a pair of flannel pajamas, and wrapped him in the warm

63

blankets lined with bottles of hot water. In a little while he was able to sit up and take the hot drink, and by evening he was enjoying the huge meal we brought to him on a tray.

The next morning I was getting breakfast in the kitchen when Daddy came in with a load of wood. "I can't wait any longer to ask you, Dad," I said, putting down the coffee I'd been measuring. "I've got to know about it now. Are we still going to sell Cirque?"

Daddy stood stock-still. "Sell him!" he exclaimed. "What an idea! Cirque can have a golden stall and feed on stardust mixed with diamonds as far as I'm concerned. Perhaps I rushed into things a bit too fast. You seem to be working matters out pretty well in your own way. I'm sorry about the camp, but all the arrangements are made, so I'm afraid you'll have to be a good sport about it this summer."

"Oh, I will, Dad," I vowed. "And I'll promise to enjoy it if only we don't have to sell Cirque."

He dropped the armful of wood by the stove and went back for another. Then I did the silliest thing. I was so glad inside—too glad for words, I guess. I just cried and cried.

Wake doesn't know I cried, though. He has often told me since that he thinks I was very brave about everything. I'd rather not let him know I cried, because I'd like him to go on thinking that.

Nicholas Kalashnikoff

The Birth of Jumper

IN THE SOFT LIGHT of the northern winter night, earth and sky lay wrapped in peace. The stars looked down from distant heights upon white-clad hills, forests, plains, and the immense expanse that was Lake Baikal, frozen over now and breathlessly quiet. Sparks from the chimneys made fantastic patterns against the heavens, then died in the mist. It was a fairylike picture, with the houses of the village of Kabansk standing out like black dominoes against nature's snowy screen.

Occasionally the anguished howls of wolves ravenous for food broke the stillness. In reply, dogs barked in excited chorus, giving notice to the marauders that they were at their posts and not to be caught napping. There was no other sound.

Except for the sparks from chimneys, the houses were dark, and even the chimneys were becoming less animated minute by minute. Siberians do not believe in wasting firewood. If at any time during the night a fire is kept actively alive, you may be sure it is not a whim but some urgent need.

Signs indicated that everyone in the village was asleep except those in the household of Gerasim Ozerov. Sparks pouring skyward singled out the house, lying prominently in the very center of the village.

It was Gerasim himself, a robust peasant with a bushy, graying beard, who threw fresh logs onto the fire and waited. He had no thought of sleep. He was greatly worried. Nine days ago, by careful reckoning, the old black mare, his favorite, was due to foal. Nine days, and still not a sign. This was bad, especially so because she refused food and obviously was suffering. Every time he approached her she breathed heavily, like a human being in pain, and yet there was nothing he could do. The bitter weather added complications. Although the stable floor was covered with straw and all cracks were stuffed against the searching wind, there was danger that the colt would freeze should he miss the foaling. This was the thing he dreaded. This was the reason he, or someone of the household, stayed awake all night.

Beside Gerasim, near the fire, a boy sat reading in a droning voice from a large book on the care of horses. The boy was Gerasim's son, Denis, ten years old and lame. Even when he was sitting, one could see that one of his legs was different from the other.

Gerasim listened, half dozing. After a time he roused himself and, picking up the lantern, left the warmth of the fire to visit the stall where the mare stood, her head drooping, her belly incredibly distended. With one hand stroking the animal's broad quarters he shook his head and plucked at his beard. "Be patient, Dowager," he said soothingly. "It won't be much longer, if God lets everything go well. Try to drop the colt. Whatever is ailing you? This is not your first. You've given me many fine colts. Now be a good girl and gladden our hearts again."

The animal's suffering gave Gerasim an odd feeling of helplessness, for in his village he was considered an authority in all matters relating to cattle and horses, a first-rate veterinarian—self-taught. The peasants always sought his help in a difficult case and he never refused. For his services he accepted trifling gifts or vodka but no money. He was very obstinate about this, being content with the esteem of his neighbors. It was cause for rejoicing when one of his patients got well, and cause for grief when one died. Then he bewailed his ignorance, which denied him the skill of trained veterinarians who, according to rumor, performed miracles by operating on animals as doctors do on human beings.

He looked at the mare and called to mind other instances of difficult foaling in his experience. Yes, all was not well. Delay in foaling was not in itself unusual. A mare couldn't be expected to drop her burden pre-

67

cisely on the minute. But nine days, and such an old mare as Dowager . . . That was cause for concern.

Before he left the stable he examined the mare, wiped her watering eyes, and crept under her and placed his ear to her belly, trying to detect signs of another life. Was there a movement? Or was the sound only a rumbling in the intestines, as it had been so many times before?

Feeling only slightly reassured, Gerasim returned to the house. The boy, who was on the verge of falling asleep, roused himself, picked up the book, and went on reading where he had left off. *The Horse and How to Care for It* was the title of the volume. Gerasim had inherited it from his father and knew most of it by heart.

Sitting there listening to the boy's droning voice, dark thoughts assailed him. Here was Denis, born with a deformed foot, a perpetual reminder of someone's carelessness. With peasant logic he thought: If my woman bore many children successfully, and yet injured the last child in her belly, then a like evil can befall the mare. Maybe she hit herself against something. Perhaps she fell. How can you tell? Maybe the colt is dead inside her.

Gerasim hated to think of it, because this time he had mated Dowager with a rare, visiting stallion, and he looked forward with more than ordinary interest to the offspring of that union.

It had happened like this. The stallion was on his way to be delivered to the owner of a nearby gold mine when he suddenly developed a lameness in one leg. An odd-looking creature, he resembled a big hare rather than a horse. The man in charge of him brought him to Gerasim.

"Help me, Gerasim," he begged. "I'll lose my job if I bring the master a lame beast. This is no ordinary horse. He has English blood and won a prize at the races in Tomsk. If you will cure him I'll pay you out of my own pocket."

Gerasim examined the animal thoroughly but could find nothing seriously wrong. One front leg was slightly swollen near the knee—the result of a slight knock or a misstep—but the bones were uninjured. After several days of poulticing with hay and bran the swelling went down. The keeper was delighted and wanted to pay Gerasim then and there, but Gerasim refused. Instead he asked permission to mate the stallion with his finest mare.

"All right," the man agreed. "But why? What do you want with this mongrel? He's useless for farming. What will you do with a horse of his breed? Parade around with him? You need an animal that is strong, one that can plow and drive across the taiga in any weather. Beasts like this are for rich people to use for sport or show. Those who have more money than they know what to do with can spend it on such playthings. What is there to him? Neither beauty nor strength."

Gerasim scratched the back of his head as he answered good-naturedly, "I don't agree with you, my friend. I have a feeling that if we mate his elegance with my Dowager we might produce an excellent breed. I have read about such things in books, also some smart people have told me. Anyway, we'll try."

The man shook his head but said no more.

The mating went off well, and Gerasim himself

69

attended the mare during the next eleven months. Never before had he given a horse such attention.

Now, thinking of all these things, he interrupted the boy and said dolefully, "We are ignorant people, Denis. We don't know anything. Maybe we shouldn't have crossed the mare with the English mongrel. But it was such a temptation. Think! If Dowager will give birth to a stallion, and we rear him, he will provide for the whole village. What a breed that will be—Siberian-English! It strikes me that it should be a mighty fine horse."

Denis answered quickly and with enthusiasm, imitating his father's voice: "Of course. It will be splendid to have a stallion. Improve the breed here, too."

It meant a great deal to the boy to be allowed to discuss such an important household matter, and to a peasant nothing is more important than the increase of his livestock. It meant that Gerasim valued his, Denis's, opinion as he would that of an adult. It confirmed the promise his father had made him only two days ago before the icon, when he had said, crossing himself, "Let God be gracious and help Dowager drop her colt. That colt will be yours. On my word of honor."

To have a horse of his very own! Since that moment Denis had been beside himself. His father's anxiety was his anxiety. There was nothing he would not do to help. When his father slept he stayed awake to keep an eye on the mare, and through the day on the slightest pretext he would grab his hat and jacket and pay a visit to the stable. His mother was provoked with both of them. "The old man and the youngster have lost their minds," she grumbled, "and we'll all die of the cold if they don't stop opening the door every other minute."

Feeling the responsibility of ownership, Denis also worried about the mare, but his thoughts were not Gerasim's thoughts. He knew something of the business of bringing life into the world—what peasant boy doesn't? It was fascinating and mysterious to think that Dowager's grotesque body, which she supported with difficulty by planting her feet wide apart, held a fully formed colt! A miracle! It was only necessary for her to let go of it, and he believed it would help if she could scream. He remembered when the wife of his eldest brother had had her child, how she had shrieked and how the midwife had soothed her, saying, "That's right, my dear. Cry out as loud as you can and push hard and you won't even notice when the baby comes."

Was it really so? At any rate the woman gave birth to a lusty girl. He thought sagely, "That's what Dowager should do—scream. It would be easier for her."

But the mare was silent. She just stood for hours at a time, not daring to lie down, because once her legs gave way under the burden she was afraid she would not rise again. Now and then she moved laboriously from one corner of the stall to another, and she drank a mixture of water and rye, though she refused food.

Such a strange thing, this giving birth. Sometimes it all went well, as in the case of his brother's wife. But you never could tell. There was that woman his mother had told him about, a relative who died in child-birth. She was young and healthy, too. . . .

71

There is no telling where the boy's thoughts would have carried him had not Gerasim just then thrown a log on the fire and startled him out of his slumber. Yawning and stretching, he rose to his feet.

"Wake me if you need me," he said apologetically. "Will you? I'll go and lie down a while."

Gerasim reached out a hand to stroke his son's thick hair. "Don't worry," he replied. "In case anything happens I'll wake you without fail."

Alone, Gerasim lit his pipe and settled more comfortably. His mind raced back and forth, seeking an explanation for the good and evil that were his lot. For it is common sense that everything has a cause. Take his life. There was nothing for him to complain about. He had a nice family. The two eldest sons were married, a third was in the Imperial Guards, in Petersburg, and Denis did well in school. His circumstances in other respects also were enviable. His granaries were full and his pantries well-provisioned. In the stables were twenty fine horses and thirty cows, while two hundred sheep ranged his land. Yes, there was plenty of everything. Moreover, Gerasim was greatly respected in the village, indeed in the entire district. It was no chance that twice he had been elected elder. Now, however, though still in robust health, he was less active in village affairs and devoted himself chiefly to his farm, to hunting, and fishing. His taxes were paid promptly, and he had an excellent record with the authorities. Nor had he forgotten God, though he seldom went to church; on occasion he showed his devotion by lighting candles before the images of the holy saints.

There, sitting by the fire with his pipe, trying to drive off sleep, he thought of these things and many more and arrived finally at an acceptable conclusion.

"Of course there is sin. Who is without it? Often you sin unknowingly. Only a fool would sin consciously. Our kind, peasants, sin only when under the influence of drink. But how can a drunkard be held accountable? Yes, everything will be well if only Dowager will not disappoint us."

While every evil must have a cause, he reasoned, if the evil that had befallen Dowager could be traced to no sin of his, then surely the outcome was not to be dreaded. His thoughts began and ended here.

At dawn the following morning, February 27, 1911, the hoped-for miracle took place, and Gerasim duly entered it in a small notebook in which he recorded important household events. It required no notebook to impress it upon the boy's memory.

He had been sleeping, when someone touched him roughly.

"Wake up."

To his startled eyes the house appeared unusually bright. Everyone was up, although it was still dark, and there was a joyous murmuring all around. The family was crowded into the corner beside the great stove. Denis ran there, and squeezing himself between the crouched bodies, was just in time to see his father wipe a wet, black colt which was lying shivering on some fresh straw.

Gerasim was saying in a happy, excited voice, "God was good and Dowager did not disappoint us. Look what a splendid young one she gave us. I almost missed it by oversleeping, old scamp that I am. The colt would have frozen to death."

When he saw Denis standing there, his eyes fairly popping from his head, Gerasim shouted, "He's yours, my boy. Come, take care of him."

The words were like sweet music to Denis. Dropping down beside the colt, he reached out with his small hand and stroked the soft, silky head.

"Look, look," he cried, "what beautiful, fine eyes he has! See how he is watching us!"

Nothing at that moment existed for the boy but the dark-eyed colt. On an impulse he gathered the wobbly head into his arms, and the sudden rush of emotion he felt toward the helpless being was not unlike a mother's feeling for her child. Then he turned to his father.

"Father, how will you christen him? What are we going to name him?"

Gerasim stroked his beard and mused.

"You are right. We must give him a name. We ought to call him after his father, but his was such a long and fancy name that I can't remember it. What we can do to honor his father is to call him Jumper. He has his mother's coloring, but his legs are slender and strong, just like his father's. Yes, we'll call him Jumper. How do you like that?"

"Fine, Father. That's it—Jumper."

While this conversation was going on the colt had gradually ceased to shiver. Lying there calmly on the

74

soft straw, he turned his head first to one side, then to
the other, and it seemed that nothing escaped his great
wondering eyes. Yet certainly he had no realization of
the joy he brought to these people who looked at him so
intently.

75

Anna Sewell

The Last Days
of Black Beauty

HARD TIMES

I shall never forget my new master; he had black eyes
and a hooked nose, his mouth was as full of teeth as a
bulldog's, and his voice was as harsh as the grinding of
cart wheels over gravel stones. His name was Nicholas
Skinner, and I believe he was the same man that poor
Seedy Sam drove for.

Much as I had seen before, I never knew until now
the utter misery of a cab horse's life. Skinner had a set
of cabs and a set of drivers. He was hard on the men,
and the men were hard on the horses. In this place we

had no Sunday rest, and it was in the heat of summer.

Sometimes on a Sunday morning a party of five men would hire the cab for the day, and I had to take them ten or fifteen miles out into the country and back again; never would any of them get down to walk up a hill, unless, indeed, the driver was afraid I would not manage it, and sometimes I was so fevered and worn that I could hardly touch my food. How I used to long for the nice bran mash with niter in it that Jerry used to give us on Saturday nights in hot weather, which used to cool us down and make us so comfortable. Then we had two nights and a whole day for unbroken rest, and on Monday morning we were as fresh as young horses again; but here there was no rest, and my driver was just as hard as his master. He had a cruel whip with something so sharp at the end that it sometimes drew blood, and he would even whip me under the belly and flip the lash out at my head.

My life was now so utterly wretched that I wished I might drop down dead at my work, like Ginger, and be out of my misery—and one day my wish very nearly came to pass.

I went on the stand at eight in the morning, and had done a good share of work, when we had to take a fare to the station. A train was just expected in, so my driver pulled up at the back of some of the outside cabs to take the chance of a return fare. It was a very long train, and our cab was called for. There was a party of four—a noisy, blustering man with a lady, a little boy, and a young girl—and a great deal of luggage. The lady and the boy got into the cab, and while the man ordered about the luggage, the young girl came and looked at me.

"Papa," she said, "I am sure this poor horse cannot take us and all our luggage so far, he is so very weak and worn out; do look at him."

"Oh! he's all right, miss," said my driver. "He's strong enough."

The porter, who was pulling about some heavy boxes, suggested to the gentleman that as there was so much luggage, he might take a second cab.

"Can your horse do it, or can't he?" said the blustering man.

"Oh! he can do it all right, sir; he could take more than that." And he helped to haul up a box so heavy that I could feel the springs go down.

"Papa, Papa, do take a second cab," said the young girl in a beseeching tone. "I am sure this is very cruel."

"Nonsense, Grace, get in at once, and don't make all this fuss. A pretty thing it would be if a man had to examine every cab horse before he hired it—the man knows his own business of course. There, get in—and hold your tongue!"

My gentle friend had to obey; and box after box was dragged up and lodged on the top of the cab or settled by the side of the driver. At last all was ready, and with his usual jerk at the rein and slash of the whip, he drove out of the station.

I got along fairly well until we came to Ludgate Hill, but there the heavy load and my own exhaustion were too much. I was struggling to keep on, goaded by constant chucks of the rein and use of the whip, when, suddenly—I cannot tell how—my feet slipped from under me, and I fell heavily to the ground on my side. The force with which I fell seemed to beat all the breath out of my body. I had no power to move, and I thought now I was going to die. I heard a sort of confusion around me and loud angry voices, but it was all like a dream. I thought I heard that sweet pitiful voice saying, "Oh, that poor horse! It is all our fault." Someone came and loosened the throat strap of my bridle and undid the traces which kept the collar so tight upon me. Someone said, "He's dead, he'll never get up again." Then I could hear a policeman giving orders, but I did not even open my eyes; I could only draw a gasping breath now and then. Some cold water was thrown over my head, and some cordial was poured into my mouth, and something was put over me.

I cannot tell how long I lay there, but I found my life coming back, and a kind-voiced man was patting me and encouraging me to rise. After some more cordial had been given me, and after one or two attempts, I staggered to my feet and was gently led to some stables which were close by. Here I was put into a well-littered stall, and some warm gruel was brought to me, which I drank thankfully.

In the evening I was sufficiently recovered to be led back to Skinner's stables, where I think they did the best for me they could. In the morning Skinner came with a farrier to look at me. He examined me very closely and said, "This is overwork more than disease, and if you could give him a rest for six months, he would be able to work again; but now there is not an ounce of strength in him."

"Then he must go to the dogs," said Skinner. "I have no meadows to nurse sick horses in—he might get well or he might not; that sort of thing don't suit my business. My plan is to work 'em as long as they'll go, and then sell 'em for what they'll bring—at the slaughterhouse or elsewhere."

"If he was broken-winded," said the farrier, "you had better have him killed out of hand, but he is not. There is a sale of horses coming off in about ten days; if you rest him and feed him up, he may pick up, and you may get more than his skin is worth, at any rate."

Upon this advice Skinner, rather unwillingly I think, gave orders that I should be well fed and cared for, and the stable man, happily for me, carried out the orders with a much better will than his master had in giving them. Ten days of perfect rest, plenty of good oats, hay, bran mashes, with boiled linseed mixed in them, did more to get up my condition than anything else could have done. Those linseed mashes were delicious, and I began to think, after all, it might be better to live than go to the dogs. When I was taken to the sale, a few miles out of London, I felt that any change from my present place must be an improvement, so I held up my head and hoped for the best.

FARMER THOROUGHGOOD
AND HIS GRANDSON WILLIE

At this sale, of course, I found myself in company with the old broken-down horses—lame, broken-winded, old, and some that I am sure it would have been merciful to shoot.

Many of the buyers and sellers looked not much better off than the poor beasts they were bargaining about. There were poor old men trying to get a pony for a few pounds, that might drag about some little wood or coal cart. There were poor men trying to sell a worn-out beast for two or three pounds rather than have the greater loss of killing him. Some of them looked as if poverty and hard times had hardened them all over; but there were others that I would have willingly used the last of my strength in serving—poor and shabby, but kind and human, with voices that I could trust. There was one tottering old man who took a great fancy to me, and I to him, but I was not strong enough.

I noticed a man who looked like a gentleman farmer, with a young boy by his side; he had a broad back and round shoulders, a kind, ruddy face, and he wore a broad-brimmed hat. When he came up to me and my companions, he stood still and looked at us sympathetically. I saw his eye rest on me; I had still a good mane and tail, which did something for my appearance. I pricked my ears and looked at him.

"There's a horse, Willie, that has known better days."

"Poor old fellow!" said the boy. "Do you think, Grandpapa, he was ever a carriage horse?"

"He might have been anything when he was young; look at his nostrils and his ears, the shape of his neck and shoulders; there's a deal of breeding about that horse." He put out his hand and gave me a kind pat on the neck. I put out my nose in answer to his kindness. The boy stroked my face.

"Poor old fellow! see, Grandpapa, how well he understands kindness. Could not you buy him and make him young again, as you did with Ladybird?"

THE LAST DAYS OF BLACK BEAUTY

"My dear boy, I can't make all old horses young. Besides, Ladybird was not so much old as run down and badly used."

"Well, Grandpapa, I don't believe that this one is old; look at his mane and tail. I wish you would look into his mouth, and then you could tell. Though he is so very thin, his eyes are not sunk like some old horses."

The old gentleman laughed. "Bless the boy! he is as horsy as his old grandfather."

The man who had brought me for sale now put in his word.

"The young gentleman's a real knowing one, sir. Now the fact is, this horse is just pulled down with overwork in the cabs. He's not an old one, and the horse doctor says that a six months' rest would set him right up, as his wind was not broken. I've had the tending of him these ten days past, and a gratefuller, pleasanter animal I never met with, and it would be worth a gentleman's while to give a five-pound note for him and let him have a chance. I'll be bound he'd be worth twenty pounds next spring."

The old gentleman laughed, and the little boy looked up eagerly.

"Oh! Grandpapa, did you not say the colt sold for five pounds more than you expected? You would not be poorer if you did buy this one."

The farmer slowly felt my legs, which were much swelled and strained, then he looked at my mouth: "Thirteen or fourteen, I should say. Just trot him out, will you?"

I arched my poor thin neck, raised my tail a little, and

threw out my legs as well as I could, for they were very stiff.

But the old gentleman must have liked what he saw, for he bought me for five pounds and had me taken to the inn.

The boy could hardly control his delight, and the old gentleman seemed to enjoy his pleasure. I had a good meal at the inn, and was then gently ridden home by a servant of my new master's and turned into a large meadow with a shed in one corner of it.

Mr. Thoroughgood—for that was the name of my benefactor—gave orders that I should have hay and oats every night and morning, and the run of the meadow during the day, and told Willie to take charge of me.

The boy was proud of his charge and undertook it in all seriousness. There was not a day when he did not pay me a visit, sometimes giving me a bit of carrot or something good, or sometimes standing by me while I ate my oats. He always came with kind words and caresses, and of course I grew very fond of him. He called me Old Crony, as I used to come to him in the field and follow him about. Sometimes he brought his grandfather, who always looked closely at my legs.

"He is improving so steadily," said Mr. Thoroughgood, "that I think we shall see a change for the better in the spring."

The perfect rest, the good food, the soft turf, and gentle exercise soon began to tell on my condition and my spirits. I had a good constitution from my mother, and I was never strained when I was young, so that I had a

84

better chance than many horses who have been worked before they came to their full strength. During the winter my legs improved so much that I began to feel quite young again. The spring came, and one day in March Mr. Thoroughgood determined that he would try me in the phaeton. I was well pleased, and he and Willie drove me a few miles. My legs were not stiff now and I did the work with perfect ease.

"He's growing young, Willie; we must give him a little gentle work now, and by midsummer he will be as good as Ladybird. He has a beautiful mouth and good paces —they can't be better."

"Oh! Grandpapa, how glad I am you bought him!"

"So am I, my boy, he has to thank you more than me. We must now be looking out for a quiet, gentle place for him, where he will be valued."

MY LAST HOME

One day during this summer the groom cleaned and dressed me with such care that I thought some new change must be at hand. He trimmed my fetlocks and legs, passed the tarbrush over my hoofs, and even parted my forelock. I think the harness had an extra polish.

"I hope the ladies take to him," said the old gentleman.

"We can but try."

We came to a pretty house with a lawn and shrubbery at the front and a drive up to the door. Willie rang the bell, and Mr. Thoroughgood went into the house. In about ten minutes he returned, followed by three ladies: Miss Lavinia, a tall, pale lady, wrapped in a white shawl, leaning on a younger lady with dark eyes and a merry face; the other, a very stately-looking person, was Miss Blomefield. They all came and looked at me and asked questions. The younger lady—that was Miss Ellen —took to me very much; she said she was sure she would like me, I had such a good face. Miss Lavinia said that she would always be nervous in riding behind a horse that had once been down, as I might come down again.

"Many good horses," said Mr. Thoroughgood, "have had their knees broken through the carelessness of their drivers, without any fault of their own, and from what I see of this horse, I would say that is his case. Why not have him on trial, and then your coachman will see what he thinks of him."

"You have always been such a good adviser to us," said the stately lady, "that your recommendation would go a long way with me, and if my sister Lavinia sees no objection, we will accept your offer of a trial, with thanks."

It was then arranged that I should be sent for the next day.

In the morning a smart-looking young man came for me. At first he looked pleased, but when he saw my knees, he said in a disappointed voice, "I didn't think, sir, you would have recommended my ladies a blemished horse like that."

"Handsome is as handsome does," said my master; "you are only taking him on trial, and I am sure you will do fairly by him, young man, and if he is not as safe as any horse you ever drove, send him back."

I was led home, placed in a comfortable stable, fed, and left to myself. The next day when my groom was cleaning my face, he said, "That is just like the star that Black Beauty had. He is much the same height too; I wonder where he is now."

A little further on he came to the place in my neck where I was bled and where a little knot was left in the skin. He started, and began to look me over carefully, talking to himself.

"White star in the forehead, one white foot on the off side, this little knot just in that place"—then looking at the middle of my back—"and as I am alive, there is that little patch of white hair that John used to call 'Beauty's threepenny bit.' It *must* be Black Beauty! Why, Beauty! Beauty! do you know me? little Joe Green, that almost killed you?" And he began stroking and patting me as if he was quite overjoyed.

I could not say that I remembered him, for now he was a strapping young fellow with a man's voice, but I was sure he knew me and that he was Joe Green, and I was very glad. I put my nose up to him and tried to say that we were friends. I never saw a man so pleased.

"Give you a fair trial! I should think so indeed! I wonder who the rascal was that broke your knees, my old Beauty! You must have been badly served somewhere. Well, it won't be my fault if you haven't good times of it now. I wish John Manly was here to see you."

In the afternoon I was put into a low park chair and

Miss Ellen tried me, and Green went with her. I soon found that she was a good driver, and she seemed pleased with my paces. I heard Joe telling her that he was sure I was Squire Gordon's old Black Beauty.

When we returned, the other sisters came out to hear how I had behaved. She told them what she had just heard, and said, "I shall certainly write to Mrs. Gordon, and tell her that her Black Beauty has come to us. How pleased she will be!"

After this I was driven every day for a week or so, and as I appeared to be quite safe, Miss Lavinia at last ventured out in the small close carriage. After this it was quite decided to keep me and call me by my old name of "Black Beauty."

I have now lived in this happy place a whole year. Joe is the best and kindest of grooms. My work is easy and pleasant, and I feel my strength and spirits all coming back again. Mr. Thoroughgood said to Joe the other day, "In your place he will last until he is twenty years old— perhaps more."

Willie always speaks to me when he can and treats me as his special friend. My ladies have promised that I shall never be sold, and so I have nothing to fear; and here my story ends. My troubles are all over, and I am at home; and often before I am quite awake, I imagine I am still in the orchard at Birtwick, standing with my old friends under the apple trees.

Anonymous

The Bell of Atri

Concerning an Alarm Bell Instituted
in the Time of King Giovanni
Italian, 13th or 14th century

IN THE REIGN of King Giovanni d'Atri, a certain great
bell was ordered to be erected for the special use of individuals who might happen to meet with any grievous
injuries, when they were to ring as loudly as they could
for the purpose of obtaining redress. Now it so fell out
that the rope in the course of time was nearly worn
away; a bunch of snakeweed had been fastened to it for
the convenience of the ringers. One day a fine old
courser belonging to a knight of Atri, which being no
longer serviceable, had been turned out to run at large
and was wandering near the place. Being hard-pressed
by famine, the poor steed seized hold of the snakeweed

89

with his mouth and sounded the bell pretty smartly. The council, on hearing the clamor, immediately assembled, as if to hear the petition of the horse, whose appearance seemed to declare that he required justice. Taking the case into consideration, it was soon decreed that the same cavalier whom the horse had so long served while he was young should be compelled to maintain him in his old age; and the king even imposed a fine in similar instances to the same effect.

Merrit P. Allen

The Mudhen, V.S.

SITTING CROSS-LEGGED on the grass of the back campus, Froggie Bates looked earnestly at the sky and repeated, " 'Breathes there a man with soul so dead who never to himself hath said—hath said—hath said—' Mud, what was it the guy said to himself?" He appealed to his roommate, known to the whole school as The Mudhen.

"It sounds like a horse," The Mudhen remarked, from his horizontal position on the ground.

"Naw! He didn't say, 'It sounds like a horse.' That doesn't make sense."

"Shut up!" The Mudhen rolled on his side.

91

"But, Mud, I've got to learn the thing before class tomorrow."

"*It is* a horse. I can hear it walking with my ear to the ground like an Indian."

"What's biting you? A horse walking with his ear to the ground like an Indian!"

"It's in the Bumble Bee's garden." The Mudhen got up with unusual speed. "We'd better see about it in case he is away."

"What harm will he do if he is away?"

"The *horse*, jughead, he'll ruin the garden."

They climbed the fence, edged through some shrubbery, and came upon Mr. Beeman digging in a flower bed. He looked up and smiled in his usual friendly way.

"I thought I heard a horse walking," The Mudhen explained.

"What you heard was probably William Shakespeare," Mr. Beeman answered and went on digging.

"I—" The Mudhen paused and blinked. "I thought it was a horse."

"William seemed restless, so I tethered him behind the barn," Mr. Beeman said casually.

They hardly expected to find the Bard there, but just to put things straight they looked behind the barn. There, walking round and round a picket pin, was a fat little horse that looked lonesome and pricked up his ears with a pleasant expression.

"This is William Shakespeare," said Mr. Beeman, coming around the corner of the barn. "He belongs to my sister, who has left him with me during her vacation."

"Swell! I love horses." The Mudhen went over and stroked William's neck. "Do you object, sir, if I come over and see him once in a while?"

"Assuredly not," Mr. Beeman said eagerly. "You may take full charge of him, if you wish."

"Mud doesn't love him that much," Froggie said.

"Yes, I do too!" The Mudhen declared warmly. "I'll be tickled pink to look after him. Frog, go bring him a pail of water."

"Me!" Froggie snorted. "He's not my baby."

"Run along and get the water—that is, if you want some help with your math tonight," The Mudhen said sweetly.

"You can't kick me around that way!" Froggie cried. "I'll get the water because I like the horse, not because you told me to." He walked away with an independent air.

So began their friendship with William Shakespeare. Why he was so called was never explained to them, nor did it matter. They, like most boys, had a fondness for animals and this one was fat and friendly and something different to play with outside of school. When it came to caring for him, The Mudhen figured out what should be done and Froggie did it, for that was the way their perfect partnership worked. And it was all right with Mr. Beeman, whose interest in horses was nil plus the square of zero multiplied by ten.

It may be that Fate arranged this setup so that when it became necessary for Mr. Beeman to be out of town for a few days the horse would not be neglected. But if

93

Fate left the cover off the grain bin that day, she was either downright careless or hopelessly dumb about the habits of horses. At any rate, William Shakespeare found the box open and ate three times as much grain as he was equipped to handle. When the boys went over to bed him down for the night they found him inflated to blimplike proportions, sweating rivulets, and breathing in a way that brought terror to the hearts of his friends.

"G—G—Gosh sakes! He's g-got the fl-flu," Froggie chattered.

"He's got the bellyache," said the practical Mudhen, pointing at the empty grain bin.

"Is that all?" Froggie looked relieved, for he had suffered that ailment and survived.

"All!" The Mudhen, who knew something about horses, gave him a look. "It's enough to kill him. Beat it to a phone and call a vet."

"But, Mud, they cost four or five bucks."

"That's cheaper than a dead horse. Scram!"

Froggie may have scrammed, but it seemed to the anxious nurse that a fossilized snail could have passed him on the first turn. Minutes masquerading as hours dragged by, while William Shakespeare groaned and sweated and finally lay down broadside on the barn floor. The Mudhen rubbed him with swabs of hay and begged him not to pass out.

"You've got to hang on, Willie," he implored. "If you croak I'll be in dutch with the Bumble Bee and he will be in dutch with his sister. No matter how punk you feel, you mustn't let us down. Please buck up."

But no vet came. Finally Froggie galloped in, carrying

an old-fashioned dinner horn and a huge pitcher full of liquid.

"Where's the vet?" The Mudhen shouted.

"Sick," Froggie panted.

"There are two in town."

"The other one is away. I called the sick one again and told him it was a matter of life and death, for William Shakespeare has an awful bellyache. He tried to be smart and said the British Museum knows more about Shakespeare than he does, so I'd better call them."

"Didn't you tell him William is a horse?"

"Sure, soon's I got a chance to. He said a name like that was enough to give any horse a bellyache."

"And he isn't coming?"

"I told you, Mud, he's sick—sick in bed. But he said to give him, that is, to give William, a pound of baking soda in two quarts of water and exercise him."

"Exercise him!" The Mudhen gestured toward prostrate William. "How you goin' to exercise a horse that can't walk?"

"How do I know? I'm telling you what the man said. So I got the soda from the Bumble Bee's housekeeper and she found a tin horn for me and—"

"For pete's sake! What are you goin' to do with a tin horn?"

"It's not for tooting," Froggie assured him. "The vet said to pour the dope down William's neck through a funnel, but we couldn't find a funnel, so Mrs. Stebbins said to use this horn. We poured some water through it and it perks."

Perking in the kitchen sink was one thing, but perking

down the throat of William Shakespeare was something else. Rank amateurs though they were, the boys knew that the horse's powerful teeth could crush a finger like a stick of candy.

"But we've got to give him that medicine," The Mudhen said grimly. "Whether he lives or dies we can't have folks sayin' we didn't try to save him."

"If he croaks, the Bears will kid us raw," Froggie prophesied.

The Mudhen nodded, well knowing the heathenish temperament of the rival fraternity.

"There must be a vet in some other town," Froggie reasoned. "I'll go ask the telephone girl to call—"

"Eureka!" The Mudhen interrupted.

"Is that a town or a vet?"

"It's this." The Mudhen dived into a dark corner of the barn and came up with a stick about a foot long with a large hole in the middle. "It's a piece of busted ladder. We'll put it between William's jaws and stick the horn through the hole. If he bites, he'll bite the wood."

"Hot dog!" Froggie's tone paid tribute to genius. "They oughta give you a vet's degree or somethin'—like H.D.—horse doctor."

"Please." The Mudhen closed his eyes in pain. "V.S.—veterinary surgeon—not horse doctor."

Deceptively, under pretense of inserting a bit, they persuaded the horse to open his mouth and accept the stick. Gently they worked it back as far as it would go and ever so carefully pushed the dinner horn into the hole, its small end aimed down his gullet. Then, naturally

96

enough, they discovered that while William was in that position nothing would run down his throat. It would be necessary to get him on his feet, pull his head up by running the halter rope through a convenient ring in the ceiling and then, standing on the stairs, transfer the bellywash from the pitcher to the tin horn.

William was, or thought he was, too ill to resist, so eventually he stood with upturned mouth wide open.

"I'll latch onto the halter. You hop up the stairs and drench him," The Mudhen said with a professional air.

"Do what?" Froggie gasped.

"Drench him. That's what vets call giving a big dose of liquid."

"Drench" was the exact word for it and Froggie was the exact drenchee. William inhaled about a quart of the stuff and then sent it back, propelled by a mighty cough and heave that first drowned Froggie, then knocked him off the stairs. The pitcher did not break because it landed on his stomach and emptied itself down his trousers legs. Intuitively The Mudhen leaped backward and let go the knotted halter rope, which flew up and smashed the electric light bulb.

"Are you hurt, Frog?" The Mudhen shouted.

But before the soggy Froggie could answer, the darkness was rent, shattered, pulverized by a blast of sound.

"Jeeeepers!" The Mudhen reeled backward, overtook the open feed bin, and jackknifed into it. The floor trembled as the ailing William bolted for the door, taking the fiendish noise with him.

"Where are you, Mud?" Froggie sounded terrified.

97

"Coming out of the feed box. What happened to Shakespeare?"

"I—I guess he exploded. It's all over me."

"But the noise? That was no explosion."

Just then it sounded again outside the barn, a terrific

metallic bray that would have raised gooseflesh on a fencepost.

"Jumping bobcats! He's blowing the dinner horn, Frog."

"William Shakespeare?"

"That board with the horn in it must be stuck in his mouth."

"Oh, my gosh! What'll we do, Mud?"

"You mean, what will he do?"

"He's doing it."

He was, with gusto. All his life William had been a well-mannered horse, and it is no disparagement to record that he suddenly abandoned his former behavior pattern. Why not? In itself a bellyache is hard to endure and when, in addition, one finds one's mouth filled with something that feels like a woodpile and sounds like the Last Trumpet, one is persuaded to get the heck out of there. So he galloped down the driveway and into the street, giving voice to what was probably the first equine horn solo.

Under ordinary conditions a stanch dinner horn of the old school can make itself heard for a mile, but when it is activated by the lung power of a panic-stricken horse its range becomes amazing. And so does its tone, which acquires not only enormous volume but a weird, unearthly note of alarm that might cause a stuffed crocodile to climb a tree. William Shakespeare made the most of his unsought opportunity by putting his four feet to the pavement in a way reminiscent of Paul Revere, or rather of Paul's horse.

Then something else happened. By one of the most remarkable coincidences in modern times, at the very moment of William's setting forth, the main electric line went flooie and the village became dark. And down the black street, hoofs pounding and horn screeching, went William Shakespeare like a messenger of doom.

"Air raid!" someone screamed, and the words took wing. "Air raid! Air raid! Air raid!" flew along streets, across gardens, over housetops. Somewhere someone snatched a phone and called emergency headquarters.

"Can you verify it?" the operator snapped.

"Don't stand there arguing. They've landed by parachute outside town. Grabbed all the cars, cut the wires, but a guy on horseback got through. Blow, you fool!"

The operator was still hesitating when a clatter of hoofs and a wild blast of alarm drew near and passed into the darkness. "That guy is a hero," the girl sobbed and threw the siren switch.

"Oh, my gosh!" Froggie caught hold of The Mudhen as the wail rose to high heaven. "They'll put us in the pedal fenitentiary for this!"

"Come on!" The Mudhen tugged at him. "We've got to hide that horse before the lights come on."

"You're nuts."

"Everybody is. Scram!"

They ran down the street, which was intermittently lighted by passing cars. By then police sirens were adding to the din and some misguided patriot was clanging a churchbell like mad.

"I can't hear William anymore," Froggie panted. "We're stuck."

THE MUDHEN, V.S.

The Mudhen stopped abruptly and pulled his partner onto a lawn.

"You know something, Frog?"

"Not a thing," Froggie admitted cheerfully.

"If that horse has any sense he'll beat it home where the Bumble Bee's sister lives. That's just outside of town. Let's go."

"There'll be nobody there. She's gone visiting."

"We don't want anybody there except William. Come on! We'll cut through this garden to the back street."

A truck backfired a few feet away and from a window above them a woman shrieked, "That was a bomb! Get ready to jump!"

"Follow me, Frog," The Mudhen shouted.

"I can't see where—" Froggie's voice stopped with a smothered squawk.

"What the heck!" The Mudhen turned back. "What's wrong, Frog?"

"They dropped a parachute on me!" Froggie sounded underground. "Pull it off me, Mud, I'm smothering!"

The Mudhen groped until he found cloth, yards of it, a great blob that seemed to cover the whole lawn. It was heaving violently and from its depths came muffled cries and grunts. There was a sudden ripping sound and Froggie began to cough and sputter like a stalling motor. The Mudhen put out his hands and found the air full of soft floating, flakelike things.

"Feathers!" he cried, enlightened. "Somebody dropped a feather bed on you. Hey, you up there! Don't throw anything more down."

"I'm going to jump on the bed before the house burns

down," the upstairs lady shrieked as the old truck back-fired again in the dark street. "They're bombing us!"

"Don't jump!" The Mudhen yelled. "There's no fire."

She caught the word "fire" and flung it around for all she was worth: "Fire! Fire! Fire!"

"I'll send in an alarm," a neighbor whooped.

"I've got my own hose hooked up," said a voice nearby.

There was a gurgle and a hiss as a vicious unseen stream of water hurtled through the night.

"Aoooow!" Froggie's voice rose and fell with a splash.

"Shut it off, you sap!" The Mudhen roared.

"I'll keep things wet," the man promised heroically.

He did, very wet, so wet that by the time the boys were out of range they made a piker of the proverbial drowned rat.

"Pft! Pft!" Froggie said.

"What ails you?" The Mudhen asked testily.

"You'd spit if you were plastered a foot thick with wet feathers."

"Snap out of it. We've got to find that horse."

"I hope he's dead."

"I don't, I'm responsible for him."

"Then you're responsible for all this mess."

"Shut up!"

They listened for a while to the wild sounds in the village, of which William Shakespeare and his horn were no longer audible parts. It was possible, as The Mudhen had suggested, that he had fled to his old home. Acting on that hunch, they made their way there and found him peacefully eating grass behind the empty house. Some-

102

where along the way he had lost his noisemaking apparatus and also his bellyache. Stealthily they tied him in an open shed and went back to the school, where their absence had not been noticed.

They spent the next day looking innocent and listening hard to various wild speculations as to what had caused last night's false alarms, but heard no word to indicate that the town guessed what it owed William. That evening, by devious back streets, they escorted him to Mr. Beeman's barn and left him to his hay.

A few days later Mr. Beeman came home and hailed the passing Mudhen.

"I chanced to meet the veterinarian this morning," he said. "He told me you phoned him that William was ill while I was away."

"Yes, sir. The vet knows his stuff. He said exercise would be good for William and it cured him."

"Thank you so much. But I regret causing you so much bother."

"Don't mention it, sir." The Mudhen gazed thoughtfully at the sky. "It wasn't the least bit of bother to anyone."

James Baldwin

Broiefort,
The Black Arabian

THE GIFT OF FORTUNE

"I would rather have that horse than aught else that now is or ever has been."

It must have been a rare animal indeed to bring this exclamation from the mouth of young Ogier the Dane while he was fighting a hand-to-hand duel with Brunamont, the giant king and champion of the Moors. He knew that his life depended upon the issue of that fight, and yet he could not think of anything but his enemy's steed; and as he stood thrusting and parrying with his

104

sword, he kept repeating to himself, "Ah! if Fortune and the good angels would only give me that horse!"

And at last Fortune did favor him. Fierce Brunamont was overthrown and left senseless upon the field, the Moorish host was routed with great slaughter, and Ogier secured the steed which he had coveted so much. And when he mounted the handsome creature and rode between the tents where flew the banners of Charlemagne, there was not a prouder man in all Europe than he. His fellow warriors cheered him for the gallant victory which he had helped to win; but his mind was all on the horse.

He kept patting the animal on the neck and saying over and over again, "Now thanks to fairy Fortune, that has given me this steed, whom I wished for more than anything else in the broad world! So long as I live there shall nothing persuade me to part with my good Broiefort—the war horse whom Fortune allowed me to win fairly at the risk of my life."

It was a matter of common talk—and therefore true—that Broiefort had been reared in Arabia, whence all the best horses come. Save for his forehead, in which there was a snow-white new moon, and his two forefeet, which were also white, he was the color of polished ebony. He was very strong, and his arching neck and slender legs and shapely head were admired by everybody who saw him. He was teachable, gentle, wise, and brave, and it was not long until he loved Ogier as well as Ogier loved him. For many years after the famous battle with Brunamont, the flaxen-haired Dane and the black Arabian were never separated for a day, and people remarked that it was as rare to see Ogier without Broiefort as to see a sword without its hilt.

There came a time, however, after both were beginning to grow old, that there was a turn in the tide of their good fortune. An accident, which had happened through no fault of Ogier's, had caused Charlemagne to become his enemy. The faithful old warrior was banished from France, and all the rich estates which had been his were forfeited. He had no longer a penny, nor even so much land as he could lie down upon. But why should he despair? He still had Broiefort. On the good horse's back he would ride out of France and seek a home and fortune among strangers. He rode over the Alps into Italy and told his story to Didier, the king of the Lombards. Didier was glad to welcome so famous a warrior; he would make him one of the foremost men in his kingdom. And so Ogier put his hands into the hands of the Lombard king and did him homage, and received in return the command of two castles on the river Rhone.

THE BATTLE

But Charlemagne would not allow his former friend and warrior chief to rest in peace, even in the domains of the Lombard king. No sooner did he hear that Didier had befriended the exiled Dane than he sent a messenger into Lombardy, demanding that Ogier should be returned to France, chained like a greyhound.

"Never will I do so base a thing!" cried Didier. "Sooner

106

than desert the friend who has sworn fealty to me, I will see all Lombardy overrun by my foes, my own palace in ashes, and myself laid low with the thrusts of Charlemagne's spears!"

The messenger returned to France with this answer, and Didier and Ogier made ready for war; for well they knew that Charlemagne was not a man to be trifled with.

Early the next spring a mighty army, led by Charlemagne himself, crossed the Alps for the purpose of overrunning Lombardy and capturing the exiled Dane. A bloody battle was fought on the plains of St. Ajossa—such a battle as neither Lombard nor Frank had ever seen before. For hours the conflict raged; and everywhere Ogier and the steed Broiefort were in the thickest of the fray. Never did man and horse fight more bravely. The old knight's shield was pierced in thirty places, his helmet was split in twain, he was wounded with seven spears; and yet, even after he knew the day was lost, he kept on fighting like a tiger.

At last Ogier is unhorsed. Broiefort, maddened for the moment, flees across the field, pursued by a hundred soldiers. Flinging right and left with his heels, he kills three squires and five horses, and puts a whole company of Frenchmen to flight. Not a weapon can be made to touch him. Men say that he has a charmed life. Coming to the top of a little knoll, he turns his head and looks back. He sees his master in the midst of the melee, surrounded by enemies, with one knee on the ground, fighting a losing fight. Shall he desert his friend in his greatest need?

He wheels about and returns to the field, scattering

107

his three hundred pursuers before him. Ogier has begun to lose hope. His sword is broken. The Frenchmen are closing upon him. Suddenly he hears a neigh, and looking up, he sees Broiefort pressing toward him through the crowd. In another moment he has swung himself into the saddle, and knight and steed are flying over the plain with—as truthful old stories tell us—fifteen thousand men in hot pursuit. But who can overtake Broiefort?

THE FLIGHT

Late in the evening, Ogier, wearied with the long ride and overcome by the pain of his wounds, thought that it would be safe for them to stop and rest. He dismounted near a spring of water which gurgled out from beneath a huge rock, and after slaking his thirst, he bathed his hot head in the stream and washed the smoking sides and mud-bespattered legs of his steed. Then sitting on the ground with his back resting against the rock, he soon fell asleep; but Broiefort stood by him to watch.

Half an hour passed quietly, and then a faint sound was heard far down the road. The horse pricked up his ears and listened. Very soon he could distinguish quite plainly the thump, thump of galloping hoofs coming closer every moment, and he knew that it meant danger. He whinnied to awaken his master, but Ogier slept on. He came closer to him and stamped his feet against the rock; Ogier stirred a little, but did not waken. Then he stamped still harder and neighed shrilly three times; but his master, dreaming of battle, did not hear him. By this

108

time their pursuers were in sight. Ten men—yes, a thousand men—with lances poised and swords drawn, ready to fall upon Ogier wherever they might find him, were coming pell-mell along the highway!

Broiefort was desperate. He seized his master by the collar, and lifting him to his feet, shook him roughly. Ogier awoke just in time. He vaulted quickly into the saddle, while the lances of his foremost pursuers almost grazed his armor. His faithful steed leaped forward, and in a few moments he was safely out of reach and out of hearing again.

For three whole days Broiefort carried his master through mountain passes and forests, so closely pressed that there was no time to stop anywhere for food or rest. For three months the chase was kept up, although the pursuers now and then lost track of the fugitives long enough to allow Ogier to rest a night in some out-of-the-way castle, where Broiefort was sure to be regaled with a measure of oats. At last, after many adventures, they reached one of Ogier's old strongholds on the river Rhone, where—according to the historian—they were besieged by Charlemagne with an army of ten thousand warriors.

THE SIEGE

There were only three hundred men—vassals of Ogier —in the castle, but the most of them were known to be good and true, and the Dane felt that, for a time at least, he was safe from any harm that the besiegers could do him. Broiefort was given a warm stall, with plenty of straw, in the cellar, and as there was a great store of provisions in the castle, the inmates were all as comfortable as need be. Ogier knew that no power on earth could batter down the walls of the castle, for they were of Saracen work—that is, the mortar had been boiled in blood—and hence they were proof against every kind of weapon. All that the garrison had to do, therefore, was to prevent the besiegers from putting up scaling ladders, and this required only a little watchfulness.

At length, however, Charlemagne caused a wooden tower to be built in front of the gate—a tower seven stories high, on which a thousand knights and 170 archers could stand, and from which they hurled missiles and shot countless arrows over the castle wall. Then, indeed, sad days began for Ogier. One by one his men were picked off the walls by the sharpshooters in the high tower; one by one his squires and faithfulest defenders of the castle met their death. Finally there was no one left alive but himself and the horse Broiefort—two besieged by ten thousand. But they had held out well; for according to the old song writers, it was now seven years since Charlemagne had begun the siege.

And now Ogier bethought him that if he could escape to his native country, Denmark, his own kinsfolk might befriend and shelter him. The chance was worthy of a trial, at least. Very early one morning, therefore, he went down to visit Broiefort in his stall. There was not another handful of oats in the castle; not a grain of corn, not a wisp of hay was to be found. Ogier himself had not had

110

a mouthful of food for two days. To hold the place longer was to starve.

"Horse," said Ogier, stroking the creature's neck and sides, "horse, so good and brave and proud! You have stood by me well. A firm friend you have been in many a strait. I wonder if you will help me once again?"

Broiefort understood every word; he whinnied softly in reply; he struck his foot upon the stone pavement as if to say that he was ready to be going. Ogier brought out his saddle, now so long unused, and the bridle with the golden bits. Broiefort leaped into the air for very gladness. And when his master threw the rich trappings upon his back, tightened the saddle girths, and laid the reins over his neck, he seemed beside himself with joy. Then Ogier donned his own armor, buckled his good sword to his side, and put his bright steel helmet upon his head. Leading the horse across the courtyard, he opened the castle gate quietly and peeped out. The besiegers were all asleep in their tents; even the sentinels were sprawled upon the ground, dreaming of their homes and their loved ones in faraway Aquitaine.

Ogier let down the drawbridge very softly, and then, mounting Broiefort, he rode out of the fortress which had sheltered him so long. Good Broiefort seemed to understand everything. With eyes open very wide and ears alert to catch every sound, he stepped so lightly that the most wakeful of the besiegers did not hear him. The birds were singing in the treetops as they passed through Charlemagne's camp, but not a soldier was stirring. Once safely outside the lines, Broiefort changed his whole

manner. Throwing up his head and pointing his ears forward, he broke into a long, steady gallop—a gait which he could keep up all day without tiring. And thus Ogier, safe out of the reach of his foes, rode northward through sunny France.

THE CAPTURE

On the fifth day they had put so many miles between themselves and the besiegers that the great Dane began to feel himself safe. In another day they would cross the Rhine, and then on to Denmark! At about noon they stopped to rest by a spring which bubbled up from the ground near the foot of a rocky hill. Ogier, very tired from his long ride, and thankful that the worst of it was over, lay down upon the grass and soon fell asleep. Broiefort, not thinking that any watch was needed, now that they were so far from their enemies, wandered here and there, nipping the young clover that was just beginning to blossom in the fields.

He was very hungry and the clover was very good, and hence he did not notice a company of priests and knights that came riding down the highway, or, if he noticed them, he did not think of their harming his master. He therefore kept on grazing and neglected to awaken Ogier and warn him of the possible danger. At the head of the company was the archbishop of Rheims, who had been making his usual rounds among the sick people of the neighborhood and was returning to his palace. He was himself a warrior of no little note, and therefore delighted always to have a retinue of knights and squires around him. One of these young men, seeing Ogier asleep upon the ground, was so struck by his noble appearance that he rode back quickly and told his master. The archbishop, curious to know who it might be, spurred his horse and, followed by his whole company, cantered down to the spring. The old man was astounded when he saw that it was Ogier, for he had marched with the Dane in many a campaign and fought by his side in many a hard-won battle.

He would have given a whole year's revenue if he had not seen him, for it pained his heart to think that he was obliged to make a prisoner of his old friend and comrade and deliver him into the hands of the king. But his oath of fealty to Charlemagne would not allow him to do otherwise. At his command, therefore, one of his knights secured Ogier's sword, another his shield, and another the good horse Broiefort. Then twenty men with drawn swords stood around the fugitive while the archbishop awakened him.

"My old-time friend, Ogier," he said, "awake and look around you! You can see that it is useless for you to resist; for here are forty men, most of them armed, while you are unarmed and alone. Yield yourself, then, as our prisoner!"

But Ogier was not the man to be taken so easily. He sprang to his feet, and with a blow of his great fist crushed the head of the knight who stood nearest to him. Then he tore the saddle from the back of one of the priest's pack horses, and with it dealt furiously about him

114

until ten of his assailants were laid sprawling in the dust and the rude weapon was broken in pieces in his hands. But the struggle was of no avail, for other knights closing in upon him, he was wounded sorely, and finally bound hand and foot with strong ropes. He begged his captors that they would kill him then and there rather than give him up to Charlemagne. They made no answer, however, but put him astride a mule, tied his feet together underneath, and took him into Rheims, where the archbishop ordered him to be placed in his own prison.

As for Broiefort, the gallant horse was taken to Meaux, where he was made to draw a heavy two-wheeled cart loaded with stones and bricks and mortar. For seven years he toiled, half-fed, broken-spirited, hopeless. His once beautiful coat became rough and ragged, showing the outlines of every rib beneath; his mane, unkempt and uncared for, was knotted in many a snarl; his long tail, which had once been his pride, was filled with burs and thorns; his breast and shoulders were galled by the ill-fitting harness; his eyes lost their fire, and his chin drooped with despair.

THE PRISON

For seven years, also, Ogier languished in prison. Charlemagne would have been glad to put him to death, but he knew that every knight in France would cry out against it. So long, however, as the good archbishop lived, the brave Dane fared much better than his horse. Every day he was given a gallon of wine to drink, and two loaves of bread and the half of a pig to eat. The ladies and squires and burgesses of Rheims came often to his cell to visit him, and the archbishop played chess with him almost every evening. His beard became white as snow, but his arms remained as big and as strong as ever, and he never lost hope.

By and by, however, sad changes came to France and to Ogier. The archbishop was slain in that famous fight at Roncesvalles, where all the flower of French chivalry perished. The prison at Rheims passed into the hands of other keepers. All of Ogier's old friends were dead, and it was not long until Ogier himself seemed to be forgotten.

Charlemagne was hard beset by his foes. A pagan king named Brehus invaded France from the south and threatened to overrun the whole empire. Battle after battle was fought, and the French, having no leaders, were beaten every time. Everybody was in despair. People began to compare the former glorious times with the present. They thought of Roland and of Oliver, and of Reinold, and of the brave archbishop of Rheims, who used to lead them in battle—all dead now. Then they thought of Ogier and wondered if he, too, was dead.

"If we only had Ogier to lead us!" said some.

And the cry was echoed by many others: "If we only had Ogier to lead us!"

"Ogier is not dead. He is still in the prison at Rheims," said a young knight, a kinsman of the late archbishop. "Let every brave Frenchman petition the king to set him free!"

116

Thereupon three hundred knights, all sons of counts, dukes, or princes, marched in a body to Charlemagne's tent, crying, "Ogier! Ogier! Give us Ogier the Dane for our leader!"

The king was angry at first, but seeing that something must be done, he said at last, "I know not whether Ogier be alive or dead. If, however, he be still alive, I will fetch him and make him your leader as you desire."

He sent at once to Rheims to inquire if Ogier were still in prison. Yes, the keeper thought that there was some such man shut up in one of the lower dungeons. The squires who had brought the king's message fancied that they heard him in his dismal cell, fighting the snakes and water rats which had come into the place from the river. They called to him, and he answered. Then ropes were let down and he was drawn up into the daylight to which he had been for a long time a stranger. He was given a bountiful meal and clad in rich garments, such as he had worn in former days, and then led into the presence of the king.

THE PARDON

Charlemagne offered to pardon the Dane and to return to him all the vast estates which had once been his, on condition that he would lead the French host against the pagan army under King Brehus. The old hero stood up, as tall and as proud and seemingly as strong as ever, and answered that if he might wear his own armor and ride the good war steed Broiefort, he would undertake to

117

drive every pagan out of France; otherwise he could not go into battle, but would return to his dungeon and leave the country to its fate.

Ogier's armor was quickly found, but nobody remembered anything about his steed. The king offered his own war horse to the Dane, but when Ogier leaned his great weight upon it the animal was crushed to the ground. Several other steeds were tried, but all with the same results. Finally an old priest who had just arrived from Meaux said that he believed that Broiefort himself was still alive and was used as a draft horse by the monks of the abbey. Ten squires were sent out at once to bring the old horse to his master.

Ogier wept when he saw the sad plight of his once beautiful war steed, and Broiefort would have done the same had it been possible for horses to weep, so great was his joy. As it was, the fire came back into his eyes; he lifted his head with somewhat of the old-time pride; he scratched his feet with delight; he fondled his master with his jet-black nose and whinnied softly, as though he wanted to speak. Ogier put his arm over him and leaned with his whole weight. The horse stood up bravely and shrank not in the least beneath him. Then the grooms washed the steed in warm spring water, and combed and oiled his mane and tail, and trimmed his fetlocks, and polished his hoofs, and covered him with a richly embroidered cloth, and put the golden bits in his mouth. You would not have known him as the draft horse that had hauled stones for the abbot of Meaux—he was the Broiefort who fought in the famous battle of St.

118

Ajossa. Brave Ogier wept again, but this time for joy, when he mounted the grand old steed and rode forth to give battle to the pagan invaders.

There is no need to describe that last fierce fight which ended in a hand-to-hand combat between Ogier and King Brehus. In all his lifetime the gallant Dane had never met so equal a foe; and had it not been for Broiefort's aid he would not have come out of the fray alive. The combat was a long one, and the fate of France depended upon the issue. The sun had set, and the twilight was deepening into darkness, and yet neither of the combatants seemed able to gain any advantage over his foe. At last the treacherous pagan, by an overhanded sweep of his long sword, struck Broiefort squarely on the neck. The faithful horse, with a cry of anguish, fell dead to the earth. Never had anything caused Ogier so great grief. But his anger held down his sorrow and nerved him to desperation. He made one final terrible thrust with his sword, and his pagan foe was stretched lifeless by the side of the steed he loved so well.

Ogier took for his own the gray war horse, Marchevalle, which King Brehus had ridden in the battle. But nothing could ever console him for the loss of his faithful friend, Broiefort, the matchless Arabian.

Marguerite Henry

Pony Penning Day

PONY PENNING DAY always comes on the last Thursday in July. For weeks before, every member of the Volunteer Fire Department is busy getting the grounds in readiness, and the boys are allowed to help.

"I'll do your chores at home, Paul," offered Maureen, "so's you can see that the pony pens are good and stout."

Paul spent long days at the pony penning grounds. Yet he could not have told how or by whom the tents were rigged up. He hardly noticed when the chutes for the bronco busting were built. He did not know who pounded the race track into condition. All he knew was that the pens for the wild ponies must be made fast. Once

120

the Phantom was captured, she must not escape. Nothing else mattered.

The night before the roundup, he and Maureen made last-minute plans in Phantom's stall. "First thing in the morning," Paul told Maureen, "you lay a clean bed of dried sea grass. Then fill the manger with plenty of marsh grass to make Phantom feel at home."

"Oh, I will, Paul. And I've got some ear corn and some 'lasses to coax her appetite, and Grandma gave me a bunch of tiny new carrots and some rutabagas and I've been saving up sugar until I have a little sackful."

In the midst of their talk, Grandpa, looking as if he had a surprise, joined them.

"I hain't rode on a roundup to Assateague for two years," he smiled, hiding one hand behind his back, "but I recommember we allus had a chaw and a goody after the ponies was rounded up and afore we swimmed 'em across the channel. Here, Paul," he said with a strange huskiness, "here's a choclit bar fer ye to take along." And he pressed the slightly squashed candy into Paul's hand.

It was dark and still when Paul awoke next morning. He lay quiet a moment, trying to gather his wits. Suddenly he shot out of bed.

Today was Pony Penning Day!

His clothes lay on the chair beside his bed. Hurriedly he pulled on his shirt and pants and thudded barefoot down to the kitchen where Grandma stood over the stove, frying ham and making coffee for him as if he were man-grown!

121

He flung out his chest, sniffing the rich smells, bursting with excitement.

Grandma glanced around proudly. "I picked the first ripe figs of the year fer ye," she exclaimed. They're chuckful of goodness. Now sit down, Paul, and eat a breakfast fit for a roundup man!"

Paul sat on the edge of his chair. With one eye on the clock he tried to eat the delicious figs and ham, but the food seemed to lump in his throat. Luckily Grandpa and Maureen came downstairs just then and helped clean his plate when Grandma was busy testing her cornbread in the oven with a long wisp of straw.

"I got to go now," Paul swallowed as he ran out the door. He mounted Watch Eyes, a dependable pony that Grandpa had never been able to sell because of his white eyes. Locking his bare feet around the pony's sides, he jogged out of the yard.

Maureen came running to see him off.

"Whatever happens," Paul called back over his shoulder, "you be at Old Dominion Point at ten o'clock on a fresh pony."

"I'll be there, Paul!"

"And you, Paul!" yelled Grandpa. "Obey yer leader. No matter what!"

Day was breaking. A light golden mist came up out of the sea. It touched the grim white houses and the white picket fences with an unearthly light. Paul loped along slowly to save his mount's strength. He studied each house with a new interest. Here lived the woman who paid Maureen three dollars for hoeing her potato patch. There lived Kim Horsepepper, the clamdigger they had worked for. Mr. Horsepepper was riding out of his lane now, catching up with Paul. All along the road, men were turning out of their gates.

"Where do you reckon you'll do most good, Bub?" taunted a lean sapling of a man who, on other days, was an oysterman. He guffawed loudly, then winked at the rest of the group.

Paul's hand tightened on the reins. "Reckon I'll do most good where the leader tells me to go," he said, blushing hotly.

The day promised to be sultry. The marsh grass that usually billowed and waved stood motionless. The water of Assateague Channel glared like quicksilver.

Now the cavalcade was thundering over a small bridge that linked Chincoteague Island to little Piney Island. At the far end of the bridge a scow with a rail fence around it stood at anchor.

In spite of light talk, the faces of the men were drawn tight with excitement as they led their mounts onto the scow. The horses felt the excitement too. Their nostrils quivered, and their ears swiveled this way and that, listening to the throb of the motor. Now the scow began to nose its way across the narrow channel. Paul watched the white hills of Assateague loom near. He watched the old lighthouse grow sharp and sharper against the sky. In a few minutes the ride was over. The gangway was being lowered. The horses were clattering down, each man taking his own.

All eyes were on Wyle Maddox, the leader.

"Split in three bunches," Wyle clipped out the directions loud and sharp. "North, south, and east. Me and Kim and the Beebe boy will head east, Wimbrow and Quillen goes north, and Harvey and Rodgers south. We'll all meet at Tom's Point."

At the first sound of Wyle's steam-whistle voice, the sea birds rose with a wild clatter.

"They're like scouts," Paul said to himself. They're going to warn the wild ponies that the enemy has landed."

"Gee-up!" shouted Wyle as he whirled his horse and motioned Kim and Paul to follow.

Paul touched his bare heels into Watch Eyes' side. *They were off!* The boy's eyes were fastened on Wyle Maddox. He and Kim Horsepepper were following their leader like the wake of a ship.

As they rode on, Paul could feel the soft sand give way to hard meadowland, then to pine-laden trails. There were no paths to follow, only openings to skin through—openings that led to water holes or to grazing grounds. The three horses thrashed through underbrush, jumped fallen trees, waded brackish pools and narrow, winding streams.

Suddenly Paul saw Wyle Maddox's horse rear into the air. He heard him neigh loudly as a band of wild ponies darted into an open grazing stretch some twenty yards ahead, then vanished among the black tree trunks.

The woods came alive with thundering hoofs and frantic horse calls. Through bush and brier and bog and hard marshland the wild ponies flew. Behind them gal-

124

loped the three riders, whooping at the top of their lungs. For whole seconds at a time the wild band would be swallowed up by the forest gloom. Then it would reappear far ahead—nothing but a flash of flying tails and manes.

Suddenly Wyle Maddox was waving Paul to ride close. "A straggler!" he shouted, pointing off to the left. "He went thataway! Git him!" and with a burst of speed Wyle Maddox and Kim Horsepepper were after the band.

Paul was alone. His face reddened with anger. They wanted to be rid of him. That's what they wanted. Sent after a straggler! He was not interested in rounding up a straggler that couldn't even keep up with the herd!

He wanted the Phantom. Then Grandpa's words flashed across his mind: "Obey yer leader. No matter what!"

He wheeled his pony and headed blindly in the direction Wyle had indicated. He rode deeper into the pine thicket, trying to avoid snapping twigs, yet watching ahead for the slightest motion of leaf or bush. He'd show the men, if it took him all day! His thin shirt clung to him damply and his body was wet with sweat. A cobweb veiled itself across his face. With one hand he tried to wipe it off, but suddenly he was almost unseated. Watch Eyes was dancing on his hind legs, his nose high in the air. Paul stared into the sun-dappled forest until his eyes burned in his head. At last, far away and deep in the shadow of the pines, he saw a blur of motion. With the distance that lay between them, it might have been

125

anything. A deer. Or even a squirrel. Whatever it was, he was after it!

Watch Eyes plunged on. There was a kind of glory in pursuit that made Paul and the horse one. They were trailing nothing but swaying bushes. They were giving chase to a mirage. Always it moved on and on, showing itself only in quivering leaves or moving shadows.

What was that? In the clump of myrtle bushes just ahead. Paul reined in. He could scarcely breathe for the wild beating of his heart. There it was again! A silver flash. It looked like mist with the sun on it. And just beyond the mist he caught sight of a long tail of mingled copper and silver.

He gazed awestruck. "It could be the Phantom's tail," he breathed. "It is! It is! It is! And the silver flash—it's not mist at all, but a brand-new colt, to little to keep up with the band."

The blood pounded in his ears. No wonder the Phantom was a straggler! No wonder she let herself be caught. "She's got a baby colt!" he murmured.

He glanced about him helplessly. If only he could think! How could he drive the Phantom and her colt to Tom's Point?

Warily he approached the myrtle thicket, then stopped as a hot wave of guilt swept over him. Phantom and her colt did not want to be rounded up by men. He could set them free. No one had brought the Phantom in before. No one need ever know.

Just then the colt let out a high, frightened whinny. In that little second Paul knew that he wanted more than

126

anything in the world to keep the mother and the colt together. Shivers of joy raced up and down his spine. His breath came faster. He made a resolution. "I'll get you both!" he promised.

But how far had he come? Was it ten miles to Tom's

Point or two? Would it be best to drive them down the beach? Or through the woods? As if in answer a loud bugle rang through the woods. It was the Pied Piper! And unmistakably his voice came from the direction of Tom's Point.

The Phantom pricked her ears. She wheeled around and almost collided with Watch Eyes in her haste to find the band. She wanted the Pied Piper for protection. Behind her trotted the foal, all shining and clean with its newness.

Paul laughed weakly. He was not driving the Phantom after all! She and her colt were leading him. They were leading him to Tom's Point!

Tom's Point was a protected piece of land where the marsh was hard and the grass especially sweet. About seventy wild ponies, exhausted by their morning's run, stood browsing quietly, as if they were in a corral. Only occasionally they looked up at their captors. The good meadow and their own weariness kept them peaceful prisoners.

At a watchful distance the roundup men rested their mounts and relaxed. It was like the lull in the midst of a storm. All was quiet on the surface. Yet there was an undercurrent of tension. You could tell it in the narrowed eyes of the men, their subdued voices, and their too easy laughter.

Suddenly the laughter stilled. Mouths gaped in disbelief. Eyes rounded. For a few seconds no one spoke at all. Then a shout that was half wonder and half admira-

128

tion went up from the men. Paul Beebe was bringing in the Phantom and a colt!

The roundup men were swarming around Paul, buzzing with questions. "Beats all!" he heard someone say. "For two years we been trying to round up the Phantom, and along comes a spindling youngster to show us up!"

"Twas the little colt that hindered her."

"Course it was."

"It's the newest colt in the bunch; may not stand the swim."

"If we lose only one colt, it'll still be a good day's work."

The men accepted Paul as one of them now—a real roundup man. They were clapping him on the shoulder and trying to get him to talk. "Ain't they a shaggy-lookin' bunch?" Kim Horsepepper asked.

"Except for Misty," Paul said, pointing toward the Phantom's colt. "Her coat is silky." The mere thought of touching it sent shivers through him. "Misty," he thought to himself wonderingly. "Why, I've named her!"

He looked out across the water. Two lines of boats were forming a pony-way across the channel. He saw the cluster of people and the mounts waiting on the shores of Chincoteague and he knew that somewhere among them was Maureen. It was like a relay race. Soon she would carry on.

"Could I swim my mount across the channel alongside the Phantom?" Paul asked Wyle Maddox anxiously.

Wyle shook his head. "Watch Eyes is all tuckered out," he said. "Besides, there's a kind of tradition in the way things is handled on Pony Penning Day. There's mounted

129

men for the roundup and there's boatmen to herd 'em across the channel," he explained.

"Tide's out!" he called in clipped tones. "Current is slack. Time for the ponies to be swimmed across. Let's go!"

Suddenly the beach was wild with commotion. From three sides the roundup men came rushing at the ponies, their hoarse cries whipping the animals into action. They plunged into the water, the stallions leading, the mares following, neighing encouragement to their colts.

"They're off!" shouted Wyle Maddox, and everyone felt the relief and triumph of his words.

On the shores of Chincoteague the people pressed forward, their faces strained to stiffness as they watched Assateague Beach.

"Here they come!" The cry broke out from every throat.

Maureen, wedged in between Grandpa Beebe on one side and a volunteer fireman on the other, stood on her mount's back. Her arms paddled the air as if she were swimming and struggling with the wild ponies.

Suddenly a fisherman, looking through binoculars, began shouting in a hoarse voice, "A new-borned colt is afeared to swim. Wait! A wild pony is breaking out from the mob. Swimming around the mob. Escaping!"

An awed murmur stirred the crowds. Maureen dug her toes in her mount's back. She strained her eyes to see the fugitive, but all she could make out was a milling mass of dark blobs on the water.

The fisherman leaned far out over the water. "It's the Phantom!" he screamed.

130

The people took up the cry, echoing it over and over. "It's the Phantom! She's escaped again!"

Maureen felt tears on her cheek and impatiently brushed them away.

The fisherman was waving for quiet. "It's the Phantom's colt that won't swim!" he called out in a voice so hoarse it cracked. "The Phantom got separated from a bran'-fire new colt. She's gone back to get it!"

The people whooped and hollered at the news. "The Phantom's got a colt," they sang out. "The Phantom's got a new colt!"

Again the fisherman was waving for silence.

"She's reached her colt!" he crowed. "But the roundup men are closing in on her! They're making her shove the colt in the water. Look at her! She's making it swim!"

Grandpa Beebe cupped his hands around his mouth. "Can the little feller make it?" he boomed.

The crowd stilled, waiting for the hoarse voice. For long seconds no answer came. The fisherman remained as fixed as the piling he stood on. Wave after wave of fear swept over Maureen. She felt as if she were drowning. And just when she could stand the silence no longer, the fisherman began reporting in short, nervous sentences.

"They're halfways across. Jumpin' Jupiter! The colt! It's being sucked down in a whirlpool. I can't see it now. My soul and body! A boy's jumped off the scow. He's swimming to help the colt."

The onlookers did not need the fisherman with the binoculars anymore. They could see for themselves. A

131

boy swimming against the current. A boy holding a colt's head above the swirling waters.

Maureen gulped great lungfuls of air. "It's Paul!" she screamed. "It's Paul!"

On all sides the shouts went up. "Why, it's Paul!"

Grandpa leaped up on his mount's back as nimbly as a boy. He stood with his arms upraised, his fists clenched.

"God help ye, Paul!" his words carried out over the water. "Yer almost home!"

Grandpa's voice was as strong as a tow rope. Paul was swimming steadily toward it, holding the small silver face of the colt above water. He was almost there. He *was* there!

Maureen slid down from her mount, clutching a handful of mane. "You made it, Paul! You made it!" she cried.

The air was wild with whinnies and snorts as the ponies touched the hard sand, then scrambled up the shore, their wet bodies gleaming in the sun. Paul half carried the little colt up the steep bank; then suddenly it found its own legs. Shouts between triumph and relief escaped every throat as the little filly tottered up the bank.

For a brief second Paul's and Maureen's eyes met above the crowds. It was as if they and the mare and her foal were the only creatures on the island. They were unaware of the great jostling and fighting as the stallions sorted out their own mares and colts. They were unaware of everything but a sharp ecstasy. Soon the Phantom and her colt would belong to them. Never to be sold.

Dodging horses and people, Grandpa Beebe made his way over to Paul.

"Paul, boy," he said, his voice unsteady, "I swimmed the hull way with you. Yer the most wonderful and the craziest young'un in the world. Now git home right smart quick," he added, trying to sound very stern. "Yer about done up, and Grandma's expectin' ye. Maureen and I'll see to it that the Phantom and her colt reach the pony pens."

133

William Cunningham

The Cloud Puncher

YOU ALWAYS HEAR a lot of stories about these cyclones blowin' straws into houses, about the feller hangin' out a sack of meal and the twister blowin' the sack away and leavin' the meal hangin' there, but I seen a thing happen when I was a boy workin' on a ranch out in Kansas, and they ain't no use talkin', that was a thing I ain't never heard anything to beat it.

They was a pony buster, name of Tiny Fallon, which was because he was so small we called him Tiny, being not five feet high. And that's why we called him Tiny. Well, Tiny was not to say very smart. That is, I guess he was bright enough. About like the rest of us when you come right down to it. But what I mean he didn't have sense enough to be afraid of anything.

They wasn't anything Tiny couldn't ride. He could ride the worst horse you ever seen. I seen horses pitch all the fleas off, tryin' to git rid of Tiny, and pitch the hair off their back, and not git out from under him. I never seen Tiny lose his head or pull leather.

Sometimes the fellers would rope up a wild steer and Tiny would git on without a string and ride that steer. And he never would ride 'em backwards, like fellers do, holdin' to their tail. You know how a steer is. Seems like his hind laigs is longer than his front laigs and his back bone slopes so that soon as he starts stickin' his front feet in the ground you jist naturally slide down on his horns. Well, Tiny never slid down like that. You wouldn't believe it, the way he could ride. He always waved his hat and yelled. You never seen a feller ride like that, I mean ride as good as Tiny.

One trouble with Tiny, he would git drunk in town and would ride home like a bat outa hell and every once in a while he'd kill a good saddle horse that way. I remember once he had the best mare in that part of the country and he rode her ten or fifteen miles on the dead lope, although he knowed she was with colt, and he killed her. Sometimes he didn't have a lick of sense.

Well, one spring they was mighty uncertain weather and bad twisters that we heard of, and sometimes we seen 'em off a little ways like funnels travelin' along in the sky and settlin' down once in a while to pull up dirt or cattle or anything that happened to be there. Them things is bad, you know. They ain't nothin' they can't do.

One day, of a Sunday afternoon, a bunch of us was loafin' around waitin' for the boys from another outfit that was gonna play baseball with us. The sky got mean-lookin' and we was talkin' about goin' to a dugout, when all at once they was a twister comin' right at us. Well, we run for the dugout, all but Tiny. It seemed like he didn't have sense enough to be afraid of the thing. That was one trouble with Tiny. He didn't have a lot of sense, and he didn't know when he ought to git scared.

We was runnin' and lookin' back, and Tiny was walkin' along not in any hurry, and that blamed twister got him. Yanked him right up, all sprawled out. And there he went. The last we seen him he was a hundred feet in the air, right side up, and he was wavin' his hat, jist from habit. He didn't know anything else to do.

We was sorry to see Tiny took off like that. He was a good feller and everybody liked him although he didn't have any too much sense. And some of the boys said it was a nice sight, him wavin' his hat, and if Tiny had to go, well, he might as well go like that.

And some of the boys said the twister would drop him astraddle of a barbed wire fence and split him length-ways, and some thought it would slide him through one along the ground and slice him the other way like a boloney. The next day when we rode fence we looked for pieces of Tiny either split or sliced, because nobody was very sure of his own opinion and you never can tell what a cyclone will do.

Well, it was about a week, and we all got over lookin'

for Tiny. We got word to the boys in the other outfits and they looked for him but didn't find him.

Then they was a bad night, and we all got scared on account of what had happened to Tiny, and we left the bunkhouse and went into the old dugout, which was safer. When things quietened a little bit we come out, not really expectin' to find any bunkhouse, but there it was, and when we went in to bed we found Tiny in his old bunk, asleep. We woke him up and asked him what in thunder had happened to him, but he was too sleepy. He said he was dog tired and he'd tell us next day. And that was all we could get out of him. He finally got mad because we wouldn't leave him sleep, so we shut up and waited to the next day.

Well, the next day we asked him again and he said, "Well, boys, it happened mighty funny, and I wished I'd had my saddle along."

And we asked him was he crazy, and he said he wasn't and he said, "You see, boys, I broke that blamed twister to ride, and I come back to git my saddle."

Well, acourse that made us mad, for him to start coddin' us, that was old friends of his and been in that country a long time. And we started walkin' off to the corral, and he said, "Wait a minute, boys," and he sounded real sincere. He said, "I don't blame you boys for takin' it like that, but it's the gods' truth. I rode it darned near to the mountains before I could git it under control, and then it wasn't no easy thing to head it back this way. I kept wishin' I had my saddle. I rode it in last night. You boys seen the storm yourself."

137

Well, he sounded so blamed sincere that we didn't feel like knockin' his head off. And we made signs to each other and decided he was crazy and we'd have to humor the poor feller for a while till he got back in his right mind.

He went on talkin'. He said, "Now the hardest thing to do was to train it not to put its foot down where it would do any hurt. It don't put a foot down very often, but when it does they's likely to be damage, and you've got to watch careful, like you do for gopher holes when you're ridin' a horse."

"Well, now, where is this twister of yours?" somebody asked him to make him feel good, and he said, "Well, they ain't no place to put one up, so I had to turn it out to graze last night, and I hope it ain't done no particular damage around here."

Now that was pretty bad, even if he was crazy, and we was sore and he seen we was, and he said, "Well, boys, I really don't blame you none. It don't sound very reasonable. I guess I'll be goin' now, and I like you boys a lot and I hope they ain't no hard feelin's."

He went in the bunkhouse and got his saddle and put it down on the ground, and we felt sorry, and we said, "You ain't goin' afoot are you, Tiny?"

And he said, "No, I ain't goin' afoot." And he whistled real loud.

Well, it was a clear mornin' up to then, but they was the blackest cloud you ever seen come whirlin' up from the west, and the dirt was foggin' over a patch of plowed ground. And we seen the twister comin', and it scared us like the devil, and we run to the dugout.

138

Well, Tiny stood there, with his saddle between his feet, and that twister swooped down. We was watchin' out of the dugout, scared to death. And it swooped down neat and it didn't touch a thing, and it picked Tiny up with the saddle under him. The way he squirted into the air would make your hair stand on end. It was the blamedest sight I ever seen. With things whirlin' all around him, he was ridin' straight, leanin' back in the saddle, and he took off his hat and waved it to us. In a couple of seconds he was just a speck, and then he was gone. The storm swung around in a big circle and headed west, and the funnel went high for a while and then settled in the brush pasture, scarin' a herd of yearlin's but not harmin' 'em a bit.

Well, that's the last we ever seen of Tiny. We heard later that he was doin' well and makin' good money further out west, herdin' clouds.

Yeah, herdin' clouds. You see, them ranchers in the dry country would git pretty hard up for rain and they was willin' to pay good money for a two- or three-inch gully washer. So Tiny would ride over the mountains, so we heard, and pick up a herd of good rain clouds and push them to a ranch. He'd bunch 'em and bed 'em down till they rained whatever the rancher was payin' for.

He charged by the inch, but the price on each inch was steeper, because rain clouds is hard to handle. They're like milk cows, you can't run 'em much or they'll lose their rain. And a good bunch ain't easy to find. Now Tiny would chase you up a shower to settle the dust for little or nothin'. An inch rain was reasonable, but two inches was more than twice as much as one inch, and so

139

on. That's the way he charged, so we heard. For a four-inch rain a rancher had to pay good and heavy, and I don't blame Tiny a bit, because of what he must of went through breakin' that twister.

It was too bad the way Tiny finally ended up. He was ridin' around at night one night, which was bad because he couldn't see where his twister was steppin', and the thing settled down on a saloon and twisted up a whole stock of liquor, includin' a bottle opener. Well, Tiny he couldn't resist, and he got drunk as a lord, and you know what he done?

He rode that twister all the way up and down the Rockies. You know, mountains is bad for twisters. They stay around the prairies mostly because they don't like rough goin' no more than a horse does. And Tiny didn't pay no mind to the condition his twister was in, and he rode it from Canada to Mexico, hell bent for election. Well, he broke its wind and a wind-broke twister ain't worth nothin'.

And besides, he musta knowed the condition it was in. All at once it started havin' a litter of whirlwinds. That's how careless Tiny was. And it dropped dead on him. Now it ain't so bad to have a horse drop dead. Maybe you git a nasty spill. But this twister died when Tiny was about five hundred feet in the air, and there wasn't nothin' left but a bunch of little orphan whirlwinds caperin' around and not one of 'em broke to ride. Anyway a young whirlwind can't hardly blow your hat off, let alone support a man.

Well, they never was much of Tiny, and after he hit

the ground he was so scattered that they couldn't hardly scrape up enough of him to make a good funeral. Which comes from not havin' common horse sense. It was too bad, because Tiny was a fine feller, when you got right down to it.

Nathaniel Hawthorne

Pegasus,
or the Chimera

ONCE, IN THE OLD, old times (for all the strange things which I tell you about happened long before anybody can remember), a fountain gushed out of a hillside in the marvelous land of Greece. And for aught I know, after so many thousand years, it is still gushing out of the very self-same spot. At any rate, there was the pleasant fountain, welling freshly forth and sparkling adown the hillside, in the golden sunset, when a handsome young man named Bellerophon drew near its margin. In his hand he held a bridle studded with brilliant gems and adorned with a golden bit. Seeing an old man and another of middle age and a little boy near the fountain, and likewise a maiden, who was dipping up some of the water in a pitcher, he paused and begged that he might refresh himself with a draught.

"This is very delicious water," he said to the maiden as he rinsed and filled her pitcher after drinking out of it. "Will you be kind enough to tell me whether the fountain has a name?"

"Yes, it is called the Fountain of Pirene," answered the maiden, and then she added, "My grandmother has told me that this clear fountain was once a beautiful woman; and when her son was killed by the arrows of the huntress Diana, she melted all away into tears. And so the water, which you find so cool and sweet, is the sorrow of that poor mother's heart!"

"I should not have dreamed," observed the young stranger, "that so clear a wellspring, with its gush and gurgle, and its cheery dance out of the shade into the sunlight, had so much as one teardrop in its bosom! And this, then, is Pirene? I thank you, pretty maiden, for telling me its name. I have come from a faraway country to find this very spot.

A middle-aged country fellow (he had driven his cow to drink out of the spring) stared hard at young Bellerophon and at the handsome bridle which he carried in his hand.

"The watercourses must be getting low, friend, in your part of the world," remarked he, "if you come so far only to find the Fountain of Pirene. But, pray, have you lost a horse? I see you carry the bridle in your hand; and a pretty one it is, with that double row of bright stones upon it. If the horse was as fine as the bridle, you are much to be pitied for losing him."

"I have lost no horse," said Bellerophon with a smile. "But I happen to seek a very famous one, which, as wise people have informed me, must be found hereabouts if anywhere. Do you know whether the winged horse Pegasus still haunts the Fountain of Pirene as he used to do in your forefathers' day?"

But then the country fellow laughed.

Some of you, my little friends, have probably heard that this Pegasus was a snow-white steed with beautiful silvery wings, who spent most of his time on the summit of Mount Helicon. He was as wild and as swift and as buoyant in his flight through the air as any eagle that ever soared into the clouds. There was nothing else like him in the world. He had no mate; he had never been backed or bridled by a master; and for many a long year he led a solitary and a happy life.

Oh, how fine a thing it is to be a winged horse! Sleeping at night, as he did, on a lofty mountaintop, and passing the greater part of the day in the air, Pegasus seemed hardly to be a creature of the earth. Whenever he was seen, up very high above peoples' heads, with the sunshine on his silvery wings, you would have thought that he belonged to the sky and that, skimming a little too low, he had got astray among our mists and vapors, and was seeking his way back again. It was very pretty to behold him plunge into the fleecy bosom of a bright cloud, and be lost in it for a moment or two, and then break forth from the other side. Or in a sullen rainstorm,

145

when there was a gray pavement of clouds over the whole sky, it would sometimes happen that the winged horse descended right through it, and the glad light of the upper region would gleam after him. In another instant, it is true, both Pegasus and the pleasant light would be gone away together. But anyone that was fortunate enough to see this wondrous spectacle felt cheerful the whole day afterward, and as much longer as the storm lasted.

In the summertime, and in the beautifulest of weather, Pegasus often alighted on the solid earth, and closing his silvery wings, would gallop over hill and dale for pastime as fleetly as the wind. Oftener than in any other place he had been seen near the Fountain of Pirene, drinking the delicious water or rolling himself upon the soft grass of the margin. Sometimes too (but Pegasus was very dainty in his food) he would crop a few of the clover blossoms that happened to be sweetest.

To the Fountain of Pirene, therefore, people's great-grandfathers had been in the habit of going (as long as they were youthful and retained their faith in winged horses) in hopes of getting a glimpse at the beautiful Pegasus. But of late years he had been very seldom seen. Indeed, there were many of the country folks dwelling within half an hour's walk of the fountain who never beheld Pegasus and did not believe that there was any such creature in existence. The country fellow to whom Bellerophon was speaking chanced to be one of those incredulous persons.

And that was the reason he laughed.

146

"Pegasus, indeed!" cried he, turning up his nose as high as such a flat nose could be turned up, "Pegasus, indeed! A winged horse, truly! Why, friend, are you in your senses? Could he drag the plough so well, think you? To be sure, there might be a little saving in the expense of shoes; but then, how would a man like to see his horse flying out of the stable window? Yes, or whisking him above the clouds, when he only wanted to ride to mill? No, no! I don't believe in Pegasus. There never was such a ridiculous kind of a horse-fowl made."

"I have some reason to think otherwise," said Bellerophon quietly.

And then he turned to the old, gray man, who was leaning on a staff and listening very attentively, with his head stretched forward and one hand at his ear because, for the last twenty years, he had been getting rather deaf.

"And what do you say, venerable sir?" inquired he. "In your younger days, I should imagine, you must frequently have seen the winged steed!"

"Ah, young stranger, my memory is very poor!" said the aged man. "When I was a lad, if I remember rightly, I used to believe there was such a horse, and so did everybody else. But nowadays I hardly know what to think, and very seldom think about the winged horse at all. If I ever saw the creature, it was a long, long while ago; and to tell you the truth, I doubt whether I ever did see him. One day, to be sure, when I was quite a youth, I remember seeing some hoof tramps around about the brink of the fountain. Pegasus might have

147

made those hoof marks, and so might some other horse."

"And have you never seen him, my fair maiden?" asked Bellerophon of the girl, who stood with the pitcher on her head while this talk went on. "You certainly could see Pegasus if anybody can, for your eyes are very bright."

"Once I thought I saw him," replied the maiden with a smile and a blush. "It was either Pegasus or a large white bird, a very great way up in the air. And one other time, as I was coming to the fountain with my pitcher, I heard a neigh. Oh, such a brisk and melodious neigh as that was! My very heart leaped with delight at the sound. But it startled me nevertheless; so I ran home without filling my pitcher."

"That was truly a pity," said Bellerophon.

And he turned to the child, whom I mentioned at the beginning of the story, and who was gazing at him, as children are apt to gaze at strangers, with his rosy mouth wide open.

"Well, my little fellow," cried Bellerophon, playfully pulling one of his curls, "I suppose you have often seen the winged horse."

"That I have," answered the child very readily. "I saw him yesterday and many times before."

"You are a fine little man!" said Bellerophon, drawing the child closer to him. "Come, tell me all about it."

"Why," replied the child, "I often come here to sail little boats in the fountain, and to gather pretty pebbles out of its basin. And sometimes when I look down into the water, I see the image of the winged horse in the picture of the sky that is there. I wish he would come down and take me on his back and let me ride him up to the moon! But if I so much as stir to look at him, he flies far away out of sight."

And Bellerophon put his faith in the child who had seen the image of Pegasus in the water, and in the maiden who had heard him neigh so melodiously, rather than in the middle-aged clown who believed only in cart horses, or in the old man who had forgotten the beautiful things of his youth.

Therefore, he haunted about the Fountain of Pirene for a great many days afterward. He kept continually on the watch, looking upward at the sky or else down into the water, hoping forever that he should see either the reflected image of the winged horse or the marvelous reality. He held the bridle, with its bright gems and golden bit, always ready in his hand. The rustic people who dwelt in the neighborhood and drove their cattle to the fountain to drink would often laugh at poor Bellerophon and sometimes take him pretty severely to task. They told him that an able-bodied young man like himself ought to have better business than to be wasting his time in such idle pursuit. They offered to sell him a horse if he wanted one; and when Bellerophon declined the purchase, they tried to drive a bargain with him for his fine bridle.

Even the country boys thought him so very foolish that they used to have a great deal of sport about him, and were rude enough not to care a fig, although Bellerophon saw and heard it. One little urchin, for

149

example, would play Pegasus and cut the oddest imaginable capers by way of flying; while one of his school-fellows would scamper after him, holding forth a twist of bulrushes, which was intended to represent Bellerophon's ornamental bridle. But the gentle child who had seen the picture of Pegasus in the water comforted the young stranger more than all the naughty boys could torment him. The dear little fellow in his play hours often sat down beside him, and without speaking a word, would look down into the fountain and up toward the sky with so innocent a faith that Bellerophon could not help feeling encouraged.

Well was it for Bellerophon that the child had grown so fond of him and was never weary of keeping him company. Every morning the child gave him a new hope to put in his bosom instead of yesterday's withered one.

"Dear Bellerophon," he would cry, looking hopefully into his face, "I think we shall see Pegasus today!"

One morning the child spoke to Bellerophon even more hopefully than usual.

"Dear, dear Bellerophon," cried he, "I know not why it is, but I feel as if we should certainly see Pegasus today!"

And all that day he would not stir a step from Bellerophon's side; so they ate a crust of bread together and drank some of the water of the fountain. In the afternoon there they sat, and Bellerophon had thrown his arm around the child, who likewise had put one of his little hands into Bellerophon's. The latter was lost in his own thoughts and was fixing his eyes vacantly on the trunks of the trees that overshadowed the fountain and on the grapevines that clambered up among the branches. But the gentle child was gazing down into the water; he was grieved, for Bellerophon's sake, that the hope of another day should be deceived like so many before it; and two or three quiet teardrops fell from his eyes and mingled with what were said to be the many tears of Pirene when she wept for her slain children.

But, when he thought of it, Bellerophon felt the pressure of the child's little hand and heard a soft, almost breathless, whisper.

"See there, dear Bellerophon, there is an image in the water!"

The young man looked down into the dimpling mirror of the fountain and saw what he took to be the reflection of a bird, which seemed to be flying at a great height in the air, with a gleam of sunshine on its snowy or silvery wings.

"What a splendid bird it must be!" said he. "And how very large it looks, though it must really be flying higher than the clouds!"

"It makes me tremble!" whispered the child. "I am afraid to look up into the air! It is very beautiful, and yet I dare only look at its image in the water. Dear Bellerophon, do you not see that it is no bird? It is the winged horse Pegasus!"

Bellerophon's heart began to throb! He gazed keenly upward but could not see the winged creature, whether bird or horse, because just then it had plunged into the fleecy depths of a summer cloud. It was but a moment,

151

however, before the object reappeared, sinking lightly down out of the cloud, although still at a vast distance from the earth. Bellerophon caught the child in his arms and shrank back with him, so that they were both hidden among the thick shrubbery which grew all around the fountain. Not that he was afraid of any harm, but he dreaded lest, if Pegasus caught a glimpse of them, he would fly far away and alight in some inaccessible mountaintop. For it really was the winged horse. After they had expected him so long, he was coming to quench his thirst with the water of Pirene.

Nearer and nearer came the aerial wonder, flying in great circles, as you may have seen a dove when about to alight. Downward came Pegasus in those wide, sweeping circles, which grew narrower, and narrower still, as he gradually approached the earth. The nigher the view of him, the more beautiful he was, and the more marvelous the sweep of his silvery wings. At last, with so slight a pressure as hardly to bend the grass about the fountain or inprint a hoof tramp in the sand of its margin, he alighted, and stooping his wild head, began to drink. He drew in the water with long and pleasant sighs and tranquil pauses of enjoyment; and then another draught, and another, and another. For nowhere in the world, or up among the clouds, did Pegasus love any water as he loved this of Pirene. And when his thirst was slaked, he cropped a few of the honey blossoms of the clover, delicately tasting them but not caring to make a hearty meal, because the herbage just beneath

152

the clouds, on the lofty sides of Mount Helicon, suited his palate better than this ordinary grass.

After thus drinking to his heart's content, and in his dainty fashion condescending to take a little food, the winged horse began to caper to and fro, and dance as it were, out of mere idleness and sport. There was never a more playful creature made than this very Pegasus. So there he frisked, in a way that it delights me to think about, fluttering his great wings as lightly as ever did a linnet, and running little races, half on earth and half in air, and which I know not whether to call a flight or a gallop. When a creature is perfectly able to fly, he sometimes chooses to run just for the pastime of the thing; and so did Pegasus, although it cost him some little trouble to keep his hoofs so near the ground. Bellerophon, meanwhile, holding the child's hand, peeped forth from the shrubbery and thought that never was any sight so beautiful as this, nor ever a horse's eyes so wild and spirited as those of Pegasus. It seemed a sin to think of bridling him and riding on his back.

Once or twice Pegasus stopped and snuffed the air, pricking up his ears, tossing his head, and turning it on all sides, as if he partly suspected some mischief or other. Seeing nothing, however, and hearing no sound, he soon began his antics again.

At length—not that he was weary, but only idle and luxurious—Pegasus folded his wings and lay down on the soft green turf. But being too full of aerial life to remain quiet for many moments together, he soon rolled over on his back, with his four slender legs in the air. It was beautiful to see him, this one solitary creature, whose mate had never been created, but who needed no companion, and living a great many hundred years, was as happy as the centuries were long. The more he did such things as mortal horses are accustomed to do, the less earthly and the more wonderful he seemed. Bellerophon and the child almost held their breath, partly from a delightful awe, but still more because they dreaded lest the slightest stir or murmur should send him up, with the speed of an arrow flight, into the farthest blue of the sky.

Finally, when he had had enough of rolling over and over, Pegasus turned himself about and indolently, like any other horse, put out his forelegs in order to rise from the ground; and Bellerophon, who had guessed that he would do so, darted suddenly from the thicket and leaped astride his back.

Yes, there he sat, on the back of the winged horse!

But what a bound did Pegasus make when, for the first time, he felt the weight of a mortal man upon his loins! A bound, indeed! Before he had time to draw a breath, Bellerophon found himself five hundred feet aloft and still shooting upward, while the winged horse snorted and trembled with terror and anger. Upward he went, up, up, up, until he plunged into the cold misty bosom of a cloud, at which, only a little while before, Bellerophon had been gazing and fancying it a very pleasant spot. Then again, out of the heart of the cloud, Pegasus shot down like a thunderbolt, as if he meant to dash both himself and his rider headlong against a rock. Then he

155

went through about a thousand of the wildest caprioles that had ever been performed either by a bird or a horse.

I cannot tell you half that he did. He skimmed straight forward, and sideways, and backward. He reared himself erect, with his forelegs on a wreath of mist and his legs on nothing at all. He flung his heels behind and put down his head between his legs, with his wings pointing right upward. At about two miles' height above the earth he turned a somersault, so that Bellerophon's heels were where his head should have been, and he seemed to look down into the sky instead of up. He twisted his head about, and looking Bellerophon in the face, with fire flashing from his eyes, made a terrible attempt to bite him. He fluttered his pinions so wildly that one of the silver feathers was shaken out and, floating earthward, was picked up by the child, who kept it as long as he lived in memory of Pegasus and Bellerophon.

But the latter (who, as you may judge, was as good a horseman as ever galloped) had been watching his opportunity, and at last clapped the golden bit of the enchanted bridle between the winged steed's jaws. No sooner was this done than Pegasus became as manageable as if he had taken food all his life out of Bellerophon's hand. To speak what I really feel, it was almost a sadness to see so wild a creature grow suddenly so tame. And Pegasus seemed to feel it so, likewise. He looked around to Bellerophon with tears in his beautiful eyes instead of the fire that so recently flashed from them. But when Bellerophon patted his head and spoke a few authoritative, yet kind and soothing words, another look came into the eyes of Pegasus; for he was glad at heart, after so many lonely centuries, to have found a companion and a master.

Thus it always is with winged horses and with all such wild and solitary creatures. If you can catch and overcome them, it is the surest way to win their love.

Aesop

The Fox, the Wolf, and the Horse
The Horse and the Laden Ass
The Horse and the Hog
The Mule

The Fox, the Wolf, and the Horse

A Fox, seeing a Horse for the first time, grazing in a field, at once ran to a Wolf of his acquaintance and described the animal that he had found. "It is, perhaps," said the Fox, "some delicious prey that fortune has put in our path. Come with me and judge for yourself."

Off they ran and soon came to the Horse, who, scarcely lifting his head, seemed little anxious to be on speaking terms with such suspicious-looking characters. "Sir," said the Fox, "your humble servants here would with pleasure learn the name by which you are known to your illustrious friends." The Horse, who was not without a ready wit, said his name was there curiously written upon his hoofs for the information of those who cared to read it. "Gladly would I," replied the sly Fox, suspecting in an instant something wrong, "but my parents were poor and could not pay for my education; hence, I never learned to read. The friends of my companion here, on the contrary, are great folk, and he can both read and write and has a thousand other accomplishments."

The Wolf, pleased with the flattery, at once went up with a knowing air to examine one of the hoofs which the Horse raised for his convenience; and when he had come near enough, the Horse gave a sudden and vigorous kick and back to earth fell the Wolf, his jaw broken and bleeding.

"Well, cousin," cried the Fox with a grin, "you need never ask for the name a second time, now that you have it written so plainly just below your eyes."

The Horse and the Laden Ass

A full-fed, lazy Horse was traveling along in company with a heavily laden Ass belonging to the same master. The Ass, whose back was nearly breaking with his load, besought the Horse, for the sake of common kindness, to take a portion of it. The Horse in his pride and ill-nature refused; and the poor Ass, after staggering on a little farther, fell down and died. The master thereupon laid the whole of the burden upon the Horse's back, and the skin of the Ass besides.

159

The Horse and the Hog

A Hog that was lazily lying in the sun on a dung heap saw a War Horse advancing on his way to the battlefield. The Horse was gaily caparisoned, and proudly spurned the ground as if impatient to charge the enemy. The Hog half lifted his head and, grunting, said to him, "What a fool you are to be so ready to rush to your death!" "Your speech," replied the Horse, "fits well a vile animal that only lives to get fat and be killed by the knife. If I die on the field, I die where duty calls me, and I shall leave the memory of a good name behind."

The Mule

A Mule, well fed and worked but little, frisked and gamboled about in the fields and said to himself, "What strength, what spirits are mine! My father must surely have been a thoroughbred Horse." He soon after fell into the hands of another master and was worked hard and but scantily fed. Thoroughly jaded, he now said, "What could I have been thinking about the other day? I feel certain now that my father can only have been an Ass."

Ernest Thompson Seton

The Pacing Mustang

JO CALONE THREW down his saddle on the dusty ground, turned his horses loose, and went clanking into the ranchhouse.

"Nigh about chuck time?" he asked.

"Seventeen minutes," said the cook, glancing at the Waterbury with the air of a train starter, though this show of precision had never yet been justified by events.

"How's things on the Perico?" said Jo's pard.

"Hotter'n hinges," said Jo. "Cattle seem O.K.; lots of calves."

"I seen that bunch o' mustangs that waters at Antelope Spings; couple o' colts along; one little dark one, a

161

fair dandy; a born pacer. I run them a mile or two, and he led the bunch, an' never broke his pace. Cut loose, an' pushed them jest for fun, an' darned if I could make him break."

"You didn't have no refreshments along?" said Scarth incredulously.

"That's all right, Scarth. You had to crawl on our last bet, an' you'll get another chance soon as you're man enough."

"Chuck," shouted the cook, and the subject was dropped. Next day the scene of the roundup was changed, and the mustangs were forgotten.

A year later the same corner of New Mexico was worked over by the roundup, and again the mustang bunch was seen. The dark colt was now a black yearling, with thin, clean legs and glossy flanks; and more than one of the boys saw with his own eyes this oddity—the mustang was a born pacer.

Jo was along, and the idea now struck him that that colt was worth having. To an Easterner this thought may not seem startling or original, but in the West, where an unbroken horse is worth $5, and where an ordinary saddle horse is worth $15 or $20, the idea of a wild mustang being desirable property does not occur to the average cowboy, for mustangs are hard to catch, and when caught are merely wild animal prisoners, perfectly useless and untameable to the last. Not a few of the cattle owners make a point of shooting all mustangs at sight, for they are not only useless cumberers of the feeding grounds, but commonly lead away domestic horses, which soon take to the wild life and are thenceforth lost.

Wild Jo Calone knew a "bronk right down to subsoil." "I never seen a white that wasn't soft, nor a chestnut that wasn't nervous, nor a bay that wasn't good if broke right, nor a black that wasn't hard as nails an' full of the old Harry. All a black bronk wants is claws to be wus'n Daniel's hull outfit of lions."

Since, then, a mustang is worthless vermin, and a black mustang ten times worse than worthless, Jo's pard "didn't see no sense in Jo's wantin' to corral the yearling," as he now seemed intent on doing. But Jo got no chance to try that year.

He was only a cowpuncher on $25 a month, and tied to hours. Like most of the boys, he always looked forward to having a ranch and an outfit of his own. His brand, the hogpen, of sinister suggestion, was already registered at Santa Fe, but of horned stock it was borne by a single old cow, so as to give him a legal right to put his brand on any maverick (or unbranded animal) he might chance to find.

Yet each fall, when paid off, Jo could not resist the temptation to go to town with the boys and have a good time "while the stuff held out." So that his property consisted of little more than his saddle, his bed, and his old cow. He kept on hoping to make a strike that would leave him well fixed with a fair start, and when the thought came that the black mustang was his mascot, he only needed a chance to "make the try."

The roundup circled down to the Canadian River and back in the fall by the Don Carlos Hills, and Jo saw no more of the pacer, though he heard of him from many quarters, for the colt, now a vigorous young horse, rising three, was beginning to be talked of.

Antelope Springs is in the middle of a great level plain. When the water is high it spreads into a small lake with a belt of sedge around it; when it is low there is a wide flat of black mud, glistening white with alkali in places, and the spring a water hole in the middle. It has no flow or outlet and yet is fairly good water, the only drinking place for many miles.

This flat, or prairie as it would be called farther north, was the favorite feeding ground of the black stallion, but it was also the pasture of many herds of range horses and cattle. Chiefly interested was the L-cross-F outfit. Foster, the manager and part owner, was a man of enterprise. He believed it would pay to handle a better class of cattle and horses on the range, and one of his ventures was ten half-blooded mares, tall, clean-limbed, deer-eyed creatures, that made the scrub cow ponies look like pitiful starvelings of some degenerate and quite different species.

One of these was kept stabled for use, but the nine, after the weaning of their colts, managed to get away and wandered off on the range.

A horse has a fine instinct for the road to the best feed, and the nine mares drifted, of course, to the prairie of Antelope Springs, twenty miles to the southward. And when later that summer Foster went to round them up, he found the nine indeed, but with them and guarding them with an air of more than mere comradeship was a coal-black stallion, prancing around and rounding up the bunch like an expert, his jet-black coat a vivid contrast to the golden hides of his harem.

The mares were gentle and would have been easily driven homeward but for a new and unexpected thing. The black stallion became greatly aroused. He seemed to inspire them too with his wildness, and flying this way and that way drove the whole band at full gallop where he would. Away they went, and the little cow ponies that carried the men were easily left behind.

This was maddening, and both men at last drew their guns and sought a chance to drop that "blasted stallion." But no chance came that was not 9 to 1 of dropping one of the mares. A long day of maneuvering made no change. The pacer, for it was he, kept his family together and disappeared among the southern sandhills. The cattlemen on their jaded ponies set out for home with the poor satisfaction of vowing vengeance for their failure on the superb cause of it.

One of the most aggravating parts of it was that one or two experiences like this would surely make the mares as wild as the mustang, and there seemed to be no way of saving them from it.

Scientists differ on the power of beauty and prowess to attract female admiration among the lower animals, but whether it is admiration or the prowess itself, it is certain that a wild animal of uncommon gifts soon wins a large following from the harems of his rivals. And the great black horse, with his inky mane and tail and his green-lighted eyes, ranged through all that region and

165

added to his following from many bands till not less than a score of mares were in his "bunch." Most were merely humble cow ponies turned out to range, but the nine great mares were there, a striking group by themselves. According to all reports, this bunch was always kept rounded up and guarded with such energy and jealousy that a mare, once in it, was a lost animal so far as man was concerned, and the ranchmen realized soon that they had gotten on the range a mustang that was doing them more harm than all other souces of loss put together.

II

It was December, 1893. I was new in the country and was setting out from the ranch house on the Piñavetitos, to go with a wagon to the Canadian River. As I was leaving, Foster finished his remark by: "And if you get a chance to draw a bead on that accursed mustang, don't fail to drop him in his tracks."

This was the first I had heard of him, and as I rode along I gathered from Burns, my guide, the history that has been given. I was full of curiosity to see the famous three-year-old and was not a little disappointed on the second day when we came to the prairie on Antelope Springs and saw no sign of the pacer or his band.

But on the next day, as we crossed the Alamosa Arroyo, and were rising to the rolling prairie again, Jack Burns, who was riding on ahead, suddenly dropped flat on the neck of his horse and swung back to me in the wagon, saying, "Get out your rifle, here's that——stallion."

I seized my rifle and hurried forward to a view over

the prairie ridge. In the hollow below was a band of horses, and there at one end was the great black mustang. He had heard some sound of our approach and was not unsuspicious of danger. There he stood with head and tail erect, and nostrils wide, an image of horse perfection and beauty, as noble an animal as ever ranged the plains, and the mere notion of turning that magnificent creature into a mass of carrion was horrible. In spite of Jack's exhortation to "shoot quick," I delayed and threw open the breach, whereupon he, always hot and hasty, swore at my slowness, growled, "Gi' me that gun," and as he seized it I turned the muzzle up, and *accidentally* the gun went off.

Instantly the herd below was all alarm, the great black leader snorted and neighed and dashed about. And the mares bunched, and away all went in a rumble of hoofs and a cloud of dust.

The stallion careered now on this side, now on that, and kept his eye on all and led and drove them far away. As long as I could see I watched, and never once did he break his pace.

Jack made Western remarks about me and my gun, as well as that mustang, but I rejoiced in the pacer's strength and beauty, and not for all the mares in the bunch would I have harmed his glossy hide.

III

There are several ways of capturing wild horses. One is by creasing—that is, grazing the animal's nape with a rifle ball so that he is stunned long enough for hobbling.

"Yes! I seen about a hundred necks broke trying it, but I never seen a mustang creased yet," was Wild Jo's critical remark.

Sometimes, if the shape of the country abets it, the herd can be driven into a corral; sometimes with extrafine mounts they can be run down, but by far the commonest way, pardoxical as it may seem, is to *walk* them down.

The fame of the stallion that never was known to gallop was spreading. Extraordinary stories were told of his gait, his speed and his wind, and when old Montgomery of the triangle-bar outfit came out plump at Well's Hotel in Clayton, and in presence of witnesses said he'd give one thousand dollars cash for him safe in a boxcar, providing the stories were true, a dozen young cowpunchers were eager to cut loose and win the purse as soon as present engagements were up. But Wild Jo had had his eye on this very deal for quite a while; there was no time to lose, so ignoring present contracts, he rustled all night to raise the necessary equipment for the game.

By straining his already overstrained credit, and taxing the already overtaxed generosity of his friends, he got together an expedition consisting of twenty good saddle horses, a mess wagon, and a fortnight's stuff for three men—himself, his "pard," Charley, and the cook.

Then they set out from Clayton, with the avowed intention of walking down the wonderfully swift wild horse. The third day they arrived at Antelope Springs, and as it was about noon they were not surprised to see the black pacer marching down to drink with all his band behind him. Jo kept out of sight until the wild horses each and all had drunk their fill, for a thirsty animal always travels better than one laden with water.

Jo then rode quietly forward. The pacer took alarm at half a mile and led his band away out of sight on the soapweed mesa to the southeast. Jo followed at a gallop till he once more sighted them, then came back and instructed the cook, who was also teamster, to make for Alamosa Arroyo in the south. Then away to the southeast he went after the mustangs. After a mile or two he once more sighted them, and walked his horse quietly till so near that they again took alarm and circled away to the south. An hour's trot, not on the trail, but cutting across to where they ought to go, brought Jo again in close sight. Again he walked quietly toward the herd, and again there was the alarm and flight. And so they passed the afternoon, but circled ever more and more to the south, so that when the sun was low they were, as Jo had expected, not far from Alamosa Arroyo. The band was again close at hand, and Jo, after starting them off, rode to the wagon while his pard, who had been taking it easy, took up the slow chase on a fresh horse.

After supper the wagon moved on to the upper ford of the Alamosa, as arranged, and there camped for the night.

Meanwhile Charley followed the herd. They had not run so far as at first, for their pursuer made no sign of attack, and they were getting used to his company. They were more easily found, as the shadows fell, on account of a snow-white mare that was in the bunch. A young

169

moon in the sky now gave some help, and relying on his horse to choose the path, Charley kept him quietly walking after the herd, represented by that ghost-white mare, till they were lost in the night. He then got off, unsaddled and picketed his horse, and in his blanket quickly went to sleep.

At the first streak of dawn he was up, and within a short half-mile, thanks to the snowy mare, he found the band. At his approach the shrill neigh of the pacer bugled his troop into a flying squad. But on the first mesa they stopped and faced about to see what this persistent follower was and what he wanted. For a moment or so they stood against the sky to gaze, and then deciding that he knew him as well as he wished to, that black meteor flung his mane on the wind and led off at his tireless, even swing, while the mares came streaming after.

Away they went, circling now to the west, and after several repetitions of this same play, flying, following, and overtaking, and flying again, they passed, near noon, the old Apache lookout, Buffalo Bluff. And here, on watch, was Jo. A long thin column of smoke told Charley to come to camp, and with a flashing pocket mirror he made response.

Jo, freshly mounted, rode across and again took up the chase, and back came Charley to camp to eat and rest, and then move on upstream.

All that day Jo followed, and managed, when it was needed, that the herd should keep the great circle, of which the wagon cut a small chord. At sundown he came to Verde Crossing, and there was Charley with a fresh horse and food, and Jo went on in the same calm, dogged way. All the evening he followed, and far into the night, for the wild herd was now getting somewhat used to the presence of the harmless strangers and were more easily followed; moreover, they were tiring out with perpetual travelling. They were no longer in the good grass country, they were not grain-fed like the horses on their track, and above all, the slight but continuous nervous tension was surely telling. It spoiled their appetites but made them very thirsty. They were allowed, and as far as possible encouraged, to drink deeply at every chance. The effect of large quantities of water on a running animal is well known; it tends to stiffen the limbs and spoil the wind. Jo carefully guarded his own horse against such excess, and both he and his horse were fresh when they camped that night on the trail of the jaded mustangs.

At dawn he found them easily close at hand, and though they ran at first, they did not go far before they dropped into a walk. The battle seemed nearly won now, for the chief difficulty in the "walk-down" is to keep track of the herd the first two or three days when they are fresh.

All that morning Jo kept in sight, generally in close sight, of the band. About ten o'clock Charley relieved him near José Peak, and that day the mustangs walked only a quarter of a mile ahead with much less spirit than the day before and circled now more north again. At night Charley was supplied with a fresh horse and followed as before.

171

Next day the mustangs walked with heads held low, and in spite of the efforts of the black pacer at times they were less than a hundred yards ahead of their pursuer.

The fourth and fifth days passed the same way, and now the herd was nearly back to Antelope Springs. So far all had come out as expected. The chase had been in a great circle with the wagon following a lesser circle. The wild herd was back to its starting point, worn out; and the hunters were back, fresh and on fresh horses. The herd was kept from drinking till late in the afternoon and then driven to the Springs to swell themselves with a perfect water gorge. Now was the chance for the skillful ropers on the grain-fed horses to close in, for the sudden heavy drink was ruination, almost paralysis, of wind and limb, and it would be easy to rope and hobble them one by one.

There was only one weak spot in the program; the black stallion, the cause of the hunt, seemed made of iron, that ceaseless swinging pace seemed as swift and vigorous now as on the morning when the chase began. Up and down he went, rounding up the herd and urging them on by voice and example to escape. But they were played out. The old white mare that had been such help in sighting them at night had dropped out hours ago, dead beat. The half-bloods seemed to be losing all fear of the horsemen; the band was clearly in Jo's power. But the one who was the prize of all the hunt seemed just as far as ever out of reach.

Here was a puzzle. Jo's comrades knew him well and would not have been surprised to see him in a sudden

172

rage attempt to shoot the stallion down. But Jo had no such mind. During that long week of following he had watched the horse all day at speed and never once had he seen him gallop.

The horseman's adoration of a noble horse had grown and grown, till now he would as soon have thought of shooting his best mount as firing on that splendid beast.

Jo even asked himself whether he would take the handsome sum that was offered for the prize. Such an animal would be a fortune in himself to sire a race of pacers for the track.

But the prize was still at large—the time had come to finish up the hunt. Jo's finest mount was caught. She was a mare of Eastern blood, but raised on the plains. She never would have come into Jo's possession but for a curious weakness. The loco is a poisonous weed that grows in these regions. Most stock will not touch it; but sometimes an animal tries it and becomes addicted to it. It acts somewhat like morphine, but the animal, though sane for long intervals, has always a passion for the herb and finally dies mad. A beast with the craze is said to be locoed. And Jo's best mount had a wild gleam in her eye that to an expert told the tale.

But she was swift and strong and Jo chose her for the grand finish of the chase. It would have been an easy matter now to rope the mares, but was no longer necessary. They could be separated from their black leader and driven home to the corral. But that leader still had the look of untamed strength. Jo, rejoicing in a worthy foe, went bounding forth to try the odds. The lasso was

173

flung on the ground and trailed to take out every kink, and gathered as he rode into neatest coils across his left palm. Then putting on the spur the first time in that chase, he rode straight for the stallion a quarter of a mile beyond. Away he went, and away went Jo, each at his best, while the fagged-out mares scattered right and left and let them pass. Straight across the open plain the fresh horse went at its hardest gallop, and the stallion, leading off, still kept his start and kept his famous swing.

It was incredible, and Jo put on more spur and shouted to his horse, which fairly flew, but shortened up the space between by not a single inch. For the Black One whirled across the flat and up, and passed a soapweed mesa, and down across a sandy treacherous plain, then over a grassy stretch where prairie dogs barked, then hid below; and on came Jo, but there to see—could he believe his eyes—the stallion's start grown longer still, and Jo began to curse his luck and urge and spur his horse until the poor uncertain brute got into such a state of nervous fright her eyes began to roll. She wildly shook her head from side to side, no longer picked her ground—a badger hole received her foot and down she went, and Jo went flying to the earth. Though badly bruised, he gained his feet and tried to mount his crazy beast. But she, poor brute, was done for—her off foreleg hung loose.

There was but one thing to do. Jo loosed the cinch, put Lightfoot out of pain, and carried back the saddle to the camp. While the pacer steamed away till lost to view.

This was not quite defeat, for all the mares were manageable now, and Jo and Charley drove them carefully to the L-cross-F corral and claimed a good reward. But Jo was more than ever bound to own the stallion. He had seen what stuff he was made of, he prized him more and more, and only sought to strike some better plan to catch him.

IV

The cook on that trip was Bates—Mr. Thomas Bates, he called himself at the post office where he regularly went for the letters and remittance which never came. Old Tom Turkeytrack, the boys called him, from his cattle brand, which he said was on record at Denver, and which, according to his story, was also borne by countless beef and saddle stock on the plains of the unknown North.

When asked to join the trip as a partner, Bates made some sarcastic remarks about horses not fetching $12 a dozen, which had been literally true within the year, and he preferred to go on a very meager salary. But no one who once saw the pacer going had failed to catch the craze. Turkeytrack experienced the usual change of heart. He now wanted to own that mustang. How this was to be brought about he did not clearly see till one day there called at the ranch that had "secured his services," as he put it, one Bill Smith, more usually known as Horseshoe Billy, from his cattle brand.

While the excellent fresh beef and bread and the vile coffee, dried peaches, and molasses were being con-

175

sumed, he of the horseshoe remarked, in tones which percolated through a huge stop-gap of bread, "Wall, I seen that thar pacer today, nigh enough to put a plait in his tail."

"What, you didn't shoot?"

"No, but I come mighty near it."

"Don't you be led into no sich foolishness," said a double-bar H cowpuncher at the other end of the table. "I calc'late that maverick 'ill carry my brand before the moon changes."

"You'll have to be pretty spry or you'll find a 'triangle dot' on his weather side when you get there."

"Where did you run acrost him?"

"Wall, it was like this; I was riding the flat by Antelope Springs and I sees a lump on the dry mud inside the rush belt. I knowed I never seen that before, so rides up, thinking it might be some of our stock, an' seen it was a horse lying plumb flat. The wind was blowing like—from him to me, so I rides up close and seen it was the pacer, dead as a mackerel. Still, he didn't look swelled or cut, and there wa'n't no smell, an' I didn't know what to think till I seen his ear twitch off a fly and then I knowed he was sleeping. I gits down me rope and coils it, and seen it was old and pretty shaky in spots, and me saddle a single cinch, an' me pony about seven hundred again a twelve-hundred-pound stallion, an' I sez to meself, sez I, ' 'Tain't no use, I'll only break me cinch and git throwed an' lose me saddle.' So I hits the saddlehorn a crack with the hondu, and I wish't you'd a seen that mustang. He leapt six foot in the air an' snorted like he was shunting cars. His eyes fairly bugged out an' he lighted out lickety

176

split for California, and he orter be there about now if he kep' on like he started—and I swear he never made a break the hull trip."

The story was not quite so consecutive as given here. It was much punctuated by present engrossments, and from first to last was more or less infiltrated through the necessaries of life, for Bill was a healthy young man without a trace of false shame. But the account was complete and everyone believed it, for Billy was known to be reliable. Of all those who heard, old Turkeytrack talked the least and probably thought the most, for it gave him a new idea.

During his after-dinner pipe he studied it out, and deciding that he could not go it alone, he took Horseshoe Billy into his council and the result was a partnership in a new venture to capture the pacer; that is, the $5000 that was now said to be the offer for him safe in a box-car.

Antelope Springs was still the usual watering place of the pacer. The water being low left a broad belt to dry black mud between the sedge and the spring. At two places this belt was broken by a well-marked trail made by the animals coming to drink. Horses and wild animals usually kept to these trails, though the horned cattle had no hesitation in taking a short cut through the sedge.

In the most used of these trails the two men set to work with shovels and dug a pit 15 feet long, 6 feet wide, and 7 feet deep. It was a hard twenty hours work for them, as it had to be completed between the mustang's drinks, and it began to be very damp work before it was finished. With poles, brush, and earth it was then

177

cleverly covered over and concealed. And the men went to a distance and hid in pits made for the purpose.

About noon the pacer came, alone now since the capture of his band. The trail on the opposite side of the mud belt was little used, and old Tom, by throwing some fresh rushes across it, expected to make sure that the stallion would enter by the other, if indeed he should by any caprice try to come by the unusual path.

What sleepless angel is it watches over and cares for the wild animals? In spite of all reasons to take the usual path, the pacer came along the other. The suspicious-looking rushes did not stop him; he walked calmly to the water and drank. There was only one way now to prevent utter failure; when he lowered his head for the second draft which horses always take, Bates and Smith quit their holes and ran swiftly toward the trail behind him, and when he raised his proud head Smith sent a revolver shot into the ground behind him.

Away went the pacer at his famous gait straight to the trap. Another second and he would be into it. Already he is on the trail, and already they feel they have him, but the angel of the wild things is with him, that incomprehensible warning comes, and with one mighty bound he clears the fifteen feet of treacherous ground and spurns the earth as he fades away, unharmed, never again to visit Antelope Springs by either of the beaten paths.

V

Wild Jo never lacked energy. He meant to catch that mustang, and when he learned that others were bestirring themselves for the same purpose he at once set about trying the best untried plan he knew—the plan by which the coyote catches the fleeter jackrabbit, and the mounted Indian the far swifter antelope—the old plan of the relay chase.

The Canadian River on the south, its affluent, the Piñavetitos Arroyo, on the northeast, and the Don Carlos Hills with the Ute Creek Cañon on the west, formed a sixty-mile triangle that was the range of the pacer. It was believed that he never went outside this, and at all times Antelope Springs was his headquarters. Jo knew this country well, all the water holes and canon crossings as well as the ways of the pacer.

If he could have gotten fifty good horses he could have posted them to advantage so as to cover all points, but twenty mounts and five good riders were all that proved available.

The horses, grain-fed for two weeks before, were sent on ahead; each man was instructed now to play his part and sent to his post the day before the race. On the day of the start Jo with his wagon drove to the plain of Antelope Springs and, camping far off in a little draw, waited.

At last he came, that coal-black horse, out from the sand hills at the south, alone as always now, and walked calmly down to the Springs and circled quite around it to sniff for any hidden foe. Then he approached where there was no trail at all and drank.

Jo watched and wished he would drink a hogshead. But the moment that he turned and sought the grass Jo spurred his steed. The pacer heard the hoofs, then saw the running horse, and did not want a nearer view but

179

led away. Across the flat he went down to the south, and kept the famous swinging gait that made his start grow longer. Now through the sandy dunes he went, and steadying to an even pace, he gained considerably and Jo's too-laden horse plunged through the sand, and sinking fetlock deep, he lost at every bound. Then came a level stretch where the runner seemed to gain, and then a long decline where Jo's horse dared not run his best, so lost again at every step.

But on they went, and Jo spared neither spur nor quirt. A mile—a mile—and another mile, and the far-off rock at Arriba loomed up ahead.

And there Jo knew fresh mounts were held, and on they dashed. But the night-black mane out level on the breeze ahead was gaining more and more.

Arriba Cañon reached at last, the watcher stood aside, for it was not wished to turn the race, and the stallion passed—dashed down, across and up the slope, with that unbroken pace, the only one he knew.

And Jo came bounding on his foaming steed and leaped on the waiting mount, then urged him down the slope and up upon the track, and on the upland once more drove in the spurs, and raced and raced, and raced, but not a single inch he gained.

Ga-lump, ga-lump, ga-lump with measured beat he went—an hour—an hour, and another hour—Arroyo Alamosa just ahead with fresh relays, and Jo yelled at his horse and pushed him on and on. Straight for the place the Black One made, but on the last two miles some strange foreboding turned him to the left, and Jo fore-

180

saw escape in this, and pushed his jaded mount at any cost to head him off, and hard as they had raced this was the hardest race of all, with gasps for breath and leather squeaks at every straining bound. Then cutting right across, Jo seemed to gain, and drawing his gun he fired shot after shot to toss the dust, and so turned the stallion's head and forced him back to take the crossing to the right.

Down they went. The stallion crossed and Jo sprang to the ground. His horse was done, for thirty miles had passed in the last stretch, and Jo himself was worn out. His eyes were burnt with flying alkali dust. He was half blind, so he motioned to his pard to "go ahead and keep him straight for Alamosa ford."

Out shot the rider on a strong, fresh steed, and away they went—up and down on the rolling plain—the black horse flecked with snowy foam. His heaving ribs and noisy breath showed what he felt—but on and on he went. And Tom on Ginger seemed to gain, then lose and lose, when in an hour the long decline of Alamosa came. And there a freshly mounted lad took up the chase and turned it west, and on they went past towns of prairie dogs, through soapweed tracts and cactus brakes by scores, and pricked and wrenched rode on. With dust and sweat the black was now a dappled brown, but still he stepped the same. Young Carrington, who followed, had hurt his steed by pushing at the very start, and spurred and urged him now to cut across a gulch at which the pacer shied. Just one misstep and down they went.

181

The boy escaped, but the pony lies there yet, and the wild black horse kept on.

This was close to old Gallego's ranch where Jo himself had cut across, refreshed, to push the chase. Within thirty minutes he was again scorching the pacer's trail.

Far in the west the Carlos Hills were seen, and there Jo knew fresh men and mounts were waiting, and that way the indomitable rider tried to turn the race, but by a sudden whim—of the inner warning born perhaps —the pacer turned. Sharp to the north he went, and Jo, the skillful wrangler, rode and rode and yelled and tossed the dust with shots, but down a gulch the wild black meteor streamed and Jo could only follow. Then came the hardest race of all; Jo, cruel to the mustang, was crueler to his mount and to himself. The sun was hot, the scorching plain was dim in shimmering heat, his eyes and lips were burnt with sand and salt, and yet the chase sped on. The only chance to win would be if he could drive the mustang back to Big Arroyo Crossing. Now almost for the first time he saw signs of weakening in the black. His mane and tail were not just quite so high, and his short half mile of start was down by more than half, but still he stayed ahead and paced and paced and paced.

An hour and another hour, and still they went the same. But they turned again, and night was near when Big Arroyo ford was reached—fully twenty miles. But Jo was game; he seized the waiting horse. The one he left went gasping to the stream and gorged himself with water till he died.

Then Jo held back in hopes the foaming black would

drink. But he was wise; he gulped a single gulp, splashed through the stream, and then passed on with Jo at speed behind him. And when they last were seen the black was on ahead just out of reach and Jo's horse bounding on.

It was morning when Jo came to camp on foot. His tale was briefly told: eight horses dead—five men worn out—the matchless pacer safe and free.

" 'Taint possible; it can't be done. Sorry I didn't bore his hellish carcass through when I had the chance," said Jo, and gave it up.

VI

Old Turkeytrack was cook on this trip. He had watched the chase with as much interest as anyone, and

when it failed he grinned into the pot and said, "That mustang's mine unless I'm a darned fool." Then falling back on Scripture for a precedent, as was his habit, he still addressed the pot.

"Reckon the Philistines tried to run Samson down and they got done up, an' would a stayed done ony for a nat'ral weakness on his part. An' Adam would a loafed in Eden yit ony for a leetle failing which we all onderstand. An' it ain't five thousand dollars I'll take for him, nuther."

Much persecution had made the pacer wilder than ever. But it did not drive him away from Antelope Springs. That was the only drinking place with absolutely no shelter for a mile on every side to hide an enemy. Here he came almost every day about noon, and after thoroughly spying the land, approached to drink.

His had been a lonely life all winter since the capture of his harem, and of this old Turkeytrack was fully aware. The old cook's chum had a nice little brown mare which he judged would serve his ends, and taking a pair of the strongest hobbles, a spade, a spare lasso, and a stout post, he mounted the mare and rode away to the famous Springs.

A few antelope skimmed over the plain before him in the early freshness of the day. Cattle were lying about in groups, and the loud, sweet song of the prairie lark was heard on every side. For the bright snowless winter of the mesas was gone and the springtime was at hand. The grass was greening and all nature seemed turning to thoughts of love.

It was in the air, and when the little brown mare was picketed out to graze she raised her nose from time to time to pour forth a long shrill whinny that surely was her song, if song she had, of love.

Old Turkeytrack studied the wind and the lay of the land. There was the pit he had labored at, now opened and filled with water that was rank with drowned prairie dogs and mice. Here was the new trail the animals were forced to make by the pit. He selected a sedgy clump near some smooth, grassy ground, and first firmly sunk the post, then dug a hole large enough to hide in, and spread his blanket in it. He shortened up the little mare's tether till she could scarcely move; then on the ground between he spread his open lasso, tying the long end to the post, then covered the rope with dust and grass, and went into his hiding place.

About noon, after long waiting, the amorous whinny of the mare was answered from the high ground, away to the west, and there, black against the sky, was the famous mustang.

Down he came at that long swinging gait, but grown crafty with much pursuit, he often stopped to gaze and whinny, and got answer that surely touched his heart. Nearer he came again to call, then took alarm, and paced all around in a great circle to try the wind for his foes, and seemed in doubt. The angel whispered "Don't go." But the brown mare called again. He circled nearer still, and neighed once more, and got reply that seemed to quell all fears and set his heart aglow.

Nearer still he pranced, till he touched Solly's nose

185

with his own, and finding her as responsive as he well could wish, thrust aside all thoughts of danger and abandoned himself to the delight of conquest, until, as he pranced around, his hind legs for a moment stood within the evil circle of the rope. One deft sharp twitch, the noose flew tight, and he was caught.

A snort of terror and a bound in the air gave Tom the chance to add the double hitch. The loop flashed up the line and, snakelike, bound those mighty hoofs.

Terror lent speed and double strength for a moment, but the end of the rope was reached, and down he went a captive, a hopeless prisoner at last. Old Tom's ugly little crooked form sprang from the pit to complete the mastering of the great glorious creature whose mighty strength had proved as nothing when matched with the wits of a little old man. With snorts and desperate bounds of awful force the great beast dashed and struggled to be free; but all in vain. The rope was strong.

The second lasso was deftly swung and the forefeet caught, and then with a skillful move the feet were drawn together, and down went the raging pacer to lie a moment later "hog-tied" and helpless on the ground. There he struggled till worn out, sobbing great convulsive sobs while tears ran down his cheeks.

Tom stood by and watched, but a strange revulsion of feeling came over the old cowpuncher. He trembled nervously from head to foot, as he had not done since he roped his first steer, and for a while could do nothing but gaze on his tremendous prisoner. But the feeling soon passed away. He saddled Delilah, and taking the second

186

lasso, roped the great horse about the neck, and left the mare to hold the stallion's head while he put on the hobbles. This was soon done, and sure of him now, old Bates was about to loose the ropes, but on a sudden thought he stopped. He had quite forgotten and had come unprepared for something of importance. In Western law the mustang was the property of the first man to mark him with his brand; how was this to be done with the nearest branding-iron twenty miles away?

Old Tom went to his mare, took up her hoofs one at a time, and examined each shoe. Yes! One was a little loose; he pushed and pried it with the spade, and got it off. Buffalo chips and kindred fuel were plentiful about the plain, so a fire was quickly made, and he soon had one arm of the horseshoe red hot; then holding the other wrapped in his sock, he rudely sketched on the left shoulder of the helpless mustang a turkeytrack, his brand, the first time really that it had ever been used. The pacer shuddered as the hot iron seared his flesh, but it was quickly done, and the famous mustang stallion was a maverick no more.

Now all there was to do was to take him home. The ropes were loosed, the mustang felt himself freed, thought he was free, and sprang to his feet only to fall as soon as he tried to take a stride. His forefeet were strongly tied together, his only possible gait a shuffling walk, or else a desperate labored bounding with feet so unnaturally held that within a few yards he was inevitably thrown each time he tried to break away. Tom on the light pony headed him off again and again, and

187

by dint of driving, threatening, and maneuvering, contrived to force his foaming, crazy captive northward toward the Piñavetitos Cañon. But the wild horse would not drive, would not give in. With snorts of terror or of rage and maddest bounds, he tried and tried to get away. It was one long cruel fight; his glossy sides were thick with dark foam, and the foam was stained with blood. Countless hard falls and exhaustion that a long day's chase was powerless to produce were telling on him; his straining bounds, first this way and then that, were not now quite so strong, and the spray he snorted as he gasped was half a spray of blood. But his captor, relentless, masterful and cool, still forced him on. Down the slope toward the cañon they had come, every yard a fight, and now they were at the head of the draw that took the trail down to the only crossing of the cañon, the northmost limit of the pacer's ancient range.

From this the first corral and ranchhouse were in sight. The man rejoiced, but the mustang gathered his remaining strength for one more desperate dash. Up, up the grassy slope from the trail he went defied the swinging, slashing rope and the gunshot fired in air in vain attempt to turn his frenzied course. Up, up and on, above the sheerest cliff he dashed then sprang away into the vacant air, down—down—two hundred downward feet to fall, and land upon the rocks below, a lifeless wreck— but free.

Frances Carpenter

The Kind Caliph
and the Horse Thief

IN BYGONE TIMES certain parts of East Asia were governed by rulers called caliphs and by judges called cadis. In those lands then, as in lands today, there were good rulers and bad rulers. There were good judges and bad judges.

Some of the caliphs thought only of their own pleasures. "Let the poor people do as best as they can," these selfish caliphs said. "It is not our affair if some are homeless and hungry, or if some are wrongly judged."

But in those times, as today, there were also good rulers. There were good caliphs who looked well after

189

their people. There were good cadis who made sure bad men were punished and good men were rewarded.

A good ruler, indeed, was one Ben-Assar, whom all called the Kind Caliph. Ben-Assar cared a great deal whether his people were fed and well housed and justly treated. Often and often, he put on the dress of a common man and went forth to find out for himself how his people fared. Many a cadis' court did he visit to see whether his laws were being obeyed.

Well, one day this Kind Caliph chose to hide himself under the robe of a merchant. So clad, he called for his horse, and so, unknown, he rode through the countryside.

Ben-Assar had not gone very far from his capital city when he was hailed from the roadside. A whining man limped to the side of his horse.

"Good sir," he cried, "I pray you, give me a ride upon your fine horse. See how lame I am! See how slowly I travel on my old wooden crutch!"

Ben-Assar's good heart was touched by the sight of the cripple. "Whither do you go, my friend?" he asked the poor, limping fellow.

"Only to the market fair in the next town, kind sir," said the lame man.

"Well, I suppose there is room for the two of us on my horse," the Kind Caliph said. "Get up here behind me. I should be hardhearted indeed if I refused to give help to a cripple like you." So, both on the horse's back, they rode slowly into the next town.

"Here is your fair, my friend," the Kind Caliph said,

190

pulling his horse to a stop on the edge of the market place. "Get you down now, and Allah go with you. Do not bother to thank me."

To the Caliph's surprise, the man did not move. No thanks were forthcoming. Instead the lame man rudely cried, "Get down yourself, merchant!" The Kind Caliph was almost speechless in his amazement.

"And why should I get down?" he demanded at last.

"So that I may ride along home on my horse," the bold cripple replied.

"But this is my horse," the Caliph cried. People from the market stalls gathered to listen to the dispute.

"Ah, no, it is my horse," said the rogue. "Nearby is the house of the Cadi, the wise judge of this town. We can let him decide which of us is the horse's master."

"Why, you bold, lying horse thief!" The Caliph was angry. "You know very well that this horse is mine. How can you think the Cadi will believe your foolish tale?"

"We shall see! We shall see!" said the crafty fellow. "He will look at you, a rich merchant, and at me, a poor cripple, whose horse is his only means of getting about. Our Cadi has a soft heart. Like yourself, he will be touched by my old, wooden crutch."

"This Cadi is a wise man, or so I have heard," the Caliph insisted. "He will soon give my horse back to me."

"Well, I shall be content with what the Cadi decides," the cripple said as he slid from the horse's back.

Before the Cadi, the Kind Caliph, still unknown in his merchant's disguise, told how he had given a ride to the lame man, and how at the end of his journey the un-grateful fellow had claimed his horse for his own.

THE KIND CALIPH AND THE HORSE THIEF

"The merchant lies, O wise Cadi," the would-be horse thief declared. "It was I who was riding my only horse to the market fair in this town. I came upon this merchant walking along on the highway. He looked tired and ill. So I gave him a ride. Now, unjustly, he wishes to take my horse from me."

The Cadi looked puzzled. He turned his eyes first on the well-to-do merchant, then on the poor, limping man with the crutch. He thought for a while. Then he spoke.

"The horse shall be put into my own stable. Each one of you, in his turn, shall go in and pick out this animal from among the other horses. That will help me do justice in this curious case."

Ben-Assar was the first to enter the Cadi's stable. He walked straight to the stall of his good horse and laid his hand fondly upon its mane.

"This is my horse, O Cadi," he said.

When the merchant had left the stable, the lame man was brought in. But he, too, pointed straightway at the merchant's horse. "O wise Cadi," the fellow said, "how could you think I would not know my own horse?"

Next morning in court the Cadi called the merchant and the cripple before him.

"By the laws of Allah," he began, "justice shall here be done. The horse belongs to the merchant. Let him ride on his way in peace!" As for this ungrateful lame fellow, let him receive one hundred lashes upon his thick hide. He gave poor return for a fellow traveler's kindness."

No sooner had these words been said than the horse thief threw down his crutch and tried to run from the court. In truth, he could walk as well as you or I can. But

193

the Cadi's men were too quick for him, and they took him away.

That evening Ben-Assar knocked at the door of the house of the Cadi. This good judge made a low bow when he learned that his visitor was the Kind Caliph himself instead of a merchant.

"Great is the honor you do my house, Ben-Assar," said the Cadi.

"Greater still is your wisdom, good Cadi," the Caliph replied. "You have proved to me that justice is done in your court. But I would know, if you please, how you could so quickly be sure the horse was mine."

"It was not easy, O Caliph," the Cadi explained. "That thief picked out your horse from among all the others as surely as you did. It was the animal itself that showed me the truth. When you went into my stable, you walked without fear to the horse's side. The horse, in his turn, welcomed you with a whinny. But I saw that the other one dared not go near the animal's head. At his approach the horse laid his ears back. He drew up his lip as though he would bite. It was easy to see which one of you that horse claimed as his master."

"Allah is good!" Ben-Assar cried. "He has given you rare wisdom. I would that the Caliph may serve our people as governor as well as this Cadi serves them as judge."

Jessamyn West

First Day Finish

"THEE'S HOME, LADY," Jess told his mare.

They had made the trip in jig time. The sun was still up, catalpa shadows long across the grass, and mud daubers still busy about the horse trough, gathering a few last loads before nightfall, when Lady turned in the home driveway.

Jess loosened the rein so that on their first homecoming together they could round the curve to the barn with a little flourish of arrival. It was a short-lived flourish, quickly subsiding when Jess caught sight of the Reverend Marcus Augustus Godley's Black Prince tied to the hitching rack.

195

"Look who's here," Jess told his mare and they came in slow and seemly as befitted travelers with forty weary miles behind them.

The Reverend Godley himself, shading his eyes from the low sun, stepped to the barn door when his Black Prince nickered.

Jess lit stiffly down and was standing at Lady's head when the Reverend Marcus Augustus reached them.

"Good evening, Marcus," said Jess. "Thee run short of something over at thy place?"

"Welcome home," said Reverend Godley, never flinching. "I was hunting, with Enoch's help, a bolt to fit my seeder," he told Jess, but he never took his eyes off Lady.

He was a big man, fat but not pursy, with a full red face preaching had kept supple and limber. A variety of feelings, mostly painful, flickered across it now as he gazed at Jess's mare.

He opened and shut his mouth a couple of times, but all he managed to say was, "Where'd you come across that animal, Friend Birdwell?"

"Kentucky," Jess said shortly.

"I'm a Kentuckian myself." The Reverend Godley marveled that the state that had fathered him could have produced such horseflesh.

"You trade Red Rover for this?" he asked.

Jess rubbed his hand along Lady's neck. "The mare's name is Lady," he said.

"Lady!" the preacher gulped, then threw back his big head and disturbed the evening air with laughter.

196

"Friend," Jess said, watching the big bulk heave, "thy risibilities are mighty near the surface this evening."

The Reverend Godley wiped the tears from his face and ventured another look. "It's just the cleavage," he said. "The rift between the name and looks."

"That's a matter of opinion," Jess told him, "but Lady is the name."

The preacher stepped off a pace or two as if to try the advantage of a new perspective on the mare's appearance, clapped a handful of Sen-sen into his mouth, and chewed reflectively.

"I figure it this way," he told Jess. "You bought that animal Red Rover. Flashy as sin and twice as unreliable. First little brush you have with me and my cob, Red Rover curdles on you—goes sourer than a crock of cream in a June storm. What's the natural thing to do?"

The Reverend Godley gave his talk a pulpit pause and rested his big thumbs in his curving watch chain.

"The natural thing to do? Why, just what you done. Give speed the go-by. Say farewell to looks. Get yourself a beast sound in wind and limb and at home behind a plow. Friend," he commended Jess, "you done the right thing, though I'm free to admit I never laid eyes before on a beast of such dimensions.

"Have some Sen-sen?" he asked amiably. "Does wonders for the breath." Jess shook his head.

"Well," he continued, "I want you to know—Sunday mornings on the way to church, when I pass you, there's nothing personal in it. That morning when I went round you and Red Rover, I somehow got the idea you's taking it personal. Speed's an eternal verity, friend, an eternal verity. Nothing personal. The stars shine. The grass withereth. The race is to the swift. A fast horse passes a slow one. An eternal verity, Friend Birdwell. You're no preacher, but your wife is. She understands these things. Nothing personal. Like gravitation, like life, like death. A law of God. Nothing personal.

"The good woman will be hallooing for me," he said, gazing up the pike toward his own farm a quarter of a mile away. He took another look at Jess's new mare.

"Name's Lady," he said as if reminding himself. "Much obliged for the bolt, Friend Birdwell. Me and my cob'll see you Sunday."

Enoch stepped out from the barn door as the Reverend Godley turned down the driveway.

"Figure I heard my sermon for the week," he said.

"He's got an endurin' flock," Jess told his hired man.

"Cob?" Enoch asked. "What's he mean aways calling that animal of his a cob? He ignorant?"

"Not ignorant—smooth," Jess said. "Cob's just his way of saying Black Prince's no ordinary beast without coming straight out with so undraped a word as stallion."

The two men turned with one accord from Godley's cob to Jess's Lady. Enoch's green eyes flickered knowingly; his long freckled hand touched Lady's muscled shoulder lightly, ran down the powerful legs, explored the deep chest.

"There's more here, Mr. Birdwell, than meets the eye?"

Jess nodded.

198

"As far as looks goes," Enoch said, "the Reverend called the turn."

"As far as looks goes," Jess agreed.

"She part Morgan?"

"Half," Jess said proudly.

Enoch swallowed. "How'd you swing it?"

"Providence," Jess said. "Pure Providence. Widow woman wanted a pretty horse and one that could be passed."

"Red Rover," Enoch agreed, and added softly, "The Reverend was took in."

"He's a smart man," said Jess. "We'd best not bank on it. But by sugar, Enoch, I tell thee I was getting tired of taking Eliza down the pike to Meeting every First Day like a tail to Godley's comet. Have him start late, go round me, then slow down so's we'd eat dust. Riled me so I was arriving at Meeting in no fit state to worship."

"You give her a tryout—coming home?" Enoch asked guardedly.

"I did, Enoch," Jess said solemnly. "This horse, this Morgan mare named Lady, got the heart of a lion and the wings of a bird. Nothing without pinfeathers is going to pass her."

"It's like Mr. Emerson says," said Enoch earnestly.

Jess nodded. "Compensation," he agreed. "A clear case of it and her pure due considering the looks she's got."

"You figure on this Sunday?" Enoch asked.

"Well," Jess said, "I plan to figure on nothing. Thee heard the Reverend Marcus Augustus. A fast horse goes

199

round a slow one. Eternal law. If Black Prince tries to pass us First Day—and don't—it's just a law, just something eternal. And mighty pretty, Enoch, like the stars."

"A pity," Enoch said, reflecting. "The Reverend's young 'uns all so piddling and yours such busters. It'll tell on your mare."

"A pity," Jess acquiesced, "but there it is. Eliza'd never agree to leave the children home from Meeting."

Enoch ruminated, his fingers busy with Lady's harness. "What'll your wife say to this mare? Been a considerable amount of trading lately."

"Say?" said Jess. "Thee heard her. 'Exchange Red Rover for a horse not racy-looking.' This mare racy-looking?"

"You have to look twice to see it," Enoch admitted.

"Eliza don't look twice at a horse. I'll just lead Lady up now for Eliza to see. She don't hold with coming down to the barn while men's about."

Jess took Lady from the shafts and led her between rows of currant bushes up to the house. Dusk was come now, lamps were lit. Inside, Eliza and the children were waiting for their greeting until the men had had their talk.

"Lady," Jess said fondly, "I want thee to see thy mistress."

The rest of the week went by, mild and very fair, one of those spells in autumn when time seems to stand still. Clear days with a wind which would die down by afternoon. The faraway Sandusky ridges seemed to have moved up to the orchard's edge. The purple ironweed, the farewell summer, the goldenrod, stood untrembling beneath an unclouded sky. Onto the corn standing shocked in the fields, gold light softer than arrows, but as pointed, fell. A single crow at dusk would drop in a slow arc against the distant wood to show that not all had died. Indian summer can be a time of great content.

First Day turned up pretty. Just before the start for Meeting, Jess discovered a hub cap missing off the surrey.

"Lost?" asked Eliza.

"I wouldn't say lost," Jess told her. "Missing."

Odd thing, a pity to be sure, but there it was. Nothing for it but for him and Eliza to ride to meeting in the cutdown buggy and leave the children behind. Great pity, but there it was.

Eliza stood in the yard in her First Day silk. "Jess," she said in a balky voice, "this isn't my idea of what's seemly. A preacher going to Meeting in a cut-down rig like this. Looks more like heading for the trotting races at the county fair than preaching."

Jess said, "Thee surprises me, Eliza. Thee was used to put duty before appearance. Friend Fox was content to tramp the roads to reach his people. Thee asks for thy surrey, fresh blacking on the dashboard, and a new whip in the socket."

He turned away sadly. "The Lord's people are everywhere grown more worldly," he said, looking dismally at the ground.

It didn't set good with Jess, pushing Eliza against her

201

will that way—and he wasn't too sure it was going to work. But the name Fox got her. When she was a girl she'd set out to bring the Word to people, the way Fox had done, and he'd have gone, she knew, to Meeting in a barrow, if need be.

So that's the way they started out, and in spite of the rig, Eliza was lighthearted and holy-feeling. When they pulled out on the pike, she was pleased to note the mare's gait was better than her looks. Lady picked up her feet like she knew what to do with them.

"Thee's got a good-pulling mare, Jess," she said kindly.

"She'll get us there, I don't misdoubt," Jess said.

They'd rounded the first curve below the clump of maples that gave Maple Grove Nursery its name, when the Reverend Godley bore down upon them. Neither bothered to look back, both knew the heavy, steady beat of Black Prince's hoofs.

Eliza settled herself in the cut-down rig, her Bible held comfortable in her lap. "It taxes the imagination," she said, "how a man churchbound can have his mind so set on besting another.

Don't thee think so, Jess?"

"It don't tax mine," Jess said, thinking honesty might be the only virtue he'd get credit for that day.

Eliza was surprised not to see Black Prince pulling abreast them. It was here on the long stretch of level road that Black Prince usually showed them his heels.

"Thee'd best pull over, Jess," she said.

"I got no call to pull out in the ditch," Jess said.

202

"The law allows me half the road."

The mare hadn't made any fuss about it—no head-shaking, no fancy footwork—but she'd settled down in her harness, she was traveling. It was plain to Eliza they were eating up the road.

"Don't thee think we'd better pull up, Jess?" Eliza said it easy, so as not to stir up the contrary streak that wasn't buried very deep in her husband.

"By sugar," Jess said, "I don't see why."

As soon as Eliza heard that "by sugar" spoken as bold-faced as if it were a weekday, she knew it was too late for soft words. "By sugar," Jess said again, "I don't see why. The Reverend Godley's got half the road and I ain't urging my mare."

It depended on what you called urging. He hadn't taken to lambasting Lady with his hat yet, the way he had Red Rover, but he was sitting on the edge of his seat—and sitting mighty light, it was plain to see—driving the mare with an easy rein and talking to her like a weanling.

"Thee's a fine mare. Thee's a tryer. Thee's a credit to thy dam. Never have to think twice about thy looks again."

Maybe, strictly speaking, that was just encouraging, not urging, but Eliza wasn't in a hair-splitting mood.

She looked back at the Reverend Marcus Augustus, and no two ways about it: he *was* urging Black Prince. The Reverend Godley's cob wasn't a length behind them and the Reverend himself was half standing, slapping the reins across Black Prince's rump and exhorting him

203

like a sinner newly come to the mourner's bench.

This was a pass to which Eliza hadn't thought to come twice in a lifetime—twice in a lifetime to be heading for Meeting like a county fair racer in a checkered shirt.

"Nothing lacking now," she thought bitterly, "but for bets to be laid on us."

That wasn't lacking either, if Eliza had only known it. They'd come in view of the Bethel Church now, and more than one of Godley's flock had got so carried away by the race as to try for odds on their own preacher. It didn't seem loyal not to back up their Kentucky brother with hard cash. Two to one the odds were—with no takers.

The Bethel Church sat atop a long, low rise, not much to the eye—but it told on a light mare pulling against a heavy stallion, and it was here Black Prince began to close in; before the rise was half covered, the stallion's nose was pressing toward the buggy's back wheel.

Jess had given up encouraging. He was urging now. Eliza lifted the hat off his head. Come what might, there wasn't going to be any more hat-whacking if she could help it—Jess was beyond knowing whether his head was bare or covered. He was pulling with his mare now, sweating with her, sucking the air into scalding lungs with her. Lady had slowed on the rise—she'd have been dead if she hadn't—but she was still a-going, still trying hard. Only the Quaker blood in Jess's veins kept him from shouting with pride at his mare's performance.

The Reverend Godley didn't have Quaker blood in his veins. What he had was Kentucky horse-racing

204

blood, and when Black Prince got his nose opposite Lady's rump, Godley's racing blood got the best of him. He began to talk to his cob in a voice that got its volume from camp-meeting practice—and its vocabulary, too, as a matter of fact—but he was using it in a fashion his camp-meeting congregation had never heard.

They were almost opposite the Bethel Church now; Black Prince had nosed up an inch or two more on Lady and the Reverend Godley was still strongly exhorting— getting mighty personal for a man of his convictions.

But Lady was a stayer and so was Jess. And Eliza too, for that matter. Jess spared her a glance out of the corner of his eye to see how she was faring. She was faring mighty well—sitting bolt upright, her Bible tightly clasped, and clucking to the mare. Jess couldn't credit what he heard. But there was no doubt about it—Eliza was counseling Lady. "Thee keep a-going, Lady," she called. Eliza hadn't camp-meeting experience, but she had a good clear pulpit voice and Lady heard her.

She kept a-going. She did better. She unloosed a spurt of speed Jess hadn't known was in her. Lady was used to being held back, not yelled at in a brush. Yelling got her dander up. She stretched out her long neck, lengthened her powerful stride, and pulled away from Black Prince just as they reached the Bethel Church grounds.

Jess thought the race was won and over, that from here on the pace to Meeting could be more suitable to First Day travel. But the Reverend Godley had no mind to stop at so critical a juncture. He'd wrestled with sinners too long to give up at the first setback. He figured the

mare was weakening. He figured that with a strong stayer like his Black Prince he'd settle the matter easy in the half mile that lay between Bethel Church and the Quaker Meetinghouse at Rush Branch. He kept a-coming.

But one thing he didn't figure—that was that the slope from Bethel to Rush Branch was against him. Lady had a down hill grade now. It was all she needed. She didn't pull away from Black Prince in any whirlwind style, but stride by stride she pulled away.

FIRST DAY FINISH

It was a great pity Jess's joy in that brush had to be marred. He'd eaten humble pie some time now, and he was pleasured through and through to be doing the dishing up himself. And he was pleasured for the mare's sake.

But neither winning nor his mare's pleasure was first with Jess. Eliza was. There she sat, white and suffering, holding her Bible like it was the Rock of Ages from which she'd come mighty near to clean slipping off. Jess knew Eliza had a forgiving heart when it came to others —but whether she could forgive herself for getting heated over a horse race the way she'd done, he couldn't say.

And the worst for Eliza was yet to come. Jess saw that clear enough. When Lady and Black Prince had pounded past Godley's church, a number of the Bethel brethren, who had arrived early and were still in their rigs, set out behind the Reverend Marcus Augustus to be in at the finish. And they were going to be. Their brother was losing, but they were for him still, close behind and encouraging him in a wholehearted way. The whole caboodle was going to sweep behind Jess and Eliza into the Quaker churchyard. They wouldn't linger, but Jess feared they'd turn around there before heading back. And that's the way it was.

Lady was three lengths ahead of Black Prince when they reached the Rush Branch Meetinghouse. Jess eased her for the turn, made it on two wheels, and drew in close to the church. The Bethelites swooped in behind him and on out—plainly beat but not subdued. The Reverend Marcus Augustus was the only man among them without a word to say. He was as silent as a tombstone and considerably grimmer. Even his fancy vest looked to have faded.

The Quakers waiting in the yard for Meeting to begin were quiet too. Jess couldn't tell from their faces what they were feeling; but there was no use thinking that they considered what they'd just witnessed an edifying sight. Not for a weekday even, that mess of rigs hitting it down the pike with all that hullabaloo—let alone to First Day and their preacher up front, leading it.

Jess asked a boy to look after Lady. He was so taken up with Eliza he no more than laid a fond hand on Lady's hot flank in passing. He helped Eliza light down, and set his hat on his head when she handed it to him. Eliza looked mighty peaked and withdrawn, like a woman communing with her Lord.

She bowed to her congregation and they bowed back and she led them out of the sunshine into the Meeting-house with no word being spoken on either side. She walked to the preacher's bench, laid her Bible quietly down, and untied her bonnet strings.

Jess sat rigid in his seat among the men. Jess was a birthright Quaker—and his father and grandfathers before him—and he'd known Quakers to be read out of Meeting for less.

Eliza laid her little plump hands on her Bible and bowed her head in silent prayer. Jess didn't know how long it lasted—sometimes it seemed stretching out into eternity, but Quakers were used to silent worship, and he was the only one seemed restive. About the time the ice around Jess's heart was hardening past his enduring, Eliza's sweet, cool, carrying voice said, "If the spirit leads any of thee to speak, will thee speak now?"

Then Eliza lowered her head again—but Jess peered around the Meetinghouse. He thought he saw a contented look on most of the faces—nothing that went so far as to warm into a smile, but a look that said they were satisfied the way the Lord had handled things. And the spirit didn't move any member of the congregation to speak that day except for the prayers of two elderly Friends in closing.

The ride home was mighty quiet. They drove past Bethel Church, where the sermon had been short—for all the hitching racks were empty. Lady carried them along proud and untired. Enoch and the children met them down the pike a ways from home and Jess nodded the good news to Enoch—but he couldn't glory in it the way he'd like because of Eliza.

Eliza was kind, but silent. Very silent. She spoke when spoken to, did her whole duty by the children and Jess, but in all the ways that made Eliza most herself, she was absent and withdrawn.

Toward evening Jess felt a little dauncy—a pain beneath the ribs, heart, or stomach, he couldn't say which. He thought he'd brew himself a cup of sassafras tea, take it to bed and drink it there, and maybe find a little ease.

It was past nightfall when Jess entered his and Eliza's

209

chamber, but there was a full moon and by its light he saw Eliza sitting at the east window in her white night-dress, plaiting her black hair.

"Jess," asked Eliza, noting the cup he carried, "has thee been taken ill?"

"No," Jess said, "no," his pain easing off of itself when he heard by the tones of Eliza's voice that she was restored to him—forgiving and gentle, letting bygones be bygones.

"Eliza," he asked, "wouldn't thee like a nice hot cup of sassafras tea?"

"Why, yes, Jess," Eliza said. "That'd be real refreshing."

Jess carried Eliza her cup of tea, walking down a path of roses the moon had lit up in the ingrain carpet.

He stood, while she drank it, with his hand on her chair, gazing out of the window: the whole upcurve and embowered sweep of the earth soaked in moonlight—hill and wood lot, orchard and silent river. And beneath that sheen his own rooftree, and all beneath *it*, peaceful and at rest. Lady in her stall, Enoch reading Emerson, the children long abed.

" 'Sweet day,' " he said, " 'so cool, so calm, so bright, the bridal of the earth and sky.' "

And though he felt so pensive and reposeful, still the bridge of his big nose wrinkled up, his ribs shook with laughter.

Eliza felt the movement of his laughing in her chair. "What is it, Jess?" she asked.

Jess stopped laughing, but said nothing. He figured

210

FIRST DAY FINISH

Eliza had gone about as far in one day as a woman could in enlarging her appreciation of horseflesh; still he couldn't help smiling when he thought of the sermon that might have been preached in the Bethel Church upon eternal verities.

Format by Kohar Alexanian
Set in Linotype Primer
Composed by The Haddon Craftsmen, Inc.
Printed by Halliday Lithograph Corp.
HARPER & ROW PUBLISHERS, INCORPORATED

Date Due

18

Oscar Hammerstein I

The Life and Exploits

of an Impresario

by

VINCENT SHEEAN

With a Preface by

OSCAR HAMMERSTEIN II

Simon and Schuster

NEW YORK · 1956

FIRST PRINTING
LIBRARY OF CONGRESS CATALOG CARD NUMBER: 56–7495
MANUFACTURED IN THE UNITED STATES OF AMERICA
BY H. WOLFF BOOK MFG. CO., INC., NEW YORK

CONTENTS

Contents

Contents

Contents

Contents

Contents

Contents

ILLUSTRATION SECTION

CULVER

OSCAR HAMMERSTEIN

Impresario

Working on his most profitable invention—a cigar-making machine

Examining scores in
the opera house he
built in London—his
last venture

Arthur Hammerstein
—Oscar's son and right-hand man

Oscar Hammerstein on the stage of the Hippodrome, after a benefit performance, surrounded by some of the best-known composers of the day. Left to right, Jerome Kern, Lou Hirsch, A. Baldwin Sloane,

Rudolf Friml, Alfred Robyn, Gustave Kerker, Hugo Feld, John Philip Sousa, Leslie Stuart, Raymond Hubbell, John Golden, Silvio Hein, Irving Berlin

Marcel Renaud
as De Nevers in *The Huguenots*

Some of the

important artists

introduced to America

CULVER

Emma Calvé

at Hammerstein's

Manhattan Opera House

Emma Trentini as Carmen

Alessandro Bonci
as the Duke in *Rigoletto*

Luisa Tetrazzini

Mary Garden

Cleofonte Campanini

Mario Sammarco as Rigoletto

Lina Cavalieri

Nellie Melba as Violetta in *La Traviata*

Charles Dalmorès

John McCormack

PREFACE

A Kind of Grandfather

by

Oscar Hammerstein II

On *August 1, 1919, he lay unconscious on his bed in the Lenox Hill Hospital. For four, possibly five, minutes I watched him and listened to his tired breathing. Then I left the room. This was the longest time I had ever spent with him.*

Outside in the hospital corridor I waited for an elevator. One came, but it was going up. A handsome, big-boned woman came out and started down the hall toward his room. Then she stopped, turned around and addressed me.

"Aren't you Oscar Hammerstein's grandson?"

I said that I was.

She said, "I'm his wife."

I said, "How do you do?"

We shook hands and smiled politely. .The downgoing elevator arrived to relieve my embarrassment and I left her.

I walked down Park Avenue feeling lost and unclassified. My grandfather was dying and I didn't know how I felt about it. I had no deep sorrow to give way to. I had no resentful memories of a domination from which I could now feel free. I could make no crass speculations concerning my probable inheritance in his will; I knew that he was broke. I had none of the conventional thoughts or emotions of a bereaved grandson. It was an uncomfortable feeling, the more uncomfortable because in some vague way my heart had been touched, and I didn't know why.

I was twenty-four that summer. I thought back on the last time I had seen him, three years before this, almost to the day. It was in

Preface

an attorney's office. I was working there during the summer to supplement my study at Columbia Law School. He was filing a petition in bankruptcy and our firm was handling it. One day I was told that my employer, Mr. Edwin Blumenstiel, wanted to see me in his room. He had a surprise for me. When I entered I saw my grandfather. He raised his eyes slowly. I felt suddenly conscious of all my defects. I had, by that time, attained my full height, six feet one and a half inches, but I had only one hundred and thirty-three pounds to account for it. My complexion was as bad as a young man's complexion can be, and I needed a haircut.

Mr. Blumenstiel beamed on us both and, turning to my grandfather, said, "You know who this is, don't you?"

My grandfather nodded his head solemnly. "Yes, a kind of a grandson."

I grinned and, forcing as much lightness into my voice as I could, answered, "That's right—a kind of a grandson."

Mr. Blumenstiel, with the deflated look of a thwarted comedian, told me I could go back to my work.

I could remember only one other "conversation" with him. It took place on the day of my father's funeral. I walked into one of the bedrooms in our apartment and found him alone, crumpled up in a chair, his face inexpressibly sad. He looked small and beaten. This made me feel strong. Surprising myself with an unnatural valor, I walked right over to him and said, "How do you do, Grandfather?" He shook my hand limply. I sat down near him. Nothing more was said by either of us. The continued silence gave me the strange feeling that I had not come into the room at all. He seemed still to be alone. Presently my Uncle Arthur entered and the ordeal was over.

Beyond these brief and unprofitable encounters, all our other meetings that I could remember had taken place in the lobby of Hammerstein's Victoria Theater of Varieties. My brother Reggie and I spent nearly every Sunday afternoon of our childhood in

xvi

the stage box of this theater watching the matinee. (The law did not permit vaudeville on the Sabbath, and so these performances were called "Sacred Sunday Concerts." They were virtually the same bills one saw on week days, made sacred only by this change of title.) Once or twice a year, as we were going into the theater, my father would lead us over to a corner of the lobby where his father was standing. Reggie and I would shake hands dutifully, but neither of us would have the courage to meet our grandfather's eyes for very long. He never said anything, not even volunteering the stale observation "What big boys you're getting to be!" He seemed as relieved as we were when these short and pointless meetings were adjourned.

Whatever hazy conception I had of him up to the day he died was based on conversations I had heard or overheard as I was growing up. Members of the family had referred to him always as "the old man." They spoke of his predilection for grand opera as if it were a sickness. They told funny stories about him. To my child's ear, sensitive more to inflections than to the specific meanings of words, it was evident that my father, my aunts and uncles and my step-grandmother, his second wife, were all afraid of him. That made me afraid of him too. It was equally evident to me that in a shy and guarded way they loved him. This puzzled me.

People outside the family seemed eager to prove to me how well they knew him. I only half listened to them, as most children only half listen to the prattle of grownups. "Young man," I would hear from an old man, "I knew your grandfather when he was in the cigar business." What did I care? It did not seem remarkable to me that he had once been in the cigar business. Making cigars seemed an unromantic and faintly humiliating occupation for a boy's grandfather. "What are you going to do when you grow up— follow in your grandfather's footsteps? You couldn't do better. He's a great man." This kind of talk bored me. What was so great about him? Why didn't anyone ever talk to me about my mother's father, Grandpa Nimmo? He seemed a much nicer man, with snow-white, wavy hair and kind blue eyes. He bought me hard candy and took me for walks in the park.

It is possible that my loyalty to one grandfather caused me to resist and resent the fame of the other, but this fame cast a broad shadow and I could never elude it. His picture kept staring at me from newspaper and magazine pages. Sometimes it was a photograph. More often it was a drawing. He was an easy subject for caricaturists. At a time when hirsute facial decoration was on the wane, he persevered with a meticulously trimmed goatee. Almost as permanent a part of his face was the cigar that protruded pugnaciously above the goatee. One more invariable symbol was the remarkable silk hat he wore day and night. It was a conically shaped topper favored by Frenchmen at that time or, at any rate, by stage comedians impersonating Frenchmen.

As a child I was not proud but ashamed of having so colorful a relative. It seemed that he was always "getting into the papers." He would arrive from Europe and announce the roster of great singing stars he had signed for the coming opera season. At another time he would be the center of a stormy fight. His adversary might be the police commissioner of New York, a society leader, or his rival, the impresario of the Metropolitan Opera House. He would write insulting letters to prominent men and they would be printed in the papers. He would write love letters to women and they would be printed in the papers. What was the matter with him? Why couldn't he be like the grandfathers of my schoolmates—nice, quiet, respectable old men? There was one thing I couldn't understand about these other grandfathers. They were always interested in mine. They would ask me questions about him, showing deep respect and admiration for the work he was doing or, at the very worst, affectionate amusement in him as a character. Those who knew him only slightly seemed to be boastful about their acquaintance. I couldn't see why. I couldn't see why he wasn't a pain in the neck to everyone, as he was to me.

Preface

Walking down Park Avenue from the hospital, recalling these vague impressions, I was astonished to realize how little I knew the man whose deathbed I had just left. I was equally astonished to realize that suddenly I wanted to know him. Perhaps for the first time it seemed safe to try. He couldn't hurt me now. He couldn't humiliate me. The fears and resentments of this remote "old man," developed in my childhood, were no longer a block to our union. It is ironic and sad and strange that I did not begin to understand or like my grandfather until the day of his death. But he was a strange man and so, perhaps, am I. On that day, thirty-seven years ago, I had only a few random patches of information about him, an unassembled crazy-quilt. Ever since then I have been sewing those patches and more patches together. Their colors clash and the pattern of the quilt is complex, but by looking at it hard and long I have grown to believe that there are a design and a theme in his life.

Some time ago my uncle, the late Arthur Hammerstein, and I began to assemble material on which to base a biographical motion picture on the life of my grandfather. Arthur himself, of course, was the best authority on the subject. He had been through the grand-opera era with his father as a kind of general lieutenant. He had a remarkable memory for actual conversations as well as the many extraordinary events that took place during that time. To supplement this first-hand knowledge we gathered data from music critics and newspaper reporters who had interviewed "the old man" during the first decade of this century. We prodded the memories of actors, actresses, opera singers, stage hands, stage doormen, property men and Lord knows how many people who knew him "when he was in the cigar business." Other surviving members of the family provided more information.

Before we had made final arrangements for producing the picture we were told that J. Vincent Sheean had expressed a deep interest in writing a biography of Oscar Hammerstein. Apart from his proven literary attainments, Mr. Sheean had one unique qualifica-

tion which set him apart from all other prospective biographers. He is the only man I have ever met whose passion for grand opera equaled my grandfather's. Believing that the book should come first and the picture second, my uncle and I immediately turned all our material over to Mr. Sheean.

The author has wisely rejected all the wild and extravagant anecdotes which could not be authenticated. The literal facts of my grandfather's life are wild and extravagant enough. An energetic young immigrant arriving in New York at the time of the Civil War with only a few coins of German money in his pocket, he remained to help build the city, establish neighborhoods, advance its culture. He made his mark as an inventor, a real-estate speculator, an editor and publisher, a producer of vaudeville and musical comedy. The energy for all these activities had one generating source—his ambition to be a grand-opera impresario. This was all he wanted. Nothing else mattered.

Having very little emotional involvement with my namesake as a grandfather, I find him nevertheless a stimulating character as he is described in these pages that follow. On behalf of my late uncle and the other members of our family, I wish to thank the author for this vivid and honest picture of a dynamic American.

Oscar Hammerstein I

I

The Top Hat of an Ego

In the time of carriages, sudden fortunes, and panics, when the snow stayed much longer in the city streets than it does today and the sleigh was still a practical vehicle, New York witnessed a phenomenon it had never seen before and has not seen since. A man impassioned for opera gave battle to the Metropolitan, an opera company and an opera house that represented the entrenched wealth of the United States.

1. The Legend of Oscar Hammerstein

While it went on, the entire population concerned itself with this man's fortunes in the battle. The name and personality of Oscar Hammerstein became as familiar to the nation as if he had been its elected President. His distinctive appearance was universally recognized. Each of his doings and sayings was chronicled. His legend, expressed in stories, songs, cartoons, and all the apparatus of legend, was spread across the land. In a period when the present use of familiar names had not yet come into fashion he was known to millions as "Oscar."

It strikes us as odd now, at this distance of time, that the American people interested themselves so intensely in Hammerstein. He fought his war on a terrain unfamiliar to most of them. Grand

3

opera in the United States has never been the preoccupation of more than a minority of the people. Compare it to baseball or the films and it is seen at once that this is not bread nor even circuses but simply caviar.

And yet Oscar Hammerstein, in his Prince Albert coat and striped black-and-white (or sometimes gray or fawn) trousers, with his goatee and his cigar and his unique top hat, commanded more space in the press than the Vanderbilts, Astors, Morgans, than William Jennings Bryan or indeed any other personage of his day except President Theodore Roosevelt.

It is true that a newsworthy quality clung about him. His wit, uttered with the German accent that he never lost, was caustic and quotable. He was not above inventing news, and some of his inventions to win space in the papers are legendary among professional publicists.

But he was, besides, the kind of person to whom things actually happened. In the Paradise Roof Garden atop his Victoria Theatre, a bear—one of the changing collection of livestock Hammerstein kept up there—escaped from its keeper and wandered loose, frightening the staff and the customers alike. Hammerstein himself, with only a siphon of soda water which he squirted into the animal's face, got it back into its cage.

This was not a stunt but an event that actually took place, without forethought on anybody's part. It happened, thanks to Hammerstein's consistent physical courage.

But it also happened because when Hammerstein built a theater —and he built thirteen of them, in New York, Philadelphia, and London—he built not merely a theater but an opera house or a music hall, possibly also a concert hall, smoking room, billiard room, vast lounges and promenades, and, to cap it, a roof garden serving food and drink as well as diversion.

To keep live animals in his aerial place of entertainment was an inspiration of Hammerstein's gift for extravagant showmanship. Thus, it was within the realm of probability that a bear should some night escape from its cage. The newsworthiness that haunted Hammerstein made it equally likely that he should be on the scene when the event took place. It might have been a waiter or it might have been a guest who grasped the seltzer bottle and stepped forward to cope with the crisis. But if Hammerstein was there, it had to be Hammerstein, because he was that kind of man.

The Top Hat of an Ego

Yet there was something more than the flamboyant talent for creating news which made nearly the entire nation his partisans. He had the kind of personality to which the people intuitively respond whenever and wherever it appears, whether in politics, art, entertainment, or sports. His quarrels were numerous and public; it is said that he once had no fewer than forty lawsuits going at the same time. He went into a quarrel, whether public or private, with a native zest, a sort of enjoyment of the fight for its own sake. Once it was over, he was quite capable of forgetting it altogether. But not always. On one occasion when he lost a battle he stood up in a box and hissed the star in his own theater. In this instance he pursued vengeance and won it, although he bankrupted himself in the process.

He was the kind of fighter who threw down as a gage in battle everything he was and had, present and future. His failures were as splendid as his triumphs, and they followed one another in dizzying alternation. The public never had to wait very long for Hammerstein to be either up or down, and both spectacularly. There was a day when he had to petition the court for entrance to a theater in which he had lost everything and from which he was barred by the receiver. He asked the court's permission to retrieve from under the pillow of his cot, in the little room over the theater marquee, the $400 he had left there, which represented all he owned in the world at that moment. In less than a year the public was again storming the doors of another and more resplendent Hammerstein theater.

He could say with perfect truthfulness to Mary Garden one night at the Manhattan Opera House: "Mary, there isn't enough money in the house to pay the light bill." That was the season that ended with a profit in the till of a quarter of a million dollars—for grand opera, which is not a profit-making enterprise. Two years later he again faced bankruptcy. That was the moment when it cost $1,250,000 of someone's money (Was it Otto Kahn's? It is still a tantalizing question) to get Oscar Hammerstein out of New York City and out of competition with the Metropolitan.

2. *The Man Who Cared Nothing for Money*

The zestful fighter, the daring gambler, the man who is down but never out—these have an irresistible appeal, and the public found them all in Hammerstein. They found still another romantic quality: he cared nothing for money. He amassed millions overnight and spent them the next day, spurning the elementary caution of keeping a little for future security or even present comfort. People living lives hemmed in by grocery bills and mortgage payments love such a man for his brave freedom from little cares.

For Hammerstein it seems to have been no struggle to rise above little cares. He was simply not aware of them. Money for itself meant nothing to him. He paid the largest fees of his time to operatic artists, and they were always fully paid. He habitually scattered silver coins, usually quarters, among the newsboys of Times Square; I have talked with one of them who is still alive and remembers Mr. Hammerstein and his largess very well.

But he spent no money on himself. He rode in streetcars rather than hansom cabs, and lived on in his two small rooms at the Victoria Theatre in preference to the more suitable quarters his son Arthur provided for him.

His sons Willie and Arthur followed the custom of sticking a five-dollar bill into the Old Man's pocket whenever he reached for his gold-topped cane to go forth into the great city. If they did not, he was likely to be stranded somewhere without even enough for trolley fare; it had happened often. He dealt in millions, but borrowed from newsboys or left his overcoat as security for a bowl of oyster stew. Arthur and Willie, practical men and wise in their generation, nevertheless understood and accepted this.

For all these reasons, and for his very bristling, belligerent, fierce individuality, Hammerstein had a fascination for strangers and a magnetism for those close to him. His clashes with his artists were famous, and so were some of the diabolical ways he had of persuading an artist to terminate a contract no longer interesting to him. Yet he won the loyalty of some of the greatest among them. He was never at a loss to find devoted employees, and although he was quite willing to sacrifice his sons as well as himself to his obsession, he had the undeviating devotion of Willie and Arthur.

6

With the public he had a fantastic personal popularity. They streamed to each of his new theaters to see what "Oscar" had done this time, to see—if possible—Oscar himself. He was drawn onto the stage by the audience's demand at opening nights, and took bow after bow. When, for a lark, he played end man once in a minstrel show—"The One, the Only, the Original Oscar Hammerstein!"—the ovation lasted fifteen minutes.

3. Lonely Triumph

If Hammerstein needed one more touch to make him appealing both as a public and as a private character, he had it. It was that touch of the puzzling, the unreachable, the enigmatic—and the lonely. In spite of the blaze of publicity in which he lived, nobody really knew Hammerstein. Many people are left alone in failure or grief, but few are alone in success, especially in the gregarious world of music and the theater. On the night of his greatest triumph Hammerstein was alone.

It was the opening night of his Manhattan Opera House. He had taken bows after the second act, and again at the final curtain he was imperiously demanded by the entire audience until he was forced to say his few words dedicating the opera house to the people of New York. After he had left the stage the calls for him continued for a long time.

When the house was dark and empty, when the last of the singers and orchestra, audience and stagehands, were gone, he emerged alone from the theater. He walked to Eighth Avenue and took the streetcar to Forty-second Street. At a Childs restaurant on Broadway between Forty-second and Forty-third streets he went in, apparently unnoticed (this, for a man of his appearance, was an achievement), ordered and consumed an oyster stew, and went home. It was late, and perhaps even Mr. Hammerstein, the most famous denizen of Times Square, could have passed unrecognized. He went to his Victoria Theatre, to his two rooms on the balcony, and went to bed.

Thus in solitude, without the host of admirers who would have been flattered to join him, or the few intimates with whom almost any man seeks to share his successes, Oscar Hammerstein savored the realization of his dream.

7

Hammerstein knew innumerable people and was known to many more, but nobody claims to have known him. He ate his frugal meals alone, and received few visitors in his rooms at the Victoria with the workbench, the drawing board, the piano, and the cot. For all his charm and geniality, for all his outbursts of merriment, enthusiasm, or anger, the essential Hammerstein remained within his self-created shell, aloof and mysterious. From the beginning— or at least from the death of his first and much-loved wife, Rose —he was, if not lonely, at least alone. The critic James Huneker said: "Hammerstein did not wear his heart on his sleeve."

His celebrated grandson, Oscar Hammerstein II, remembers how in his childhood people were always speaking to him of his grandfather, and he describes in the poignant preface to this volume the "paradox of fear and affection, of disapproval and admiration which the 'old man' excited in all who knew him." Arthur Hammerstein, who knew his father about as well as anybody did, and who was inextricably, though reluctantly, involved in all his fortunes, also spoke of that quality in Oscar Hammerstein which drew people magnetically to him and yet held them at arm's length.

For all that he kept them at a distance, they were drawn to him. They all must have felt in him some greatness that they were willing to serve, even though the life was precarious and the hurricanes frequent.

4. Magnificent Obsession

To know such a man is difficult, but perhaps less difficult for us than it was for his contemporaries. That the greatness they felt in him was there we now no longer question. His achievement is a matter of record.

He was no architect, but he designed all his theaters, opera houses, music halls, roof gardens, and they were wonders in their time, with a spaciousness and elegance that drew as much admiring space in the press as the artists who performed in them, although the artists were, many of them, of the highest quality. He was no engineer, but his theaters were all remarkable for their acoustics. All of them, no matter what their ostensible purpose, were theaters for the ear—in effect, for opera.

8

The Top Hat of an Ego

He was single-mindedly dedicated to opera. It was toward the production of opera that all his enterprises tended for more than thirty years. At the very time of his death he was contemplating another foray into that perilous and expensive fairyland. He might make or lose money on the various theaters he built. He certainly did make a great deal of it in some of his real estate and a good many of his theatrical efforts aside from opera. And he made money whenever he needed it by inventing a new machine or a new process for the cigar business, in which he had made his start.

But the purpose of getting money was only to be able to get back again to the production of opera. It was a ruling passion, and to it he was ready to sacrifice not only himself but his family, his friends, and whatever business interests he or they might have in other directions. When his sons made money in enterprises of their own he had no hesitation in taking it from them —not for himself but for the opera, always for the opera. We find few such disinterested and uncompromising obsessions in the history of the theater.

Why did he love the opera so much? His whole fantastic life is probably the answer to that question. At every performance of opera that he gave, without exception, he sat in the wings on a kitchen chair, cigar between his teeth, watching and listening, from the curtain's rise to its final fall. This is not myth but fact. When, in his glittering new opera house in Philadelphia—"the most beautiful opera house in the world"—a kitchen chair was not at hand before the curtain rose, someone had to be sent out to find one for him.

He was, by any standard, a great opera impresario. He had a nearly infallible flair for a coming public taste, and was often ahead of the critics but in tune with the audience. He knew how an artist should be presented, and when he got a cast for a particular opera he kept it together; this was an idea that did not reach the Metropolitan for decades. He gave attention to stage direction, chorus, and orchestra as none had done up to his time. He sat on his chair in the wings for his own good reasons, but there can be no question that his presence kept artists, musicians, even stage crew on their mettle.

Artists such as Melba, Garden, Tetrazzini, McCormack appreciated the character, the temperament, and the innumerable peculiarities of their very original impresario. But this same originality and

9

abounding ego frightened others. They seemed to feel menaced, as on a lowering, smoky day in the neighborhood of a volcano.

Caruso, for example, may have been afraid of Hammerstein in this intuitive way, as many were. We know that the extraordinary tenor was strongly tempted to leave the Metropolitan for Hammerstein, and his hesitations have never been fully explained. If Hammerstein had won Caruso, the end of the story might have been different. Hammerstein's very personality, his greatest asset, may in this case have cost him the complete fulfillment of his lifelong dream.

Yet Hammerstein reached fantastic heights of success—alone and by his own efforts, without a board of directors, without patrons, with no help but the devotion of his lieutenants, his two capable, patient sons. And while it lasted, his achievement was phenomenal. He introduced standards of performance never before known in the United States; works hitherto unheard, some of them masterpieces; artists new to this country and some of them the greatest; musical and dramatic revelations to the operagoers of America.

It took years for some of the Hammerstein ideas to penetrate the Metropolitan, and that they did so at all was because he had seriously endangered that great monopoly in its complacent rut of gold. Long after he had been banished from opera in New York by a contract unique in theater history, his ideas were germinating in other fields, as they still are, and his repertoire, not to speak of his artists, bejeweled the theaters of his rivals and successors.

And he did all this in eminently American terms. He was no reticent, art-loving intellectual. He was no intellectual at all. He was a showman who disdained no trick of his trade and made use of them all as occasion offered.

He crystallized his own personality, furthermore, in an easily recognizable form—the beard, the cigar, and especially the silk hat—so that not only was he physically known himself, but for years it was hardly possible to represent any other impresario without this same regalia.

Oscar Hammerstein's career began in the era of gaslight and went on to triumph in the modern glare of electric bulbs. His perilous zigzag progress in finance, the extremes of his fortunes, the bewildering succession of theaters built and lost, millions squandered and regained, became a story told and retold. In such a picaresque tale it is inevitable that much should be invented, much exaggerated. But there was enough truth in it all to catch the imaginations of countless people who did not care anything at all about opera.

There have been, of course, other impresarios colorful and original in their own ways. But there has never been another Hammerstein, any more than there has been another top hat like Hammerstein's—the top hat of an ego.

II

Beginnings

HAMMERSTEIN said once to Mary Garden, when she was the bright particular star of his opera company: "Mary, we've got our house in New York and our house in Philadelphia. I'll get one in Boston and one in Chicago and one in, say, Denver, and of course one in San Francisco, and we'll have a bridge of opera across the whole country. Then you'll see!"

The bridge of opera got no farther west than Philadelphia and then with the transient brilliance of a comet rather than the solidity of a bridge. Yet Oscar Hammerstein did more for opera in this country, and imprinted a more dazzling image of himself on the public consciousness, than many a man who has realized his ambition to the full, and mainly because he was a man possessed by a single idea.

We know that all he wanted was to produce grand opera. But in tracing his beginnings we are puzzled to find the source of the dream, the birth of the obsession.

1. The Hammersteins in the Theater

Both before his day and since, the Hammerstein family and its connections have displayed uncommon talent for the theater. Bertha Valentine Hammerstein, Oscar's mother, came of a French

12

Huguenot family that had a persistent interest in music and drama. The actress Rosa Valetti was Oscar's aunt, and another of his aunts was the first wife of Josef Kainz, celebrated in Germany for his Hamlet.

In America the Hammerstein gift for the stage has had an abundant flowering. Oscar's sons, Arthur and Willie, produced, managed, and directed—Arthur in operetta and musical comedy, Willie chiefly in vaudeville. Arthur, at the age of eighty, still found expression for his talents in song-writing, and not long before he died (in 1955) he composed the music of a widely popular song, "Because of You." Arthur's daughter Elaine was a beautiful and well-remembered star of silent films. Willie's son Oscar, namesake of his opera-bewitched grandfather, has written the book and lyrics and been the co-producer of an entire new genre of musical plays known to the whole English-speaking world and the continent of Europe. Some of his successes, notably *Oklahoma!* and *South Pacific*, have made theater history.

It is rare even in theater families to find such a range of activity and success. In the old days Francis Galton might have listed and tabulated the doings of the Hammerstein family, as he did those of the Bach family, to illustrate a sort of statistical heredity. The modern way is to attribute almost everything to environment.

Environment may well have played a part for the descendants of Oscar Hammerstein in America, an environment of opera, music, and every kind of theater, created by Oscar himself. But we are hard put to find a model for him in the house in Berlin when he was a child.

We are balked at the very start even for the exact date and place of his birth: whether it was in Hamburg or Berlin, in 1848 or 1847. He himself gave his birth, for the 1906 edition of *Who's Who in America*, as occurring on May 8, 1847, in Berlin. Other books of reference gave 1848 as the date and Hamburg as the place. (The *Dictionary of American Biography* offers still a third date, August 1, 1841, but this we may discard as incompatible with other dates in his history.)

It is not in the least out of character for Hammerstein to have given different dates and places for his birth on different occasions, either in absent-mindedness or from some impulse of mischief. More than once in his career we find an ambiguity of fact, or at least a choice of alternatives. As one of the oldest and best-known stories about him is that he ran away from home at the age of fifteen and came to New York "before the end of the Civil War"—by most accounts in 1863—we cannot go far wrong if we accept the date supplied by himself to *Who's Who* as the correct one.

2. *Young Oscar in Berlin*

The place of his birth is less important than the place where he spent his early, formative years, and this, we can be certain, was Berlin. To the home established here by his father, Abraham Hammerstein, a building contractor originally from Stettin in Pomerania, we must look for the influences that converged to form Oscar's unique personality. If the clue to his obsession with opera eludes us, we can find clues of another kind—to his rebelliousness, his appetite for unchallenged power, perhaps also his courage and tenacity once the dream had taken possession of him.

The Hammersteins in Berlin were a Jewish family of substance, with devout habits and an ingrained respect for culture. Typically for German-Jewish families of their time and status, they combined a loyalty to Jewish tradition and learning and an unquestioning identification with the Germany of their birth. Typically, too, the home was dominated by the absolute authority of the father and was warmed and softened by a gentle, submissive mother.

Oscar was the eldest of five children, with two brothers, Emile and Paul, and two sisters, Augusta and Anna. There is no indication that he had more than a routine brotherly relationship with any of the younger children, and there is every sign that his attitude toward his father was resentful and hostile. Abraham Hammerstein may have done no more than act out the part of the good German father, as tradition required of him. But his spirited eldest son could neither accept nor tolerate his domination.

His mother, the gentle soother and peacemaker, seems to have kept the boy's antagonisms from explosion while she lived, or perhaps he was too young still to try his strength against his father. But Bertha Hammerstein died when Oscar was about fourteen, precisely at the point of adolescent rebellion and self-assertion.

One might muse on the possible effects of the loss—at this critical moment between boyhood and manhood—of all that was tender and softening in his life. It comes to mind that fate was to deal him this same blow a second time, when he stood on the brink of his career, in the death of his wife Rose.

Death is inexplicable to the child—and to the child that lives in every adult—and the death of someone loving and loved is taken as a rejection. "How could she leave me if she really loved me?" may remain an unanswered question far below the level of consciousness. It is provocative to consider how much the untimely deaths of the two women, perhaps the only two human beings who loved him and whom he loved in return, may have shaped the superficially genial but profoundly lonely and withdrawn personality of the Hammerstein the world later knew.

3. German Discipline and German Music

Through his childhood years, however, above the strong tide of rebellion which must have been building in the boy Oscar, life in the Berlin house was comfortable, stable, and rooted in the past. There were good old pictures and books, family objects and bibelots of all kinds, articles of furniture which were good without being greatly valuable. It was a household that, without wealth or display, gave every evidence of a relish for the good things and an ability to hold on to them.

In such a family, study, music, discipline, and love of the Fatherland were considered the proper diet for children. Oscar, as the first-born and a boy, received a full measure of each, and especially of the discipline. The traditional Jewish reverence for learning in itself imposed a heavy curriculum on the eldest son. With this was coupled the high standard of education and culture in a German middle-class family of the time. It will be readily seen that a normal, healthy boy could hardly be kept to such a schedule without a parental scowl constantly at his shoulder.

Music was an inevitable part of the family life and the children's training. Oscar's father played the violin, his mother the piano. When he was five years old his mother began giving him piano lessons, and by the time he was six he was able to play some simple accompaniments to his father's violin. He studied flute very early, too, but gave it up for the violin at his father's desire. He had a tutor for ordinary studies until the age of seven, when he went to school.

Up to the time he was fifteen, young Oscar had the benefit of all the family could afford on his education, and to our eyes it seems a good deal. The elder Hammerstein apparently went on from contracting to trading on the stock exchange, but even so his income never rose very high. Yet Oscar had his private school, his lessons in violin and piano, and, from the age of twelve, his studies at the Conservatory in harmony and counterpoint. He had a tutor in Latin and Greek, and he had daily instruction from a Hebrew scholar in religion and language. To the boy, this meant a day filled with studies and lessons from early morning until bedtime. Such a schedule, and the discipline required to enforce it, could never have been congenial to the spirited boy who grew up to be the fiercely independent Hammerstein.

At the same time, a childhood of such intense application could not help establishing habits of solitude and industry. We begin to foresee the small, bare rooms over the theater marquee; the workshop with the piano, the drawing board, and the cot; the satisfaction in lonely accomplishment rather than gregarious pleasure. Another equally rebellious temper might have thrown off all shackles, even those of diligence. But without diligence, without the capacity for work which his restless ambition demanded of him, he would not have been the Oscar Hammerstein who left his mark on the theater and opera world.

One requirement of his studies at the Conservatory, we are told by his grandson Oscar, was that he must attend performances of the Opera. This, we can imagine, was one requirement he needed no parental prodding to fulfill. He went sometimes with fellow students, sometimes with his mother. How welcome was the escape into a world of illusion, glittering with light and color and filled with the melody of voices and instruments, we hardly need to ask. Perhaps it was in this very required attendance at the Opera that the magic of a bustling audience and an orchestra tuning up, of footlights going on and a curtain rising, took possession of his spirit with a hold that never slackened.

From the time he entered the Conservatory, tutors came to the home to continue his general education, and his formal studies were concentrated on music. He studied harmony, composition, and music-appreciation, and spent many hours in practice on the violin. Although he worked hard, his talent was not equal to any expectation that he would become a violin virtuoso. If this was the family's hope for him, and if perchance he shared in the hope, we might give some credence to the "disappointed violinist" theory so blithely offered to explain many a career in the musical world which was managerial, critical, or of almost any kind other than performing. His frustration with the violin seems too feeble a spark to burst into the blazing ambition that was Hammerstein's drive. And, as we shall see, when he struck for freedom the first object he chose to sacrifice was his violin.

For the next two years he was absorbed, perhaps even happy, in his music. Then Bertha Hammerstein died. In the anguished void that her going left, there loomed after a decent interval a new mistress of the household, the Dutch Widow. This was the only name the Hammerstein children had for her, and, according to family recollection, she was an austere, heavy blonde. She may have been a very good woman indeed, but probably it would have been beyond any woman's power to win the affection of the bereft, angry adolescent boy.

Meanwhile, beyond the trembling walls of the Hammerstein household a young Kaiser had been crowned, Bismarck had returned from Paris, and Germany was embarking on an aggressive new policy of "blood and iron." Pride in Prussia's expanding future was the theme in the streets and—as the elder Hammerstein shared the patriotic fervor of every good Berlin burgher of the day—no doubt of the dinner table as well. The flags and bands and military parades reminded a boy constantly that he must one day exchange music conservatory for army barracks. And we can be certain that by the time he was fifteen, young Oscar had many times faced the fact that a lad of small stature, and Jewish besides, could expect no distinction in the army except the contempt of his officers, the Prussian military elite.

4. Escape

In that year of 1862 the winter came early. Ponds froze over, including the pond near home where Oscar liked to spend his infrequent leisure. Perhaps his fondness for skating had caused trouble before; it does not seem probable that there was only one such time.

At all events, there was a night when he skated long, arriving home well past the hour for his evening instruction in religion and Hebrew. His father, infuriated, seized the skates from the boy's shoulder, detached the strap, and proceeded to administer a very sound thrashing.

The punishment was apparently unusual and must have been even more severe than the elder Hammerstein intended. The strap buckle cut a gash in the boy's forehead, and, according to Oscar's account of it years later to his own son Arthur, a doctor was called to take stitches in the wound. Hammerstein carried the scar all his life and often referred to this visible evidence of his father's severity, which he never forgave.

With or without the wound, young Oscar had evidently had enough. The boy's mind, as he sat brooding in his room afterward, turned toward an idea that boys in such circumstances have often had before and since: running away.

He knew something of America—chiefly, perhaps, that it was a long way from Berlin. But without money he could hardly undertake this or any other journey. It was then that he thought of his violin and the neighborhood pawnbroker—or perhaps, as his mind was so active, he had thought of them before. Now they became definite as the means of escape.

The pawnbroker's shop stayed open late. Young Oscar waited until he was sure his parents were asleep and then crept out of the house with his violin under his arm. It was his recollection afterward that the pawnbroker asked no questions, but paid him the equivalent of thirty-five dollars for the fiddle. With that and the clothes on his back and a very little cash he had saved, he set out for America.

The first step was a third-class ticket to Hamburg that same night, and among the other passengers were a number who were bound for America. He learned from their talk that a steerage passage to New York would cost thirty dollars (about 150 marks at that time) and that no cheaper way could be found. This involved passage on a cattle boat from Hamburg to Hull, in England, where the steerage passengers would be transferred to a freighter called the *Isaac Webb*. Trailing along behind the westward-bound passengers, he too bought passage on the following morning, and the cattle boat sailed for England in the afternoon. It took four days to get to Hull, which the steerage migrants left later the same day aboard the *Isaac Webb*.

The discomforts of the journey seem to have been exceptional even for those days, when immigrants were prepared to suffer. The old sailing ship was driven off its course by storms, the journey from Hull to New York consumed eighty-nine days (as Oscar remembered afterward), and long before the journey's end rations had begun to run short. The seventy immigrants on board were crowded into quarters below decks, where, when the hatches were battened down for the long storm, there was never any fresh air. Thus, young Hammerstein made his American entry in the classic manner: virtually penniless, friendless, hungry, and dirty, but with high hope and certainty, if the child *is* the father of the man, with boundless ambition.

III

Young Man on the Town

HIS EARLY DAYS in the New World might have been terrifying to a less confident youth. Hammerstein himself said afterward, more than once, that from the beginning he had been certain he would get work and make his way. As it happened, there was a labor shortage everywhere: this was the winter of 1863, the middle of the Civil War.

1. Oscar Discovers New York

Young Oscar found both a roof and a job almost at once. A sailor from the *Isaac Webb*, seeing the young immigrant in the street, advised him to go to a German boardinghouse across Bowling Green in Greenwich Street, where the lodgings were clean and cheap and where there would be no language difficulty. There he found a haven of sorts and a kindly landlady who produced for him the German newspaper with its advertisements of help wanted. Early on the morning of the next day (his second in New York) he applied for a job at the Pearl Street establishment of a cigar-maker named Levine, who wanted a boy to learn the trade and do odd jobs while learning.

His wages at first were two dollars a week, raised to four in the third week and five in the fourth. He was quick-witted, as always, and a demon of industry, for he was working not only in the cigar factory from seven to six every day but also extra hours in the German boardinghouse to pay his expenses there. In addition to all this, he had begun to study English immediately, and was hard at his books whenever he had an hour free for them.

It is recorded on his own authority that by this method of ceaseless labor and application he learned the cigar-maker's trade in six months and was paid accordingly, with constant raises, until he was earning as much as any experienced man. The demand for skilled labor—indeed, for any kind of labor—was great, and a capable worker had no worry about a job. Oscar gave up his handyman's work at the boardinghouse, moved to a new establishment in Ann Street, and began to look about him a little at the splendors of the brave new world.

The New York of 1864 was given to fantastic luxury in some areas, to professional vice and crime in others, to corruption pretty well everywhere, especially in politics. The flow of gold into the city after 1848 had caused the growth of many enormous fortunes and the building of great palaces in which the scale of entertainment on state occasions was far beyond anything known today. Most of the great houses were provided with ballrooms, art galleries, and general reception rooms of a size to cause even European visitors amazement. Along with wealth and display there was a great deal of vulgarity, but, as nobody seemed to notice, it can hardly have caused much suffering.

By contrast, the tenement districts and slums were deplorable, fires were very frequent, there were some areas (such as "The Five Corners," a rabbit warren off Worth Street) where murder was common and policemen ventured only in numbers. There was practically no limit to the possibilities of profit or the rewards of speculation; Vanderbilt (the original one) boasted of receiving twenty-five per cent annually on the $11,000,000 of his declared fortune at the time.

Much of the life of the city was in the lower part of Manhattan Island, around the City Hall and on Broadway a little farther north. The great restaurant of the whole period, and for years afterward, was Delmonico's, at Fourteenth Street and Fifth Avenue. A tendency on the part of the rich to build their great houses farther and farther uptown had begun to appear, and there were some notable ones already in Twenty-third Street and even as far north as Thirty-fourth, but Fifth Avenue had not yet fully come into its own. The theaters were all in the lower part of the island. The Academy of Music, where opera had been performed for the fashionable since 1849, was in Fourteenth Street; it was here that the great ball had been given for the Prince of Wales (Edward VII) in 1860.

It is hardly likely that the sixteen-year-old immigrant boy, enjoying his first evenings of leisure and sensation of success, saw much of all this. The families that were to play a considerable part in his own destiny (Morgan, Astor, and Vanderbilt) were all still in various stages of ascendancy, and in fact one of them, the Vanderbilts, had not yet begun to climb. Old Commodore Vanderbilt lived in immense luxury, but was "not received"—indeed, not even personally known—in New York society. A. T. Stewart, as rich or richer, was equally ignored, although the marble palace that he built in 1867 at Thirty-fourth Street and Fifth Avenue was the most pretentious of all.

We can imagine young Oscar Hammerstein walking of an evening up Fifth Avenue from Fourteenth Street—or anywhere "north of Bleecker Street"—to stare at the mansions of the rich, but we cannot imagine that he ever wanted to live in them. From all that we know of him in later years, his ambitions were not of that kind. He may have looked, but he certainly never envied.

2. The Magic of the Theater

What did arouse him to great excitement and dreams of a roseate future were his first visits to the theater.

There were about fifteen theaters in New York at the time, all handsome and most of them new, offering a variety of entertainment seldom surpassed since. The minstrel show was giving way slowly to music-hall entertainment in London style, where the restaurants, "conversation rooms," and promenades were as important as the show itself. To these theaters came the graduates of the "concert saloons" scattered through the city, and from them were to come eventually the American vaudeville. There were recitals and concerts at the new Steinway Hall (Fourteenth Street near Irving Place), where Charles Dickens gave his celebrated

series of thirteen readings. The most favored of the legitimate
theaters was Wallack's, originally at Broadway and Broome Street,
which built its luxurious new home at Thirteenth Street and
Broadway not long before Oscar arrived in New York. Wallack's
was for legitimate plays what the Academy of Music was for
opera—a center of taste, fashion, and display—and it maintained
a high standard throughout this decade.

Joseph Jefferson in *Rip Van Winkle* and Edwin Booth in the
Shakespeare tragedies were unfailing favorites at any theater
where they appeared. (It was not until the very end of the
1860's that Booth built his own theater at Twenty-third Street
and Sixth Avenue.) There were repertory companies playing in
New York in German, Italian, French, and Spanish from time to
time during this decade, as well as a good many visitors from
England; it was the period when the Italian tragedienne Ade-
laide Ristori made her American visit and subjugated all the
cities, like Duse long afterward.

In addition to all this, it was the moment when Offenbach and
the general style of French *opéra bouffe* were made known to New
York by two companies from Paris. The beauties of the undraped
female form were so generally concealed in the age of the crinoline
that any show which contained dancers in ballet costume was
eagerly attended, at least by the men of the town. The ballet-
spectacle *The Black Crook*—something like a modern musical
comedy, only much more clad—achieved a run of almost five
hundred performances at Niblo's Garden toward the end of the
decade.

Hammerstein remembered long afterward that the first time he
had ever been inside a New York theater was in March, 1864,
when he was taken by a fellow worker from the cigar factory to
hear and see the Bryant Brothers' Minstrels. This was at Mechan-
ics' Hall, 472 Broadway, when he was sixteen, and it seems to
have aroused in him the sense of wonder and delight which the
born man of the theater never quite loses even though he never
experiences it again to quite such a degree.

As a Conservatory student he had already thrilled to theater
magic at the Berlin Opera. Now the misty wish began to form
that he might one day work in the theater. From now on he went
as often as he could, sampling various kinds of entertainment
and unconsciously seeking his own. During this early period of

theater-going he was present at one famous performance: that of *Julius Caesar* given by the Booth brothers at the Winter Garden as a benefit for the fund to erect a statue of Shakespeare in Central Park. Edwin Booth played Brutus, Junius Brutus Booth played Cassius, and John Wilkes Booth Mark Antony. It was on November 25, 1864; less than five months later John Wilkes Booth was to assassinate Lincoln and cause his grief-stricken brothers to retire from the stage, as they thought and intended, forever.

Whether Hammerstein's English was yet equal to such performances is doubtful, but he felt in them the magic fire that was to be (according to testimony fifty years later) his own best contribution to the production of opera.

His epochal experience in this year of new experience was the rediscovery of opera.

3. Opera in the 1860's

There was a flourishing German-language life in New York then, with theater stock companies, newspapers, beer halls, choral societies, and a population that, being mostly of the first generation in the country, had not yet learned English. (Oscar could have lived quite well at that time without learning English at all if he had wished to do so.) The Academy of Music, the social center of New York, dominated by boxholders of the so-called "Knickerbocker aristocracy," leased its theater to German opera impresarios and to Italians alternately, and the financial conditions were precarious for anybody undertaking such a season. The season in German did not mean that only German operas would be given: it meant that all performances, whatever the origin of the operas presented, would be given in German. The Italian season meant that everything for a given number of weeks would be in Italian. This was the usual operatic fare in New York for another forty-odd years, until the principle of performing operas in their original languages was established. All the standard nineteenth-century works reached New York in this form—*Faust* in German, *Lohengrin* in Italian, depending on the resources of the performing company.

Maurice Strakosch's season of German opera in 1864 opened with *Faust*. Hammerstein, now seventeen and a bit, sat in a gallery seat, dazed by the splendor, the mysterious but imperative irrationality of opera. He went to performances of *Marta, Der Freischütz,* and *La Juive* that season, and in a beer hall he made the acquaintance of Adolf Neuendorff, chorus master and assistant conductor of the organization. Neuendorff was to become a friend for years, a friend of considerable power in influencing Hammerstein's mind. Later on, when Max Maretzek's Italian season took over the Academy, young Hammerstein was present, as he remembered it, almost every night. That was not one of the most brilliant seasons at the Academy of Music, which reached its heyday only in the 1870's, but the standard repertoire, usually not well rehearsed or produced, was at least opened to a young and thirsty spirit.

The old Academy of Music gave opera in New York from 1849 until 1885, three years after the opening of the Metropolitan. The lessee of the theater was the only arbiter of performances. There was no resident company, no real director, no planning. The Academy was often on the rocks, sometimes forced to close its doors through the difficulties of a temporary impresario.

The house was careless of scenery and properties, mixing them up and using bits from one opera in another without a qualm. It had very poor standards for rehearsal, especially for principals, and it was a time when the purchaser of a ticket had no real assurance that he would get what he had paid for. Casts and operas were liberally changed. Colonel Mapleson, the lessee at the Academy of Music a decade and a half after this, tells in his *Memoirs* of a certain day on which he changed the opera no fewer than six times between four o'clock in the afternoon and the performance at eight. A doctor's certificate arrived at four; a prima donna had diphtheria; *William Tell* was changed to *Lucia,* to *Aïda,* to *Rigoletto, Les Huguenots,* and finally *La Favorita,* each time for a different reason. With all the prompters in the world, singers cannot be letter-perfect in every role all the time, and the results of these swift changes of plan must have been startling.

And yet, in its slipshod way, the Academy contributed greatly to American knowledge of opera. It brought to this country some of the most eminent singers and conductors of the time. Almost all the principal operas of the nineteenth century had their first American performances at the Academy—works of Verdi, Wagner, Bizet, Gounod, Massenet, as well as Rossini and Bellini. The debuts of many renowned singers took place there: Adelina Patti, at the age of seventeen, in 1859; Clara Louise Kellogg, a purely American phenomenon. Here was stimulation for a mind like Oscar Hammerstein's. We can hardly be surprised that forty years later he spoke of having gone to the Academy "every night."

It was in this house, with all its faults, that Hammerstein at seventeen and eighteen undoubtedly acquired his lifelong ambition. It was years before he avowed it, but he looked back upon this as the formative moment, the time when he first felt the strange longing to bring opera to performance himself. It was no doubt too much for him to express clearly to himself or to others—there were limits even to his confidence—but it was there.

4. Rose

And another element of his long, variegated career had its beginnings, more unconsciously perhaps, during these same early years. The young man lived in Ann Street, not far from Barnum's Museum at the corner of Ann Street and Broadway. Here he spent many long hours looking at the strange exhibits of human and animal life to be seen there—the fat woman, the giant, the trapeze artists, the remarkable midgets Tom Thumb and his bride Lavinia.

Barnum had contrived an outburst of publicity about an alleged rivalry between General Tom Thumb and another midget named Commodore Nutt for the hand of the fair Lavinia, ending with a wedding of the victorious Tom Thumb in Grace Church. Barnum had brought Jenny Lind to America fifteen years before, for the most extraordinary popular success any singer had had. He was now engaged in the "museum" or circus business with equal brilliance; he could turn anything into a show and attract huge audiences for it.

Hammerstein has said he spent many hours in Barnum's Museum; it may be conjectured that some notion of Barnum's peculiar talent may also have penetrated his mind. The Museum at Ann Street burned down in July, 1865, in the midst of a huge crowd collected to see the showman's last show; Barnum rebuilt it farther up Broadway.

Young Man on the Town

All these sights and sounds of New York did not keep the young Hammerstein from becoming a first-class operative in his own trade and receiving the highest wages paid for it. He displayed very early that extraordinary ingenuity which was to help him in many a crisis thereafter, and small gadgets of his—inventions of one sort or another—were put into use in Levine's cigar factory before he had ever heard of the system of patents.

He showed no inclination to save money even then: he spent it on clothes and on the opera, perhaps a little in the café or beer hall. That little, too, was chiefly for company and talk, as he was never at any time fond of the pleasures of the table. Years later his idea of supper was often a bowl of milk with crackers in it, just as his form of meditation was a journey in a trolley car. He was growing up rapidly, and we can be sure he worked at his English throughout, because the time was coming quite soon when he would take to writing the language, first in letters to the press, then in a paper of his own.

At some time after his eighteenth year he acquired a roommate named Blau, perhaps a fellow worker, whose chief claim to a biographer's attention is that he had a sister Rose. Rose was very young when Hammerstein first met her (so was he, of course). That far-off romance is impossible to reconstruct now. Rose shared his love of the theater, his ambition, and his confidence in his own future.

They were married, after what seemed to him a long courtship, in 1868. He was still not twenty-one and she was just over seventeen. Little though we know of that first marriage, it seems to have been the great love of Hammerstein's life: he said so often enough at various times afterward. Rose bore him a son at the end of the first year, who died in infancy, and then successively Harry (1869), Arthur (1872), William (1874), and Abraham Lincoln Hammerstein (1876). Not long after the birth of the youngest son Rose died.

There were a good many women in Hammerstein's life during the next forty-three years, but it seems clear enough that the one who clung to his memory throughout was Rose. His son Arthur, years later, asked him why he had married his last wife, Emma Swift, in his old age. He replied: "Because she looked like your mother."

27

IV

First Forays

OMESTIC HAPPINESS was not to be Hammerstein's good fortune for long. He had it now, briefly. And he was bounding with energy for experimental forays in a variety of directions.

He was at the beginning of his assorted careers, so curiously related from now on to the end of his life: the theater, cigar-making and inventions for cigar-making, plus a kind of journalism all his own. It is recorded (by Carl Van Vechten, among others) that Hammerstein made his own cigars up until about two weeks before his death—made them for his own consumption, that is, because he preferred his own. His first efforts to write English for publication, his first important inventions for cigar-making (including the first of about a hundred patents he was to hold), and his first venture into opera all took place during his happy early marriage. He was quite evidently quivering with life, alert to every opportunity, determined to get on in the world, sure of what he wanted, and willing to take a chance whenever it was presented.

1. Cigar Inventions and Musical Compositions

He had also, in all this, the stimulus of some mild adversity. It was not so bad for him as for many others, but the impatient, speculative gains of the Civil War years and those immediately afterward were followed by the usual collapse and the "great panic" of 1871. The cigar business felt it as much as any other. Oscar for a time had difficulty, good as he was, in finding work, and perhaps this pushed him on to his inventions. His first was a wooden cigar-mold to ensure uniformity of size for the product: it was good, but in his innocence he sold it to a cigar-manufacturer for $300 outright. Within a short time (a month, it is said) he had produced another mold on the same principle which would make a dozen cigars at a time; this time, upon advice, he consulted a lawyer and obtained a patent.

His first published letters in English, of which he was very proud, appeared in the *Post* at about the same time, complaining of the lamp-lighting system in his neighborhood and the dangers an orderly citizen endured from footpads.

He and Rose began their life together in Anthony Street (now Worth Street), downtown. On one of their rambles along the East River much higher up—indeed, almost out of New York as people counted it in those days—Rose and Oscar saw some new flats in Fifty-second Street, not far from the river. They found one that suited them and moved in: it was to be their home until her death and his home for some years afterward. It was so far from the Wall Street district, in a time before the rapid-transport systems had developed, that Hammerstein had to go to and from his work in a steamboat that made stops up and down the island.

Into this flat there came as frequent visitors Adolf Neuendorff and his wife—that same Neuendorff who had worked with Strakosch at the Academy of Music. Neuendorff was an enthusiast for opera, which was all Hammerstein needed in the way of conversation, and the two of them discussed endlessly the various ways in which operatic production could be brought about without financial loss.

Neuendorff also encouraged his young friend to play the piano and to compose. Hammerstein needed little encouragement: the first article of new furniture he had bought for the flat in Fifty-second Street was a piano. At about this time (1870) Neuendorff got a beer-hall orchestra to play a composition of Oscar's—a march—which gave the young man great delight and caused him to spend many evening hours at further composition.

2. Friend of an Impresario

Neuendorff's difficulty, like that of many an aspiring impresario before and since, was money. He had none himself and could not find enough believers in his cause to advance what was needed. He was able, sometime in the spring or summer of 1871, to get the interest of Carl Rosa, the well-known conductor and producer (Parepa-Rosa's husband). Carl Rosa and some of his friends put up the chief part of the funds; Neuendorff's share was still short; Hammerstein, in his enthusiasm, characteristically took the entire family savings—$500—and gave them to his friend, without telling his wife. The deed was done: Neuendorff leased the Stadt Theater for a series of performances of opera in German beginning September 18, 1871.

The principal bait for his season was to be Theodor Wachtel the elder, a tenor whose great New York success was in part based upon the fact that he had once been a coachman and was therefore particularly appreciated in *Le Postillon de Longjumeau*. This circumstance aside, he was a singer of excellent voice and style, and later on he was to sing many more serious roles (he was Raoul in the first really successful performance of *Les Huguenots* at the Academy of Music in 1872). He consented to Neuendorff's proposals—no doubt with a sound guarantee in the bond—because he had been brought to America by a manager who was unable to carry out his obligations.

The opening night of the season at the Stadt Theatre—the opera was *Le Postillon de Longjumeau*, in German—was tremendously exciting to young Oscar Hammerstein, who promptly resigned all his jobs and devoted himself to writing publicity for the opera company and doing anything else he could about the premises. He had gone through some moments of altercation with Rose, who was not at all content to see their savings put into a crazy scheme in which she was sure they would be lost; he was sure, on the contrary, that money would be made; but, whether it was or not, the fever of opera was upon him and he could not stay out of the theater.

As a matter of fact, the first night was triumphant. After that, as does happen, curiosity cooled and interest died. Performances of *Lucia, Der Freischütz, Marta*, and *Il Trovatore* filled in between *Postillons*, and then the season closed on November 15 and young Oscar went back to cigar-making. His savings were gone, but he had never enjoyed any enterprise so much; the idea of producing opera dwelt in his mind thereafter. He held no grudge against Neuendorff, who continued to be his friend, and there can be little doubt that the post-mortems between them on why their opera season had failed must have consumed many a long evening over the beer.

Two great events in Oscar's life took place in the following summer: he opened a bank account and became an American citizen. The tale is told that he got into a bout of fisticuffs with a local politician, the alderman of his district, and threatened to "go into politics" as the alderman's opponent. He then found out, apparently for the first time, that he was not an American citizen, and promptly took steps to become one.

The bank account was from his first patent, the multiple cigar-mold, which he had been in no great hurry about selling. Now another son was on the way (Arthur, born December 21, 1872), and expenses promised to be considerable. He sold the multiple mold for $1,500, which was the equivalent of about five times that amount today, and opened an account in the Butchers' and Drovers' Bank on downtown Broadway.

3. A Newspaper on a Shoestring

During the next two years, although he wrote some unpublished short plays and music, Oscar's mind was bent, apparently, on some way of making more money than he could count upon in the cigar business. He had by now done a good deal of writing in English—chiefly letters to the press, but at least he had demonstrated that he could use the language effectively. His acquaintance in the cigar trade was wide, and a good many men in the business agreed with him that a trade journal would be useful in giving information both to wholesalers and to retailers, who had little direct acquaintance with each other. Again Rose was against the new venture, which seemed to her dangerous, but she yielded when he showed her the first promises of advertising.

Once more he started on a shoestring. By his own account, he had only fifty dollars in hand (and although he sometimes exaggerated these exploits, they were all essentially true). He found a basement in Maiden Lane, near Water Street, for twelve dollars a month, bought some white paper, and found a trusting printer. The *United States Tobacco Journal*, Oscar Hammerstein, Editor and Publisher, appeared for the first time on May 5, 1874. On the day of publication, Hammerstein used to relate, he made the rounds of his advertisers and prospective subscribers, collecting $120 from the first and $100 from the second.

This was a one-man job in the beginning: Oscar wrote everything in the four-page paper, solicited the advertising, delivered the papers, and collected the bills.

The *Tobacco Journal*, from the beginning, printed accurate credit lists of retail tobacconists—which were in good standing, which had gone bankrupt, and which had sold out without notice. The wholesalers found the information valuable and the retailers found it frightening; consequently, advertising grew apace.

Hammerstein could never resist the chance of making a sharp phrase, and his combative instincts were always alert. Furthermore, any tobacconist who refused to buy space in the *Journal* might see a picture of himself in the paper, disheveled, clinging to a lamp post, his hat in the gutter, with a caption underneath remarking that So-and-So "was on another drunk."

In one way and another the paper prospered, and Oscar needed assistance in his work. Meanwhile, his enemies in the trade (those who had suffered from his attacks in the paper or simply those who did not like him) combined to publish a rival sheet called the *Tobacco Leaf*. The exchanges between the rivals were acid indeed, and Hammerstein had a chance for his favorite rhetorical form, vituperation. It was common at that period in all the press: if you disagreed with a man, you called him a "morally depraved individual, a shyster and a bilk." Neither libel nor blackmail could be invoked, for the methods were common to both sides and were expected as part of the entertainment value of the paper.

Hammerstein burgeoned with ideas for his paper during these years of the late 1870's. He began a registry for brand names of cigars, thus making the *Tobacco Journal* almost official in its rank: there had been no registration before, and much trouble had resulted. He formed an Inquiry Service to operate in the leaf-tobacco markets and quoted prices every day in a special bulletin for subscribers. He organized, or helped to organize, the New York Leaf Tobacco Dealers' Protective Association and the New York Leaf Tobacco Board of Trade, which, when fully operative, took over his Inquiry Service and its bulletins at a good price. The *Tobacco Journal* thus in a very short time became an important—even indispensable—adjunct to the whole cigar trade.

4. *A Little Real Estate, a Little Opera*

It was just about now, in one of his money-making moods, that Hammerstein took his first leap into real-estate speculation. His brother-in-law, Blau, told him of some land in 116th Street, then very far away, which could be bought and then quickly sold to an interested builder. Hammerstein made $1,600 on this within a single week, an experience that may have helped to create his lifelong weakness for real-estate buying and selling.

From what we know of the later Hammerstein we must assume that his desire to make money at this period, as at all others, was connected with his obsessive desire to work in the theater, and particularly in opera. His friendship with Adolf Neuendorff never lapsed, and through Neuendorff he met numbers of other people involved in music and production. He was himself composing music and writing sketches or short plays in German all the time. There is a strong probability that his brief experience in the opera season at the Stadt Theater was actually at the base of his desire to make money, for the entire complex of later evidence indicates that money was valuable to him only because it enabled him to produce opera. A character as sharply individual and consistent as Hammerstein's must have been more or less the same in essence when he was twenty-seven as when he was sixty.

The opportunity, such as it was, did not fail to come along. Neuendorff had a new scheme in 1874. Part of the old Tammany Hall structure in Fourteenth Street had been turned into a theater for Bryant's Minstrels, but was now available at a low rent; it was an opportunity to produce German music, plays, sketches, revues. Hammerstein was willing, of course; with what money he had, and with some from other sources, Neuendorff opened the

"Germania Theatre" on September 27, 1874. In the opening night's revue there was a short play with music by Oscar Hammerstein. It was called *Solo Sechzig* and is otherwise lost to fame.

The Germania Theatre lasted until the season of 1877, and during those four seasons (or three and a half) five short plays by Oscar Hammerstein were produced there, as well as a good deal of his music—some of it incidental to his playlets, some of it written for revues or sketches by others. He lost money from time to time, as one of the guarantors, but the work in the theater was his delight and undoubtedly confirmed him in his conviction that this was where he belonged.

He had another splendid inspiration at this period, but it came to rest, as so many do in his field, upon the hardheaded business instincts of a prima donna. At his friend Hermann Grau's Terrace Theatre in Fifty-eighth Street, which offered operatic concerts at intervals, he heard the celebrated coloratura soprano Ilma di Murska. This lady, whom the critic Hermann Klein had called "the most nearly perfect Queen of the Night" who ever came to London, was willing, at Hammerstein's suggestion, to become the star of a traveling opera company in the United States, but she required guarantees of first-class productions and a deposit of $10,000 in the bank against her own salary. Oscar retired from the engagement, perhaps a little sadder, but no wiser; he still had his private determination.

When the Germania Theatre disappeared in 1877—to give way to Tony Pastor's variety theater—Neuendorff went to the Academy of Music for a Wagner season in which he was the chief conductor. *Tannhäuser, Lohengrin, Der Fliegende Holländer* and *Die Walküre* were given, the last-named for the first time in the United States (April 3). Neuendorff had also had the honor of the first American performance of *Lohengrin* six years earlier.

At these Wagner performances Hammerstein was an assiduous attendant—"every night" is the story again—although he was never a Wagner enthusiast. In this company he was at home, even though his friendship with Neuendorff had been sorely strained by the heavy financial losses on the Germania Theatre. He met many singers and musicians and cultivated their acquaintance for the sake of the opera talk and the familiarity it gave him with their ways of thinking.

We can hardly doubt that his vocation—or, in any case, his aim

34

—was perfectly conscious and deliberate by now, especially after the Di Murska episode. He knew where he was going. He used to take singers to Lorenzo Delmonico's fine restaurant, now moved from Fourteenth Street to Twenty-sixth, and regale them with handsome suppers that he could ill afford, just for the sake of the métier. That endless story-telling and reminiscing which is part of all opera talk seems to have filled him with delight, and he could participate in this way in all the weird happenings of opera companies he had never seen. It was a sort of fertilization of the ground—by this time an almost scientific fertilization, in view of the experiences he could already foresee.

5. Loss and Remarriage: The Legend Begins

In 1876 Rose died, and Oscar was left with his brood of small boys to care for in some way. His sister Augusta, now married and living in Selma, Alabama, advised him to cable to Germany for their youngest sister, Anna, who wanted to come to America. Anna arrived promptly and took over the household for two years, at the end of which time she elected to marry Henry Rosenberg, a prosperous harness-maker in Selma, whom she met on a visit to her sister, Augusta. The consternation of Oscar at this event was calmed by a suggestion: there was a young lady in Selma who wanted to come to New York and might be very good for the children.

To all intents and purposes it was an arranged marriage, just as marriages had been arranged in similar circumstances for generations in the old country. The young lady was called Malvina Jacobi. Oscar went to Selma and married her at once. She was a devoted mother to his boys and herself bore him two daughters, Rose and Stella, but her interest in his various ventures seems to have been restricted indeed. She did not often accompany him on his forays into the theater world.

Hammerstein's pattern of solitude seems now to have begun. Although wives in those days did not share their husband's activities as a rule, Rose seems to have been a loved companion as well as the manager of his household and mother of his boys. With her loss, in spite of a devoted second wife and a lively crowd of boys and girls growing up at home, he began to live an increasingly lone-wolf existence and his family knew him less and less. Arthur remembered the musical instruments in the house—this, more than seventy years ago—and how he and the other children were forbidden to touch them. He remembered how his father would come home in the evening and go straight to the piano without a word for the family. His domestic life was, apparently, the least part of his existence. In fact, with the exception of the last, there is little to be learned about Oscar Hammerstein's marriages.

We do not know precisely when he began to acquire the characteristic appearance that was to make him in later days as recognizable to all Americans as, for example, Theodore Roosevelt. The little pointed beard came fairly early, probably by the time of Rose's death, and the eternal cigar was undoubtedly an affectation of his first youth, a sort of advertisement of his trade. But, like all persistent affectations, it gradually became natural, and Hammerstein from about this time onward was never seen without it. Whether he was smoking it or not did not seem to matter. It would be difficult to find any caricature of him which did not show the cigar; I have seen none. It appears in newspaper accounts and newspaper photographs of the 1890's, but was obviously a fixture long before.

The high hat, the Hammerstein topper, is another matter. It must have been a deliberate creation from a variety of motives, deepest of which was the desire to make himself seem taller. He was about five feet five inches tall, by most accounts, but perhaps he was an inch less than that (there is no firm agreement). In any case, he felt himself to be short and probably resented it fiercely, in his usual angry way.

We are told that he designed the original top hat himself and had it made for him by a Jewish hatter in one of the lanes near his *Tobacco Journal* downtown. Thereafter, each new one was copied after the old one, or with alteration (if any) according to Oscar's own stipulations. It was a very deliberate, determined, and persistent assertion of some kind or other—not merely to call attention to himself, as top hats were quite usual in those days, but to emphasize by its slightly extravagant design the defiance he felt toward a world that placed obstacles in his way.

He wore this hat not only out of doors but inside the theater at all times—in the dressing rooms or on the stage, in his office or elsewhere. Perhaps one reason why he disliked any sort of formal society was that he had to remove his hat in such surroundings. The hat was so much a part of him at the time of his greatest fame that (like the cigar) it appears in all photographs, caricatures, or sketches.

These elements of the finished product, the complete Hammerstein, were all in rapid formation in the late 1870's and early 1880's. The Prince Albert coat and striped black-and-white, gray, or fawn trousers were adopted probably a little later, but they, too, became standard in the 1880's, and the ferociously distinctive little man presented an appearance unlike that of anybody else in New York. This must have been his wish, a wish sharply at variance with that of most human creatures, who want to resemble one another as much as possible; but, however much we may wonder at it, we see that it was a kind of fulfillment while awaiting others.

V

Harlem Adventure

Hammerstein would have made money more safely, and would have hung on to it longer, if he had stayed in the cigar business. But we have seen that he was barely adult before he was writing plays and music for the theater, pouring all his savings into theater and opera ventures, and slipping back into the cigar business only to make more money for the same purpose.

It is possible that, just as his restless young spirit aspired at first to the New World, so perhaps by this time he was yearning toward the theater as another sort of new world, a magical world that might conform more obediently to his imperious will. A born autocrat has few opportunities to practice autocracy in the United States, and the theater may have offered this illusion, as well as others. Certain it is that he had already begun to dream of a theater of his own, built with his own money, housing plays, concerts, and ultimately opera of his own choosing.

Now the dream sent him adventuring in Harlem.

1. Juggler of Lots and Mortgages

Hammerstein's simple and easy first transaction in real estate—$1,600 in a week—had been above Central Park, and it took him more than a decade to recover from its success. He continued to believe that real-estate speculations meant quick money without much trouble, and he persisted also in the theory that New York was growing so fast that the upland wastes beyond the park would rapidly be settled. In this last idea he was only ahead of his time—and not much, at that; but the notion of quick and easy speculation was less defensible. He never fully got over that notion, in spite of bitter experience, because the gains, when they did come, seemed so disproportionate to effort.

He became expert in the juggling of titles and mortgages. We shall see him from now on performing tricks of prestidigitation which take the breath away—pulling the money out of one hat to put it into another; making it vanish and reappear; materializing it out of nothing. He was bent on making money, but not to amass riches nor even for the comforts and pleasures that riches could buy. The time was not far off when he would declare his mission in no ambiguous language. It was 1889 when he said, in effect, to James Gibbons Huneker in the offices of the *Musical Courier* that all the failures of opera in America had only blazed the trail for him. This was seventeen full years before he opened the Manhattan Opera House.

Even now in the early 1880's, when he was busy making money in Harlem real estate, he never lost interest in the theater. He wrote a German farce called *The Knight Errant* and produced it with his own money. It failed immediately, but is of interest because its leading actor was Heinrich Conried, fresh over from Germany and looking for a job.

When, in 1882, Hammerstein again wanted to back a play— something called *The Perjured Peasant*, which had been popular in Germany—he employed Conried once more, and with dire results. The play was liked by the New York Germans, but Heinrich Conried was even more liked: he became a sort of matinee idol. Perhaps Hammerstein was jealous; perhaps Conried became unruly because of success. Certain it is that they quarreled repeatedly and parted company on the bitterest terms. Conried's departure probably cost Hammerstein money, for the play had to close. The rancor left over from these experiences never was quenched entirely, and years later, when Conried was general director of the Metropolitan Opera and Hammerstein opened his Manhattan Opera, it flared into open warfare.

But the main occupation of these years was real estate in Harlem. Hammerstein bought and sold properties in that area with great speed and generally at a profit; his transactions in 1884 alone were numerous enough to attract notice. Meanwhile, he was busy with his inventions, and succeeded at about this time in producing a pneumatic cigar-making machine that would save a good deal of hand labor. It afterward made millions, but Hammerstein—hard pressed for money to pay mortgages on his various holdings—sold it for $6,000.

2. Hammerstein the Builder

The game of real estate led Hammerstein to a new creative adventure: he discovered the joys of building. He was a natural-born builder and took a peculiar delight in it, almost as keen as his delight in the production of opera. He was the architect and engineer of all his theaters. He was perhaps not an architect at all—the architects would say certainly not—but he built well, constantly better, and was impatient of every curb put upon him and even of well-meant advice.

His first actual building, so far as we know, was a row of seventeen houses between Seventh and Eighth avenues in Harlem, part on 141st Street and part on 142nd Street. A new invention in 1887 brought him more money from the cigar business as advance on royalties, and with this, plus his gains from real-estate transactions, he felt emboldened to begin his next project, the most ambitious one he had yet undertaken. This was a big block of flats, an apartment house, on Seventh Avenue between 136th and 137th streets, to be called "The Kaiser Wilhelm." The name was given, he afterward explained, in the hope of attracting German and German-Jewish residents to Harlem.

Hammerstein could never merely build. He had to invent and innovate. In the Kaiser Wilhelm he invented a concealed bathtub and an easily operated new dumb-waiter, and he built a small theater in the basement. His son Arthur, who had been apprenticed to learn bricklaying and plastering, was put to work on the Kaiser Wilhelm; it was Hammerstein's principle that all his sons must learn trades and learn them well. Arthur was then sixteen.

3. Good-by to the Tobacco Journal

The building of the Kaiser Wilhelm was one of the minor Hammerstein epics. He had run out of funds and could get no more until the roof was on the building, and on March 12, 1888, the greatest blizzard Manhattan has ever known paralyzed the city. The Kaiser Wilhelm was buried in snow for a month, but it is on record that Oscar himself, as well as his sons Harry and Arthur, helped to shovel it away.

For the Kaiser Wilhelm and some simultaneous ventures, Hammerstein was now forced to mortgage his income from the *Tobacco Journal.* The paper had grown until it occupied three floors of a building in Burling Slip; it had a manager and a staff. Hammerstein went there less and less often, but he directed its policy and always wrote its editorials. His income from the paper was $25,000 a year. He obtained a loan of $12,500 by pledging the whole year's income for repayment—a rate of one-hundred-per-cent interest, which even Oscar had never been forced to pay before.

By thus consolidating mortgages and getting new ones, he opened the Kaiser Wilhelm for tenantry. Other houses were put on the market for sale. A year or so earlier Hammerstein had moved from Fifty-second Street to 115th Street to be nearer his operations. Now he moved again with his brood to a "Moorish castle," as Arthur called it, at 142nd Street and Seventh Avenue. Oscar built it himself. It seems, indeed, to have been of the purest Moorish or Turkish-bath style, and at the age of eighty Arthur was unable to mention it without laughing.

All this passionate interest in the development of Harlem was, to state it moderately, premature. The dwellings north of Central Park could probably still be numbered in the hundreds. There were no systems of transport by which persons living so far north could get to work in the city and back home again in a reasonable time. Oscar discovered this, certainly, when he had difficulty selling his houses. And yet he conceived, at this precise moment, the masterly notion that what this sparse and scattered population required was a theater. Perhaps he thought a theater would bring

41

more tenants, more purchasers of houses. He did not say so. What he said was that the inhabitants of Harlem, once they got home from the city, would be too tired to go back again for an evening's entertainment, and that it should be provided for them near at hand.

We may not go far wrong if we say simply that Oscar wanted to build a theater. It made little or no difference whether anybody else wanted a theater. If he had been at the North Pole and money had been in any way obtainable, he would have wanted to build a theater there. To New Yorkers of that day Harlem was, practically speaking, at the North Pole.

Hammerstein bought land between Seventh and Eighth avenues, in the middle of the block and running through from 125th Street to 126th. He had not anticipated finding hard rock near the surface of the land, and the excavation costs nearly bankrupted him again. His brother-in-law Harry Rosenberg from Selma, Alabama—his sister Anna's husband—appeared at the providential moment with $10,000 to lend, and the building went forward. By Hammerstein's own account, he was actually standing in front of the excavation early one morning, arguing with a recalcitrant dealer in building materials who would unload nothing unless $10,000 were paid on arrears, when brother-in-law Harry came up with a request for some kind of work in the new theater. Oscar agreed at once on condition of a loan of $10,000, which was provided on the spot. Thus Oscar; but we know he was not above making a story slightly more dramatic than life.

He was compelled, just the same, to part with the *Tobacco Journal*, and, although he was a remarkably unsentimental man, it must have cost him a pang. He received $50,000 in cash for it, plus $11,000 payment of the mortgage on his income from the *Journal*. By this means, after all the crises and recurrent trepidations that were customary with him, he was enabled to complete his theater. He called it the Harlem Opera House.

4. A Theater without a Box Office

Headlong, impetuous, and obsessed, Hammerstein seems in this, as in so many other cases, to have forgotten half a dozen of the most essential practical considerations. The really astounding Freudian lapse—key to all the rest—is that he forgot to put in a box office. He had built the theater himself, planned it and supervised it without the assistance of any architect or engineer. It was his first theater. Architects were called in to list the building laws and obtain a permit; after that, it was Oscar's job. And when the theater was completed, it had no box office.

It was necessary to correct a good many other oversights besides. Oscar had paid no attention to the building regulations the architects had provided for him. With the building completed, the legal requirements still had to be met. The running fight he then conducted with the authorities was characteristic of many others that followed during the years.

Hammerstein was now forty-two years old and at last he had a theater of his own. But he had no plan for what to put on its stage or how to fill its seats. It was bad enough to forget the box office, but he had also forgotten both stage and audience. He must have known that there were hardly enough people in Harlem to fill his theater even if they all came. He must also have realized that it would be difficult to find players and plays of the first quality for a theater so far removed from the center of the city. If he did realize all this, he simply ignored it until the theater was finished and the problem was before him.

This was his first theater and the first occurrence of this peculiar omission. But it was to become a recurrent theme. One assumption explains this seemingly inexplicable lapse in a mind as shrewd as Hammerstein's: that he had built the theater with opera in mind from the beginning—not as a clear and definite plan but simply as the glowing light at the end of the labyrinth. Yet he must have had this illumination in his busy brain all along. And, to be sure, he did end with opera, even in Harlem.

It is no accident that every one of his theaters was remarkable for its acoustics, although he had neither architect nor acoustical engineer. The Lexington Opera House, his last, was an acoustical marvel to every audience as well as every performer who appeared there. Theaters had their evocation for him, I believe, chiefly aurally. Obviously he also took pleasure in proud arches, handsome lines, and a certain amount of plush and gilt; his theaters were, without exception, sumptuous and grand. But his particular characteristic as a builder was that he used shapes and materials for sound. When he built a theater, he built it for the ear.

5. The Best Is None Too Good

So opera must have been his goal, even in Harlem—it was in the name he gave his theater—and he must have been willing to improvise until the goal could be achieved. Now the theater was finished, but his resources were exhausted. To produce any opera at all on the wind-swept heath of 125th Street was out of the question. Even the more modest costs of producing spoken drama were beyond his present means. His only possible move was to take productions complete as they left the theaters of New York. He could have found touring companies of the second, third, and fourth categories, no doubt, but he could not content himself with such fare. He wanted the best that New York had to offer. It was then his discovery, the old and the ever new, that New York's best is extremely expensive.

There were a good many productions of high quality available to Hammerstein in his first season, but all demanded heavy guarantees or payments in advance. The alarm of the great theater stars of the day at being asked to play in Harlem may have had something to do with the high fees, but it seems more likely that their astute managers took advantage of the novelty and precariousness of Oscar's position, perched as he was in a shiny new theater halfway to Canada with nothing to put in it.

Daniel Frohman's Lyceum Theatre was then as prosperous and fashionable in New York as Wallack's had been a generation before. It was in Fourth Avenue near Twenty-third Street—not at all in the theater district of that or any other time. Perhaps that was what made it "society's" favorite, but its repertoire of highly polished and empty dramas of high life may also have contributed. One of the wits of the period said that New York society went to the Lyceum to see how to behave, how to enter a room, how to wear clothes and place furniture. Whatever the reason, Frohman's company was chic, and there is a strong probability that Oscar thought chic was what he needed to take the curse off 125th Street. At all events, he went to see Daniel Frohman and asked for a great current success to open the Harlem Opera House.

The play was *The Wife*, by David Belasco and William de Mille, both of whom attained great celebrity in their fields afterward. It was played by Frohman's stock company, headed by Georgia Cayvan and Herbert Kelcey, two society favorites who have left little imprint on history; with them were William Faversham, an actor of talent and distinction, and the perennial Mrs. Thomas Whiffen. Mr. Frohman provided this feast for the sum of $5,000 in advance. (It must be mentioned again that the value of $5,000 was then five times, at least, what it is today, and perhaps more.)

The Harlem Opera House opened on September 30, 1889, with Oscar resplendent in the entrance to greet his audience. He was then much less known in New York than he was to become in the next few years, and it seems that his characteristic appearance—in particular, the remarkable top hat and the Prince Albert coat—was on view for the first time to many of those present. He beamed with a pleasure only slightly dampened by the realization that he could not possibly make money on this week's offering, but no doubt the thought that it was the Lyceum company he was presenting—the favorite repertoire company of New York—made up for any such trifles. And, besides, was it not the first night in the new theater? Only a grub would expect to make money out of an epithalamium. As James Huneker remarked years later, Hammerstein spent his own money as lavishly as most managers spent the money of other people.

The second week's bill at the Harlem Opera House was *Little Lord Fauntleroy*, then not far along in its almost endless run in America and England. "Little Tommy Russell" played the title role, as he did hundreds of times everywhere, alternating with Ray Maskall. The season continued with some of the most famous of actors and actresses: Joseph Jefferson, Dame Madge Kendal and her husband, E. H. Sothern, Fanny Davenport, and a remarkable week when Mme Modjeska played with Edwin Booth in a repertoire that included *The Merchant of Venice, Hamlet, Much Ado About Nothing*, and *Macbeth*, along with some contemporary plays. The Harlem Opera House also seems to have had one week dark; Hammerstein either could find nothing to put in it or was looking for money again.

Hammerstein had his week of private joy when he brought in an opera company for seven performances. It was not his own opera company and he did not actually supervise matters as he delighted to do afterward, but he was never out of the theater and it may be certain that the week gave him a particular personal pleasure that even Booth and Modjeska could never have provided.

In presenting the Emma Juch Opera Company for this week (November 4–9), Hammerstein advertised himself as "owner and manager" for the first time. Emma Juch was a German soprano whose company played *Faust, Der Trompeter von Säkkingen, Mignon, The Bohemian Girl, Carmen, Maritana,* and *Der Freischütz.* Juch herself sang four parts: Marguerite, Mignon, Carmen, and Agathe in the *Freischütz.*

For the Christmas holiddays Hammerstein committed another extravagance: half the week was taken by Fanny Davenport in Sardou's *La Tosca* and the other half by Joseph Jefferson with William J. Florence and Mrs. John Drew in *The Rivals.* The payments required were ruinous: for Jefferson's engagement Hammerstein was required to turn over ninety per cent of the receipts. These were then reigning deities of the theater, at the very height of their sovereignty, and their reluctance to try a new theater, a new management, and an unknown audience in the wilderness may be understood.

It could also be that rumors of Hammerstein's financial jugglery had penetrated all New York by now; if so, the rumors had been misunderstood. However precarious his financing with regard to real estate and building operations, and whatever his difficulties in obtaining money for production, Hammerstein never failed to pay an artist. There is not one case recorded in which he defaulted on a financial engagement with an actor, singer, or musician.

Later he paid his opera artists—and at the highest scale known in the world—when he was unable to defray his own family expenses. There seems to have been in this some element either of superstition or of special esteem for artists, and perhaps of both: certainly he did not hesitate to make builders and the suppliers of materials, as well as many other business enterprises, wait for their money. In the case of artists, he even went further: he quite fre-

Harlem Adventure

quently gave them advances when they declared the need or made the request. At the Harlem Opera House no such need ever arose, of course, because his payments were made direct to the manager of the week's company and salaries were not his concern.

As the first season wore on into February and March, Hammerstein's fortunes and those of his theater grew steadily worse. He was at a serious moment in his activity, a moment to give even his ebullient spirit pause. He had lost money on everything he had presented in his theater. He had tried opera, too, and failed—the Emma Juch company had lost money for him, as had all the rest.

This critical moment was the one he chose, and farthest Harlem was the place, to initiate his first independent venture into opera.

VI

Opera in Ultima Thule

H AMMERSTEIN'S DECISION to form an opera company for his Harlem theater, where nothing, not even opera, had yet succeeded, and at a time when his resources were at a very low ebb, was not mad, however mad it may sound. It was a piece of shrewd, though daring, thinking. In other words, it was characteristically Hammerstein.

His obstinate drive toward opera was based primarily, of course, upon his delight in it. He may also have felt by now that he had some kind of talent for opera, even if nobody else recognized it in him. But in this instance he had sound practical motivations as well. The geographical handicap of a theater in Harlem might be overcome by first-class opera performances as by nothing else. In reasoning thus he was perfectly correct. Those who want opera are quite willing to travel in order to get it, and this is not the case with most other forms of entertainment.

1. First Brush with the Metropolitan

Up to this point, everything Hammerstein had put into his theater, even though played by the greatest actors of the day, had been seen in New York recently and for varying lengths of time. Productions that had completed their downtown runs could not be counted on to entice audiences up to 125th Street. He had been obliged to depend upon the scanty population of the Harlem area and such enthusiasts—the adorers of Modjeska, Booth, or Jefferson—as would make the journey. Opera, however familiar, has no such frequency of repetition. Three performances in a season for one work were about average for those days, so that a further taste of it in Harlem might be welcome even to the dwellers in lower Manhattan.

All these considerations operated upon his mind, we may be sure, for, in spite of his apparent forgetfulness, he was extremely shrewd. And underneath it all was the same old passionate desire to give opera—and this time really to give it, to be responsible for everything, to put everything together and see that everything worked.

Creased and shining and top-hatted, he called in state upon Mr. Edmond Stanton, general director of the Metropolitan Opera Company, to propose some arrangement by which members of that institution might come to Harlem for a brief period. Mr. Stanton, outraged, showed him to the door.

The Metropolitan Opera had then existed for seven years. The theater itself had been built in 1882 under the financial leadership of William Henry Vanderbilt, who had inherited ninety-four millions of tax-free dollars from his father, the Commodore, and with it the social cloud that had always hung over that uncouth old pirate. Mrs. William Henry Vanderbilt, his wife, or Mrs. William Kissam Vanderbilt, his daughter-in-law—it has never been clearly established which it was—wanted a box at the old Academy of Music and bitterly resented the refusal of it. The "Knickerbocker aristocracy," so-called, still wanted no contamination by Vanderbilts.

The "Knickerbocker aristocracy" was led by the Astors, who were in fact just about as Knickerbocker as Oscar Hammerstein, at two or three removes. William Henry Vanderbilt, aware that he could buy and sell most of the Knickerbocker aristocracy at will (except, of course, the Astors), proceeded to build the Metropolitan Opera House and create a "Metropolitan Opera Company" to operate it. The theater remained the property of the original stockholders, all of whom had boxes in it, and the operating company took its chances with the public.

The excitement created in New York by the opera rivalry of

1881–1883 furnished columns to the newspapers, and Hammerstein must have been aware of it, although he no doubt cared little about the actual feuds of the maharajas involved. In their way, all these new people—the Vanderbilts, Morgans, Huntingtons, Ogden Millses, and the rest—represented some kind of progress over the stagnation in which the Academy of Music had gone on for years. The refusal of a box to Mrs. Vanderbilt was, by the way, nothing extraordinary at the Academy of Music. There were only eighteen boxes in that old theater, and all were the inherited property of descendants of the older families, Schermerhorn, Astor, Belmont among them. Many besides Mrs. Vanderbilt had been refused admittance. One very rich man had offered $30,000 for a box at the Academy for a season, and had been refused. This was not a contest over music—indeed, music had nothing to do with it. It was simply a matter of social distinction, the eternal preoccupation of the *bourgeois gentilhomme*.

Old Mrs. William Astor, the consecrated queen of New York society until her death in 1908, called upon Mrs. William Kissam Vanderbilt for the first time in March, 1883, thus terminating the hostilities and admitting the Vanderbilts to court. The Astors then took a box at the Metropolitan themselves. The Academy of Music ceased operations in 1885, with its dauntless manager, Colonel James Mapleson, uttering a farewell that might have rung in Hammerstein's ears: "I cannot fight Wall Street."

It was this formidable new monster that Hammerstein had gone to see toward the end of the season of 1889–1890. It was not Edmond Stanton alone who showed him unceremoniously to the door: it was the whole system of the Metropolitan Opera. The episode rankled in Oscar's mind and spirit for the rest of his life.

2. Sensible Lilli Lehmann

Hammerstein was in such severe trouble by now—this was February, 1890—that he was obliged to sell his latest patent outright. He had already received and spent substantial sums in royalties; he now sold his rights for $65,000. Altogether, this invention brought him about $115,000. But he was beset by demands for money not only for his theater, but for the banks and on real-estate obligations. His encounter with the Metropolitan Opera did not diminish but rather increased his determination to try first-class opera in Harlem as a chance of making money.

He had recourse to Marc Blumenberg, publisher of the *Musical Courier*, whom he probably already knew. Huneker, afterward a friend of Hammerstein's for years, was then editor of that paper and was present at the first interview. To Blumenberg and Huneker, in the course of a long talk, Hammerstein warmed up and revealed his true intention: he would produce opera or die. He would even produce opera in English. This was when he declared, in bold words, that the failures of the American opera had only blazed the trail for him. Huneker remarked in his memoirs (*Steeplejack*, published in 1920) that Hammerstein "came to seek Blumenberg's advice and went away advising us." He went away, nevertheless, with a letter from Blumenberg to Lilli Lehmann, who lived across the street from the Metropolitan at the Hotel Normandie.

Lehmann and her husband, the tenor Paul Kalisch, were people after Hammerstein's own heart. Even though she was the *prima donna assoluta* of the opera at that time, Lehmann used horsecars and liked to cook; from the photographs, it seems likely that she also made her own clothes. She had—as she shows in her memoirs —a deep inner scorn for what may be called the Vanderbilt view of art and for some of the other vagaries with which she was surrounded at the Metropolitan. When already established as a leading soprano at the Berlin Opera, she had volunteered for minor roles in the very first performance of the Nibelungen Ring at Bayreuth in 1876, actually singing the first words of the first performance as the Rhinemaiden Woglinde in *Das Rheingold ("Weia! Waga! Woge, du Welle!")*. Subsequently she had gone on to eminence in every opera theater in the world, admired not only for her Isolde and Brünnhilde but for an enormous variety of roles from every repertoire, including the great Meyerbeer parts and numerous roles from the Italian and French. Her Metropolitan debut had been in *Carmen* (November 25, 1885), a little over four years before, and she had just chosen *Norma* as her benefit performance and farewell for the season in New York (February 27, 1890). It netted her $8,000.

For a Wagnerian soprano to sing Norma was regarded as very daring, but her performance was a sensational success in New

York as everywhere else because she actually could sing this music as few Italian sopranos ever can. Her cantilena and her coloratura and her portamento and her staccati and her glissandi and her pianissimi and all the rest of the technical proficiencies were adjudged to be phenomenal even by the sourest critics.

Hammerstein found in this sensible, unpretentious, highly intelligent woman a person who could understand his needs and sympathize with his ambition. Her husband was also eager to help. It is not impossible that they shared his resentment of his treatment by the Metropolitan; the Stanton regime, which had only one more year to go, was unsympathetic to them, too, and they were not to return to New York until it had changed.

Lilli Lehmann was just Hammerstein's age. Her life span (1848–1929) was greater than his, but of course the limitations of the human physical machine retired her from the stage before he reached his great days. She made her farewell to the Metropolitan in 1899 and a farewell concert tour the following year, and was not heard in America again. One is tempted to speculate on what difference it might have made to his plans, his repertoire and achievement at the Manhattan Opera House, if she had been a dozen years younger. With Lehmann added to Mary Garden, Tetrazzini, and the rest, he would have had an opera company even more extraordinary than the one he did assemble.

3. The Magic of a Name

Lehmann and Hammerstein were friends from the start, and although her engagement with him was only for one week, it was momentous in his life. He never forgot it; it was his real beginning as an opera manager; they remained friends. As he had been treated so cavalierly by the Metropolitan, he was unable to borrow scenery, costumes, or anything else from that establishment, and Lehmann obviously could not provide them. She did suggest to him certain singers—the baritone Theodor Reichmann, who had sung *Don Giovanni* and the Wagner parts at the Metropolitan, the soprano Sophie Traubmann, and the tenor Julius Perotti—who were happy to take the post-season engagement in Harlem. She was always patient and ready with advice, but there were innumerable things that Hammerstein had to do for himself.

Opera in Ultima Thule

He flung himself into this work with enormous zeal: it was what he felt he was born for. He had to rent secondhand scenery and costumes, engage orchestra and chorus, find the innumerable properties and accouterments necessary for opera production. The operas chosen by Lehmann for the week were *Norma, Les Huguenots,* and *Il Trovatore.* These were among the most successful in her own repertoire. She herself sang in only one performance, *Norma,* but it was enough.

In the course of the enterprise Hammerstein discovered another thing that was to be a key to production in the future: the magic of a very great name. The fact that Lehmann was going to sing for him opened the theatrical warehouses of New York. He had no real difficulty getting what he wanted, even though he was short of money. Nor was there any difficulty about singers, orchestra, and chorus. For the conductor he had quickly hit upon Walter Damrosch, whose father, Leopold, had died in harness five years before as director of the Metropolitan. Lehmann's name paved the way everywhere.

And he made a great deal of money out of his week of opera. New Yorkers were willing to go far to hear Lehmann under comfortable conditions, without the then intolerable pretentiousness of the Metropolitan Opera House. He was to find that his success with the Lehmann week also made it quite easy to book other productions for his theater in what was left of the season. With this name-magic Hammerstein had had no direct personal experience until now; he never forgot it, and in the years of his greatest activity he made the most of it.

The Metropolitan Opera may not have liked all this, and probably did not. However, its own season was over and it had no right to object to the after-season activities of its singers. It had leased the opera house for a spring season to Henry Abbey, who had been first director of the company (1883–1884) and now returned every March for a while with some bright stars of his own. Abbey, like Hammerstein himself, was an opera enthusiast. He was making large sums out of the dramatic company of Sir Henry Irving and Ellen Terry, but was not content until he had lost it all in opera.

Abbey's spring season at the Metropolitan this year (1890) opened with Tamagno in *Otello,* with Albani as Desdemona and Del Puente as Iago. His second performance gave New York Patti in *Semiramide,* the third Nordica in *Il Trovatore.* Such fare was

53

heady for New York. With the single exception of Lehmann, the Metropolitan at that time possessed no great singer of international renown, and Abbey's galaxy was well received.

4. *If One Is Too Many, Try Two*

Hammerstein's opening occurred on the night after Abbey's. Lehmann's Norma, which had been heard only once in New York, was as much of a novelty as Tamagno's Otello. For the rest, despite Abbey's success at the Metropolitan, there were still enough opera-followers to flock up to Harlem and fill Hammerstein's opera house at every performance. This evidence that there was a very big public for opera in New York was not lost on Hammerstein.

The chronicler Odell, noting these occurrences, inquires: "Was the Harlem outburst a song of defiance?"

It was, of course. But it was also a remarkably good piece of management on the part of Oscar Hammerstein, who found himself in pocket at the end of this week beyond anything he had ever hoped.

His pleasure would have been extreme without the profit. Earlier in the evening he stood in the entrance as usual, surveying the audience, but before each performance he took his place on a kitchen chair in the wings (stage right, theater left) and watched everything intently. With his top hat and his unlighted cigar, his Prince Albert and spotless linen, he was the same Hammerstein as the one known to fame sixteen years later, and his behavior was the same. He never missed a moment of any performance, and he always watched from this same place in the wings, just as he was to do in his apotheosis at the Manhattan.

Moreover, he never ceased asking questions when he was not physically busy doing something. He questioned stagehands, chorus, and orchestra; he questioned stage manager and wardrobe mistress and light engineer; there was nobody concerned in the enterprise who did not submit to a running catechism all week long on the business of putting on an opera. His curiosity on the subject was insatiable, and for reasons that he no longer bothered to conceal: he was going to be an opera manager himself and he did not care by now who knew it, or how fantastic the ambition might seem. As on this occasion his own contribution had been, practically speaking, that of manager—aside from the casting, which was Lehmann's—he had some reason for feeling when the week was over that he had not only learned something but accomplished something.

His natural response to this first honey-sweet success was fatally his own: he wanted to build another theater.

In the very week after the Lehmann triumph Hammerstein traded in some Harlem lots he owned for a new piece of property on the south side of 125th Street, between Lexington and Fourth avenues, whereupon to build the Columbus Theatre. Opera had left Harlem with the *Trovatore* of March 29, and on April 2 the excavations began for the new theater. Thus, two theaters, by some strange Hammerstein logic, were to grace a district which had already abundantly shown that it could not support even one.

VII

And Another Harlem Theater

ALMOST ANY EXCUSE would do to get Hammerstein started building a new theater. Arthur said: "If Father could buy enough plush to make a theater curtain, there would be a theater built around it!" At the same time, some special intoxications were at work in this case. He had, by his own lights, emerged into the great world in his Lehmann week.

1. No More the Anonymous Hammerstein

There is a certain pathos in the fact that to Mme Lehmann it meant almost nothing: she does not even mention it—or Hammerstein—in her book of memoirs called *Mein Weg*, translated into English as *My Path Through Life*. To her it was merely another engagement on the road: the only American performances she mentions are those at the Metropolitan and at the Auditorium in Chicago, which, in her day, had a Metropolitan season either before or after the one in New York.

But to Hammerstein it was a release from the shackles not only of failure, but of anonymity. He had been treated badly at the Metropolitan Opera House mainly because nobody there had ever heard of him. He had been given cavalier treatment also by the great actors and their managers in the woefully unsuccessful season that preceded Lehmann. In spite of his glistening new theater, he was so new in the business of theater management that he had to explain himself wherever he went. His productions were not reviewed in the press because they had all been seen before. His advertisements, headed "Hammerstein's Opera House, 125th Street near Seventh Avenue," were put lower down in the advertising columns of the papers than all the rest of the New York theaters because he was not "in the city." And even the expression "Hammerstein's Opera House," which he employed in the paid advertising, was not current: the theater was called the "Harlem Opera House" when it was called anything. Even the notices of the Lehmann week were headed, in the New York *Times:* "Opera in Harlem."

Now, with a little unexpected cash in his pocket and a glow in his breast, he set out to build a new theater, also in 125th Street, a bare five streets farther east than his opera house. His opera house had been called "one of the handsomest and most modern in the world," but this apparently was not enough for Oscar.

The Columbus Theatre arose from nothing during the summer and was scheduled to open on October 6, 1890. Meanwhile, the Harlem Opera House completed its season, down to June 7, with the Conried Light Opera Company filling the house for the last four weeks. The losses had been considerably reduced by the Lehmann week and by the popular appeal of Conried's company, but Hammerstein still was lighter by $50,000. He had booked Theodore Thomas and his symphony orchestra for the week following Lehmann, had been obliged to pay Thomas $2,000, and had a gross in the box office for the whole week of $700. His highest-priced seats were never very expensive: indeed, they could not be so in 125th Street. For Lehmann's week he had charged $2.50 for the best seats, ranging down to fifty cents. For the Theodore Thomas week he charged $1.25 for the best seats and twenty-five cents for the cheapest.

During the summer, while the Columbus Theatre was being built, Hammerstein rid himself of all the other real estate he possessed in Harlem. He had built, in all, some twenty-four apartment houses and thirty separate houses. It was his intention henceforth to concentrate any time or money he had for real estate on theaters.

The fire hazards in theaters entirely lighted by gas were such that every building was an adventure. The Columbus, all of whose fixtures, including footlights, were gas, was no exception. Arthur Hammerstein remembered an occasion when a Negro boy in a straw skirt, dancing near the footlights in *In Old Kentucky*, found himself ablaze and started to run offstage; one of the attendant firemen struck him on the head with a stage jack to prevent a panic and the flames were extinguished with blankets, but the boy died in the hospital. The fireman's defense was that it was better for one to die than for 1,500 to be seized by panic.

2. Opera in English

The Columbus Theatre was finished not quite on schedule but near enough to have a gala opening on October 11, 1890, with Margaret Mather as Juliet and Otis Skinner as Romeo. On the same night the Harlem Opera House had its formal opening with an opera company performing *Ernani* in English. As the singers' names were Tagliapietra, Montegriffo, and Collini, aside from Miss Charlotte Walker, it may be inferred that the English was not much better than is usually heard in opera.

The Harlem Opera House had actually housed three other productions in a sort of pre-season run, beginning on September 1 with a musical show called *The Seven Swabians*, in which Chauncey Olcott had a small part. But it was Oscar's whim to designate as the official opening the October 11 performance of *Ernani*, followed by *Faust, Mignon, Il Trovatore, The Bohemian Girl*, and a final week divided between *Masaniello* and *Carmen*, all in English. The tickets were cheap and the house was beginning to be known, so that on this venture Hammerstein was at last beginning to make a little money.

Things were never smooth in the house, however, even with money coming in. Hammerstein was even then extremely assertive and did not always get on well with the visiting companies. One very starry star of the time was Richard Mansfield, with whom Oscar had a violent quarrel during the week of *Beau Brummel*. In his rage at Mansfield and all other supercilious visitors from downtown New York, Hammerstein decided to operate a stock company of his own. This was notable because one of the plays he chose was Ibsen's *The Pillars of Society*, which had never been done in the United States. It was a dire failure, and he had to disband his stock company and keep his theater dark for two weeks for want of anything to put in it.

From the outset, the Columbus Theatre did better than the Harlem Opera House. It had a larger local audience to draw upon, as its immediate area was more populous and its tickets were usually cheaper; moreover, Hammerstein's policy was to open it to vaudeville, minstrel shows, and the other forms of entertainment which he tried to avoid in his Harlem Opera House. The Columbus made profits on the Boston Howard Athenaeum Specialty Co. (vaudeville) and on thrillers and popular plays from Broadway, as well as on such offerings as the prizefighter John L. Sullivan in a work called *Honest Hearts and Willing Hands*. Even at the Columbus there were, of course, weeks of drama: Margaret Mather and Otis Skinner returned for a repertoire of Shakespeare and other plays in late November; Clara Morris played her famous and, by this time, extremely familiar *Camille* in April; Rose Coghlan appeared in *Peg Woffington* later in the same month.

Then Oscar, with a shout of glee, descended at the end of the season upon the Columbus Theatre, too, with a brief season of opera. This time it was called the Metropolitan English Opera Company, organized by himself around the soprano Georgine von Januschowsky, wife of his friend Adolf Neuendorff. He made up his roster mainly from the remains of the Emma Juch Opera Company, his first operatic tenant of the Harlem Opera House the year before, which had just folded its tents through lack of business.

This experiment with opera in English lasted three weeks and made money for all concerned. Neuendorff conducted everything and his wife sang in most of the works. The lady's repertoire was astonishing—it ran from Gilda in *Rigoletto* to Leonore in *Fidelio* —but such a range was not so uncommon then as it would be now. The operas given were *Rigoletto, Carmen, The Bohemian Girl, Il Trovatore, Maritana, Der Freischütz,* and *Faust*.

3. On to Broadway

Once the Columbus Theatre had weathered its first season, Hammerstein began to lose interest in Harlem. The theaters there engaged less and less of his attention. He had house managers for them: John Donnelly, from Daniel Frohman's staff, was installed at the Columbus, and Oscar's brother-in-law Harry Rosenberg took over the Harlem Opera House. The Columbus did very well with variety shows, musical comedies, and Broadway thrillers, and occasionally an exceptional offering such as Georgie Drew Barrymore in *Mr. Wilkinson's Widows* and Robert Mantell in repertoire. Loie Fuller made her first New York appearance as a "serpentine dancer" there, in a play called *Quack, M. D.* The United States Marine Band played a Sunday concert.

The Harlem Opera House continued to glitter unprofitably with Broadway's best: Pauline Hall, Richard Mansfield, Nat Goodwin, E. H. Sothern, Mrs. Leslie Carter in their current vehicles, and repertoire weeks for Rose Coghlan, the Kendals, and Margaret Mather with Otis Skinner. Obviously the level was too high for the neighborhood, but Hammerstein was obstinate enough to cling to it just the same. There were also a few performances of the new opera sensation *Cavalleria Rusticana*, the production of which was a venture in true Hammerstein style; of this, more in a moment. On the whole, the Harlem season was a success. The Opera House again lost money, but much less than in the previous season, and the Columbus made a profit.

With even a small balance in the bank, Hammerstein considered himself entitled to new adventures. As usual, this meant a new theater.

The logical and relentless development of his ambition was drawing him toward the center of the American theater, somewhere in the Broadway area between Twenty-third and Forty-second streets. He was magnetized in that direction from now on, inescapably, and during his forays downtown from Harlem in search of productions to put into his two theaters, he was forever poking about in vacant lots and derelict buildings, looking for a place where he might build what he wanted. There is no doubt that a theater suited to music and especially to opera was what he had in mind, but it had to be a theater in which any and all other forms of entertainment could also be given.

He bought land on the north side of Thirty-fourth Street in February, 1892, and immediately began tearing down the old buildings that stood there. His property was between Broadway and Seventh Avenue in the space now occupied by the R. H. Macy department store, and, in the state of theater geography at that time, it was almost the center of New York.

This season, too, brought a florescence of Oscar's own compositions for orchestra—marches, gavottes, waltzes, and diversions of various sorts to be used before performances or as intermezzi. He rehearsed these works himself every Monday morning while the new show for the week was moving in. The house orchestras in both theaters were his own, and the one at the Harlem Opera House must have been of good quality, for he gave it most of his own compositions.

There is a fairly strong suggestion that at this time Hammerstein wanted to write a comic opera and produce it in a theater of his own—still another reason for the purchase of the site in Thirty-fourth Street. There is no reliable evidence of how fully he was able to write out these compositions of his. He undoubtedly composed them at the piano; he continued this exercise to the end of his life. We do not know how much of his early harmony and counterpoint he remembered, or whether he had ever learned how to write for specific instruments; but we do know that his time was preternaturally occupied, and even if he had been able to undertake orchestrations, it defies reason to see when he could have done them. He was busy with plans for his new theater; he was downtown a great deal of the time; he was never content to let a day go by without working in his workshop at new inventions for cigar-making and other things; he was embroiled in endless financial transactions.

My guess is that Hammerstein wrote out his melodies with simple harmonizations and left the rest to the professionals. There are many popular composers of the present day, among them the most popular, who never put pen to paper; not only harmony and orchestration, but even the writing out of the melody is left by them to "technicians." Hammerstein's compositions—and, counting the various stage attempts, ballet and opera and the rest, which came later, they are voluminous—may have had no other merit, but he did turn them out himself.

4. *The Race for* Cavalleria Rusticana

His friend Neuendorff was responsible for one of Oscar's most spectacular exploits of these earlier days, one that peculiarly appealed to his temperament: the race for the first American performance of *Cavalleria Rusticana*. That work had won a prize in Italy the year before in a competition organized by the Sonzogno music-publishing company of Milan—no doubt as a device to help break down the quasi-monopoly of the Ricordi company—and had received its first production at the Costanzi in Rome on May 17, 1890. Its tuneful passion, or its passionate tunefulness, swept the whole world in about a year and a half and made the fortune of its twenty-seven-year-old composer, Pietro Mascagni, who never afterward wrote anything that could remain in opera repertoire more than a few weeks.

The reigning conductor of the moment, Anton Seidl, was giving a series of summer symphony concerts, the first being at Brighton Beach. Neuendorff asked Hammerstein to go to this opening concert, undoubtedly on free passes, and it was there that they heard the first American performance of the Intermezzo and other excerpts from *Cavalleria Rusticana*.

Oscar seems to have been overwhelmed by the freshness and strength of this music, particularly of the Intermezzo. He hastily made inquiries about performing rights to the whole opera and cabled an offer to the Italian publisher, Sonzogno, for an American production. He paid $3,000 cash down as an advance on a royalty of fifteen per cent of the gross receipts, handsome terms for an opera then or even now. Debussy got only $100 a performance for *Pelléas* from this same Oscar, plus $400 for the season as a sort of bonus.

Hammerstein's purpose was not only to produce an opera that, by report from Europe and by Seidl's excerpts, had interested him. It was also to advance his own career as an impresario by sponsoring the American première of something that, his instinct told

him, was bound to be a permanent success. He was seldom wrong
when this weird instinct, which was in sum about three-quarters
of his genius, prompted him powerfully to choose this or that
work, this or that artist.

The copyright laws in 1891 were full of holes and had not yet
been fully internationalized, so that each nation had variants upon
the code of artistic property. In America, it seemed, "exclusive"
rights could be obtained from Italy, but not if the Italian work in
question had been performed outside of Italy. This neither Hammerstein nor the Milanese publisher realized. Perhaps they did
not realize, either, to what an extent *Cavalleria* was already sweeping the world: it was, in fact, running over Europe like a pesti-
lence, and by the time the summer was ended it had had performances pretty well everywhere. Hammerstein's rights were not
worth much under the law, except that he could rightly claim
official precedence in having the authorization of composer and
publisher for his production.

He wanted to give *Cavalleria* a downtown New York performance, realizing that at last he would obtain ample attention from the
newspapers. The late summer was spent on the *Cavalleria* project,
getting together scenery, costumes, singers, orchestra, and properties. The problem of a theater proved insoluble: everything suitable was booked for the end of September and the beginning of
October, the earliest time Hammerstein could be ready. In grim
necessity he was obliged to take a hall called the Lenox Lyceum,
at Fifty-ninth Street and Madison Avenue: this was in "the city,"
of course, but a considerable distance from the theater district,
which was then, roughly speaking, on Broadway between Madison
and Longacre squares (i.e., Twenty-third to Forty-second streets).
He was guaranteed his newspaper attention—this he would have
had with a *Cavalleria* production even in his own theater in 125th
Street—but it was not the kind of theater he wanted, and he
fumed.

He was to fume more. Every manager in America had his eye on
Cavalleria, and the work had two *premières* outside of New York
before Hammerstein could be ready. One was at the Philadelphia
Grand Opera House on September 9, the other in Chicago on September 28. Hammerstein meanwhile learned to his horror that
even in New York he had a rival for the honors of the first performance. Rudolph Aronson, manager of the Casino Theatre,

experienced with both opera and operetta, prepared a production and announced it for October 12. Hammerstein suspected, or perhaps was privately informed, that this announcement was a deception, and that Aronson actually would put on the work at some earlier date. His own announced date was Thursday, October 1, and he was unable to make it any earlier because of the difficulties of the production.

Hammerstein worked like a demon during the second half of September, trying to get his production together. His difficulties were great because the Lenox Lyceum was in no sense a theater. It had no stage to speak of, no proscenium arch, no room for scenery, and no orchestra pit. It had been built for concerts and lectures or other meetings. Aronson, at the Casino, had a properly built theater with dressing rooms, an orchestra pit, and a roomy stage. Hammerstein went to court and, citing his contract with the owners of *Cavalleria*, got an injunction forbidding Aronson's performance, but the injunction was thrown out of court three days before his announced *première*, on the ground that the copyright laws did not validate an exclusive right because the work, except orchestral parts, was published.

Aronson quickly improvised a stratagem: he would have a *répétition générale*, as in Paris, on the afternoon of October 1, with an invited audience, and thus cheat Hammerstein out of the first performance and at the same time guard against any possible legal action that might be taken if he sold tickets. He invited not only the critics of all the newspapers, but also a large number of friends and the merely curious: on the day itself he sent ushers out to bring people in off the streets to fill the house. He did not, however, gain much by doing so, because his performance was adjudged inferior to Hammerstein's. Nor did he rob Oscar of the coveted newspaper attention: he may even have added to it. Hammerstein's production was reviewed as the official first night, quite sympathetically on the whole, by the entire New York press.

The cast for this *Cavalleria* consisted of Mme von Januschowsky as Santuzza, Louise Pemberton-Hicks as Lola, Payson Clarke as Turiddu, and Hermann Geraldus as Alfio, with Neuendorff conducting. Unlike the Philadelphia and Chicago performances, which were in Italian, this one was sung in English.

The New York *Herald*'s review, observing that Hammerstein had presented the opera "after Aronson had given it away," said:

And Another Harlem Theater

"The performance was creditable to Mr. Hammerstein, who organized it, and to most of the artists in the cast. Two of the chief singers, the baritone and the contralto, had no time allowed them to learn their parts. The wonder is that under the circumstances they did not break down altogether. One or two more rehearsals would have added vastly to the efficiency of the chorus. An extra day of preparation would have averted the small errors in stage management which compromised the fate of the work before it was well under way. Fortunately, the beauty and dramatic inspiration, which made the success of the opera abroad, saved it from failure here—this, and the admirable art of Madame Januschowsky, who threw her soul into the part and was repeatedly applauded, the splendid tenor of Mr. Payson Clarke and the conscientious efforts of the chorus, who sang and played with feeling, taste and intelligence. At the end of the evening Mr. Neuendorff, with the leading interpreters of the opera, were recalled. It was not altogether to the credit of the New York public that the audience was not larger last night.

"To give the platform the semblance of a stage, a canvas proscenium was hung up all awry in front of it. The orchestra, composed of some of the best musicians in New York, sat out in front of the platform with nothing to separate them from the audience. The property man must have been negligent in his duties, for when Turiddu sang his drinking song the chorus regaled itself with supposititious Chianti which they drank with Teutonic gusto from beer mugs."

One wonders, in spite of the beer mugs, what made this critic think Sicilian villagers could ever afford to drink Chianti.

The *Times* remarked:

"The opera was pitchforked into an open concert room, and a bad one at that. But the musical forces were superior to Aronson's and had there been a better theater, the Casino performance would have been greatly surpassed. The cardboard-like construction called a proscenium arch afforded such a view that you were practically behind the scenes when you were in front."

The remaining performances of *Cavalleria*, both in Hammerstein's house and in Aronson's, were accepted by New Yorkers with what somebody (I think it was Alexander Woollcott) used to call "a frenzy of indifference." In both cases, one week's run was adjudged sufficient; the Hammerstein production was then moved to the Harlem Opera House for a few additional performances. One wonders what a dramatic soprano would say nowadays if anybody asked her to sing Santuzza for eleven nights running with only Sunday off.

Cavalleria's great fortune in the American opera houses dates from the arrival of Emma Calvé two seasons later. She was to sing Santuzza at the Metropolitan and all other principal houses for years to come—until, in fact, *Cavalleria* had become a standard opera almost wearisomely familiar. It has seldom been absent, even for one season, from the repertoire of any established opera company since then.

Again Hammerstein had not only his share of bad luck, particularly as regards the theater available to him, but was ahead of his time. His instinct about *Cavalleria* had been perfectly correct, but he had been unable to materialize it in objective fact.

As we have seen, Hammerstein's interest in Harlem was waning. He performed one more service for the area by building another theater—a concert hall—next door to the Harlem Opera House, but the failure of music to fill it caused him to lease it to a vaudeville management, which occupied it for many years. From now on his concern with Harlem was manifested chiefly from a distance. He retained his Harlem theaters for years, and quite profitably, until they, too, were engulfed in the debacle he was now preparing.

VIII

Broadway Invaded

BEDEVILED AS HE WAS by the idea of opera, Hammerstein could hardly have built any edifice without calling it an opera house. His new theater in Thirty-fourth Street, accordingly, opened as the Manhattan Opera House. He was prevailed upon later to rechristen it the Manhattan Theatre, but he never gave up the name or the idea. His titanic effort, the opera house that at last crowned his life, came to fruition in the same street and under the same banner.

1. The Theater That Was Too Big

Obviously he had opera in mind all through the building of this structure. It was too big for plays: it had 2,600 seats. There were fifty-two boxes in it, placed under the balcony as in a regular opera house. Acoustically it was superb for music, like all of his theaters, but the speaking and singing voices have such different resonances that from the very beginning the discrepancy was noticed. Hammerstein's unconscious was always building opera houses, but his conscious mind was busy putting plays into them because opera on the grand scale was still too expensive for him. It took him another decade and more to resolve this fundamental contradiction.

The plan of the theater was his own. He employed the architectural firm of McElfatrick, as he had done before, to file the plans and obtain the building permits, but all the designs and almost all the details were his doing. He spent many hours of many days during the early part of 1892 working at his drawing board, adopting and discarding idea after idea. Whenever possible, he introduced an invention, a novelty; and, as far as the utilization of space was concerned, he had already become as skillful as the most practiced architect. For example, he got all of his fifty-two boxes aligned so that they faced the stage. Such a design had not been seen before.

Ground was broken even while it was still frozen; fires were built to thaw out the earth so that excavation could begin. Hammerstein was, as always, in a hurry. He wanted to open his new house in the autumn, and by spring he had already announced a date. His haste did not keep him from attending to every detail of decoration and equipment. His theater, when completed, was declared by the press to be "one of the handsomest and most modern on earth."

In the greater world to which Hammerstein, in his fine theater in the center of New York, now prepared to introduce himself, Grover Cleveland had just been returned to the White House after a Republican interlude, and Adlai Stevenson was his Vice-President. There was a cholera scare in western Europe and the United States, and in Paris the Panama Canal scandal was ruining reputations and political careers. There had been street demonstrations outside the Paris Opera, where *Lohengrin* was being performed for the first time, and—a recurrent phenomenon of the day—the young German Emperor had just made a provocative chip-on-the-shoulder public speech.

In New York, Daniel Frohman's Lyceum Theatre was still extremely fashionable and E. H. Sothern was its particular star. Daly's company, with Ada Rehan, was showing its mettle in Paris and London. Mrs. John Drew, Ethel Barrymore's grandmother, was still playing Mrs. Malaprop to crowded houses, with Joseph Jefferson and William Florence. Anton Seidl was conducting symphony concerts either in Madison Square Garden or the Lenox Lyceum; Walter Damrosch had organized the Symphony Society in the Music Hall, as Carnegie Hall was then named; and Arthur Nikisch and the Boston Symphony were visitors to New York at Chickering

Hall. Most important—to Hammerstein—was the single fact that the Metropolitan Opera House had suffered a disastrous fire during the summer and had not opened for the season.

Hammerstein was now forty-five. His Harlem offerings were noticed in the newspapers nowadays, almost as if they were new productions. Even his operatic aspirations had been mentioned in print a whole year before, although not flatteringly. The New York *Times*, in an account of *La Belle Hélène* at the Harlem Opera House, remarked: "Mr. Hammerstein, whose ambition it is to be the impresario of German opera, should see to it that his musicians are well rehearsed."

Again he had a new theater, and again he had the problem of what to put into it. Again, too, opera must wait on his resources. Now he wanted something to launch his theater among the elegant, the curious, the snobs. The London newspapers were printing enthusiastic notices of a lady named Mrs. Bernard-Beere, who had recently abandoned the drawing rooms of Mayfair for the theaters of the West End. Hammerstein thought that this lady, who was said to resemble Lily Langtry, would bring the "Four Hundred," as they were called (the four hundred persons invited to Mrs. Astor's annual ball), into his theater. He also thought that the intimate connection between London and New York society would ensure Mrs. Bernard-Beere a large number of ready-made friends on her arrival in New York.

The theatrical manager Marcus Mayer went to London to get Mrs. Bernard-Beere and recruited for her season a company of actors in New York, American and English, including Maurice Barrymore and Guy Standing. The opening of the new theater took place on Monday, November 14, 1892, with Mrs. Bernard-Beere in *Lena Despard*.

The new theater brought out a great crowd, and the structure was much admired. The *Times* critic thought that the preponderance of buff and blue in its decoration was a little monotonous: the description given of the alternation of these colors sounds like a theater of at least forty years later, or even today, for those were still red-plush days. The great curtains, of some "expensive-looking blue stuff," parted in the manner of grand opera to allow for the bows of the artists. The vast foyer, as the newspapers pointed out, was surpassed only by the foyers in the great opera houses of Paris and Vienna. The trouble was, apparently, that the theater was too big. "The stage was obviously designed for grand opera," said the *Times*. "The boudoir of Mrs. Despard at Monte Carlo is . . . vast. . . . The auditorium must be 100 feet deep."

The *Times* critic thought *Lena Despard* "a better piece than the incongruous and invertebrate version of the same tale used here some years ago by Mrs. Langtry," but, even so, it was an exceedingly dull play. The star, although not beautiful, had a commanding stage presence and a full, rich voice when it could be heard. She was, said the *Times*, a "thoroughly competent actress" who would be very well received in New York if she had a play worthy of her talents.

Back of the fifth or sixth row of the orchestra it was difficult to hear anyone—even Maurice Barrymore, who had a reputation for stout and brusque delivery. Most audible was a Frenchman, in the role of a Russian prince, who delivered his lines with a strong accent but loudly and slowly.

At the end of the first week *Lena Despard* gave way to *Ariane*, also a dismal failure—"even stupider than its predecessor," said the *Times*.

2. Opera—Briefly—in Thirty-fourth Street

Hammerstein had waited only until the morning after the first night. When he saw that the critics unanimously condemned *Lena Despard,* he set to work at once on the formation of an opera company. No doubt he had had this in mind all along, but the *Times* spurred him on by saying: "This theater is suited only to grand opera, which Mr. Hammerstein will have to provide if he hopes to fill it."

Mr. Hammerstein was as busy as he could be, providing. Meanwhile, Mrs. Bernard-Beere, having failed also with *Ariane*, made one last attempt with *Adrienne Lecouvreur*, and when this, too, failed, her engagement was terminated. Mayer, with whom she had her contract, was perhaps not solvent enough to be worth a suit for damages; she sued Hammerstein instead, and the case was fully reported in the press.

Hammerstein's position was quite clear: he had booked the actress and the whole company into his theater as he might book any other offering, in order to fill the house, and he had no further obligation: so the court ruled. But his droll remarks on the witness stand, and his equally droll appearance, caught the public fancy for the first time. He was becoming a "Broadway character," and the legend was to grow from this time on.

Hammerstein now filled in with a musical show called *The Isle of Champagne*, with Thomas Q. Seabrooke. Meanwhile, the formation of "Hammerstein's English Opera Company" was announced before Christmas, and early in January it was further announced that the composer Moszkowski would come from Europe for the opening-night production of his comic opera *Boabdil*, then a success in many countries. The rest of the repertoire was to consist of *Carmen*, *The Bohemian Girl*, *Rigoletto*, *Fidelio*, and *Il Trovatore*. The inclusion of *Fidelio* was undoubtedly a concession to Neuendorff's ideas of the proper repetoire for a great theater in the center of New York; it received only one performance by Mme von Januschowsky and Payson Clarke, and although they were good, the public did what it usually does at performances of *Fidelio* unless they are graced by a very famous soprano: it stayed away. The reviewers praised Mme von Januschowsky, as was an invariable custom, for her "comprehension" of her part and the "vigor" of her singing; the main musical honors went to Neuendorff, but "the rest of Mr. Hammerstein's cast was distinguished chiefly by its unevenness."

It must be admitted that the operas received shoddy performances with insufficient rehearsals and warehouse scenery. The one exception was *Boabdil*, the comic opera receiving its first American performance Tuesday, January 24. It was to have opened the night before, but was held off so as not to conflict with the first American appearance of Eleonora Duse. Hammerstein wanted an elegant first night for *Boabdil*, and he got it.

Moszkowski's opera, with a libretto about Moors and Spaniards in the fifteenth century, had been produced at the Royal Opera in Berlin the year before with great success, and Moszkowski's salon music and some pieces for orchestra were well known in this country. The composer, it need hardly be said, did not come to America for the *première*. It was already Hammerstein's habit to announce as certainties notions that existed merely in his fertile brain.

Nevertheless, a great deal of space was given to the first performance of *Boabdil*. Hammerstein's production, said the *Times*, was "better than some recently witnessed at the Metropolitan Opera House." The press, as a whole, wished Hammerstein well with his English-opera venture.

3. Too Many Good Things

But by now the theater in New York was at midseason and the competition was severe. Duse seems to have stunned critics and audiences; her season was extended from four weeks to seven. Ada Rehan had returned from abroad to revive *As You Like It* at Daly's Theatre. Lillian Russell was playing to packed houses in *The Mountebanks*, by W. S. Gilbert and Alfred Cellier. Miss Russell's fame as a professional beauty has obscured the fact that she was originally a gifted singer. Critics of the time said that only Lilli Lehmann could produce tones as ravishing as Russell's, and her generosity with high notes (five or six high C's in an evening—so many that Melba is said to have remonstrated with her for lowering the market) must have delighted the groundlings. Meanwhile, there was always Daniel Frohman's Lyceum with its matinee idols, and, furthermore, Charles Frohman had opened the new and elegant Empire Theatre, opposite the Metropolitan Opera, with *The Girl I Left Behind Me*.

Hammerstein never acknowledged discouragement. But now the steady failure of everything he had put into his beautiful new theater was climaxed by the public's indifference to his productions of opera in English, which survived hardly more than a week. He tried a rather tawdry spectacle, *The Wonders of America*, for a few days in February, and then allowed his theater to remain empty for almost two months, probably because he could find nothing suitable to put into it.

Ironically, this was the year when Hammerstein could have done something in real opera with such a theater. The Metropolitan was closed. There were a good many competent singers in the country—Juch, Campanini, Galassi, Plunket Greene, and others were constantly giving concerts—and some of the finest conductors, including Seidl, Damrosch, and Nikisch, were working in New York, Boston, Chicago, and Philadelphia. Without a doubt

Hammerstein thought of it all the time, but his problem was forever the same: he had no money. It is true that the theaters on 125th Street were making money. The Harlem Opera House booked numerous well-known companies, including those of Marie Wainwright, Chauncey Olcott, Joseph Jefferson, and Mrs. John Drew, as well as the celebrated light-opera aggregation called The Bostonians. The Columbus Theatre housed popular plays, magicians, vaudeville, and other lucrative entertainments, including an effort on the part of the pugilist James J. Corbett. But the big house on Thirty-fourth Street swallowed every cent.

4. How Not to Fill an Empty Theater

Hammerstein had various schemes, of course. One that received great attention from the press was a plan to bring the French Opera company from New Orleans. The expansive interview Oscar gave out on that occasion appeared in the press on the very day when the Manhattan closed for lack of a booking. It was a weird foreshadowing of the interviews he was to give in profusion fifteen years later.

The French Opera in New Orleans was the oldest established company in the United States. Its principals came chiefly from Paris, and many modern French works received their first American performances there. The fame of the establishment had spread, and there was lively curiosity in New York when Hammerstein made his confident announcement. According to him, the whole French Opera company would arrive in a week's time and settle down to an ambitious repertoire including operas that had never been heard in New York. The first performance would be Reyer's *Sigurd*, to be followed by Lalo's *Le Roi d'Ys*, etc., etc.

He went so far as to list all the principals and a good many of the minor members of the New Orleans company, and the tone of the interview implied that the railroad tickets had been bought, the hotel reservations made, and the stage already set for rehearsal. The *Times* interview went on: " 'I am tired of opera in English,' continued Mr. Hammerstein, 'and I shall not try it again. The people don't want it. Italian grand opera is all right but the Italian grand artists want the price of the earth to sing.' " This was true, as it happens, but it took a decade and a half for it to be realized. The New Orleans company did not come because Hammerstein did not have the money to bring them.

During this period of idleness in his beautiful theater Hammerstein must have had a good many moments of anger and frustration, if not of discouragement. He was always busy, of course—his workshop and piano took up his time when nothing else did—and there is a fair certainty that he explored all the financial possibilities. Meanwhile, after considerable debate by the board of directors at the Metropolitan (then headed by James Roosevelt, father of F.D.R.), it was decided to repair that opera house and open it in the autumn under the management of Henry Abbey and Maurice Grau. It must have galled Hammerstein to see this one particular season go by without giving him a real chance at the production of opera. From now on, anything done in the field, unless it were second-rate, would entail direct competition with the Metropolitan.

The Manhattan opened again on April 3 for a brief season by Alexander Salvini, son of the great Italian tragedian, who played in English. The general feeling seemed to be that it was a pity he was not his own father. When his unsuccessful season ended on May 20 the Manhattan was closed again for a month. Hammerstein made one more try, putting some of his own money into the production of an operetta called *The Talisman* by Planquette, composer of *The Chimes of Normandy*. The failure this time was definitive: he could take no more.

When we look over the contemporary accounts of this year at the Manhattan, we are forced to the conclusion that Hammerstein had put the cart before the horse, as he so often did, in the entire enterprise. He had, as one of the comments says, "the pleasure of building the house and the anxiety of realizing that it was a complete frost." He did not need a theater just for the sake of owning one: he needed or wanted it for the sake of what was to be played upon its stage. Yet this consideration came last of all in his conscious thinking.

We know that all the substructure of his mind was filled with opera, but the only attempt at opera which he made in this theater was a makeshift affair with nothing much to offer the public either musically or otherwise.

With time and money he could have formed an opera company

of quality, and his handsome theater in Thirty-fourth Street would have been stormed by the hungry opera audience of New York. But he would allow himself no time and he had, by the time the theater was completed, very little money. It took him years to learn how far in advance it is necessary to plan an opera season, how many details must be foreseen, how many catastrophes avoided by precaution. Perhaps he did learn by his unlucky experience with the English Opera Company. His one really successful venture in opera had been with Lilli Lehmann and other artists from the Metropolitan who were used to singing together and required scarcely any rehearsal.

It was his fortune, or misfortune, to be obsessed by the costliest and least lucrative form of theater art, one that can scarcely pay its own way in the best of circumstances. That he later did make it pay, and handsomely for at least one season, is one of his several astonishing achievements. Opera appeals to a huge audience in the largest cities, but there is a limit to what any management can charge for tickets, and the paradox therefore occurs in which even sold-out houses do not pay all the expense of production.

The "backer," the philanthropist, is then called upon, and this is what Hammerstein could never accept. He was fiercely protective of his own authority, and his one venture into partnership split on the rock of his independence even while it was making him a handsome income, as we shall presently see. The strange and wonderful thing is that he never lost faith in his ability to do the impossible. He went on each time in the confidence that if he tried again, he would succeed.

Now there was one avenue still open: spectacular or musical shows, vaudeville or pictorial diversions of some kind, ballet, acrobatics, anything that could be seen in such a big house and did not depend primarily on the spoken word.

IX

A (Little) Time of Milk and Honey

NEW YORK boasted at the time a "concert hall" of renown, profitable to its owners, which had to turn customers from the door with great regularity because it lacked space to accommodate them. This was Koster and Bial's, in West Twenty-third Street, where many of the best variety artists displayed their wares to an audience that was comfortably eating or drinking the while. The "concert hall" was a larger and more prosperous version of the "concert saloon" that had flourished all over New York two decades earlier.

It occurred to Hammerstein, brooding on the handsome but empty shell on Thirty-fourth Street, that his opera house was big enough to supply the wants of Koster and Bial's clientele and a whole new public as well. He went to them with his proposal, demonstrating that with the Manhattan Opera House their profits would be so huge that they could afford to engage the most expensive variety acts in the whole world. Koster and Bial accepted, and at the end of July a new corporation was formed to take over the Manhattan.

1. A Field Day in Variety

Hammerstein threw himself into the variety business with the impetuosity and completeness that were to be seen in most of his enthusiasms while they lasted. He was in charge of all the book-

A (Little) Time of Milk and Honey

ings for the new establishment and, in a general way, of everything else that concerned it as a theater. Koster and Bial were interested, above all, in the profit to be derived from the sale of food and drink. While they attended to this part of the operation, they were happy to allow Oscar a free rein in all the rest. He established an office near the entrance of his theater and interviewed the agents for variety acts there on Tuesday mornings. With Al Aarons as stage manager and with plenty of money to spend on the actual entertainment, Hammerstein had a field day making up programs.

To accommodate the new audience for Koster and Bial's Music Hall, as it was called, alternate rows of seats in the auditorium of the Manhattan were torn out and tables were put in. A huge bar was added, and a Green Room was provided for customers who wished to entertain artists from the variety show. The establishment was, in effect, a huge cabaret, like the Folies Bergère in Paris, but nothing like it had been seen in the United States before and it quickly became known throughout the country. Hammerstein's name, so recently unknown on Broadway, was now one of the most familiar to press and public, and the numerous devices he adopted to obtain publicity for the new variety acts did nothing to draw a veil over it.

During his tenure of this pleasing office—from August, 1893, to February, 1895, about a year and a half—Hammerstein brought to America such entertainers as Cissie Loftus from London, an inspired imitator; the beloved Cockney singer Albert Chevalier; Otero, Cléo de Mérode, and Anna Held from Paris; Marie Lloyd, whom older Londoners even now can remember as the funniest singer they ever heard; various trapeze performers and acrobats from Berlin; and a sprinkling of dancers (La Carmencita, La Tortajada) from Spain. He became known as the most prodigal and successful of variety managers.

There was plenty of money for all concerned; tickets for Koster and Bial's Music Hall were bought up weeks in advance. It was a time of milk and honey.

2. *An Opera on a Bet*

Just at this moment (1893) when all was going well, Hammerstein indulged in one of those escapades which contributed so much to his legend and clung to his name through all the years afterward: on a bet of $100 he composed an opera in forty-eight hours.

The story has been told many times, best of all by Huneker in *Steeplejack*. Five men were lunching together at the Gilsey House, a hotel much frequented by theater people, at Broadway and Twenty-ninth Street. They were Hammerstein and Huneker; Gustave Kerker, the composer of *The Belle of New York*; Charles Alfred Byrne, critic of the *Journal*; and the comedian Louis Harrison. Both Byrne and Harrison had written for the stage. An argument arose about how long it took to turn out an operetta. Kerker declared that it could not be done in less than two months at a minimum, and received support from others at the table. Hammerstein swore that it could be done in much less time, and finally was led by his own excitement into declaring that he could do it himself —words and music—in forty-eight hours. Faced with laughter and unbelief, he offered to bet $100 that he could do it, and Kerker accepted the bet. There was one condition: if he succeeded in turning it out, Kerker would do the orchestration.

Hammerstein engaged rooms on the top floor of the Gilsey House and locked himself in with a piano and plenty of paper. His good friends did everything possible to distract him from the undertaking; Louis Harrison hired organ-grinders to play under his windows and even sent one of their monkeys climbing to the top floor. Huneker relates that cocktails were insidiously sent up by the floor waiter; but these were never any temptation to Hammerstein. News of the crazy bet spread through the theater district and a good many people gathered around the Gilsey House to see what would happen.

When the forty-eight hours were over, the triumphant Hammerstein exhibited his work to his four friends, played some of it, explained what he could and sang what he could, and claimed the $100. He was unable to understand why they did not appreciate the product! Kerker refused to pay the bet because, he said, this nonsense could never be produced: one of the conditions had been that the work created in forty-eight hours should be "fit for production."

Oscar's answer to that was to produce it.

The status of his friendship with Gustave Kerker after this is not quite clear. According to some accounts, he was furious with Kerker for not paying his bet and they were never friends again. Nevertheless, it is a fact that when Oscar announced his intention of producing his work at Koster and Bial's Music Hall, Kerker set to work and orchestrated it as skillfully as he knew how.

The Kohinoor, an opera in three scenes, was produced at Koster and Bial's on October 30, 1893, and played there for six weeks as part of the current variety show. It was greeted throughout this run with roars of laughter. Huneker's account says:

"The first night of *The Kohinoor* was a side-splitting one. The audience, of pure tenderloin variety, laughed themselves blue in the face. I remember that the opening chorus consumed a third of the first act. Oscar knew the art of camouflage before the word was invented. Two comic Jews, alternately, for half an hour sang 'Good morning, Mr. Morgenstern, Good morning, Mr. Isaacstein,' while the orchestra shifted the harmonics so as to avoid too much monotony."

This last, Huneker tells us, was Kerker's contribution.

Hammerstein even thought of sending *The Kohinoor* on the road, apparently not realizing how much of its success depended upon Broadway's relish of a Broadway joke; however, after a one-week trial at his Harlem Opera House, his losses made him think better of that.

3. The Milk Sours

Koster and Bial, meanwhile, were not at all pleased by the turn of events. They were making a great deal of money, but this, except quantitatively, was nothing new to them. What they disliked was the way in which their music hall had become in the eyes of New Yorkers Oscar Hammerstein's music hall. They did not appreciate the way Hammerstein's name effaced their own in all press references to their theater. They were irked by the sudden celebrity of their partner, who had become such a "Broadway character" that he was known everywhere and was generating a whole mythology. They thought that success had gone to his head, as it probably had.

Perhaps Oscar had been rude to them; it seems likely, in view of the fact that he later referred to them publicly as "liquor dealers and restaurateurs." It is certain that if they attempted to interfere with his direction of the theater, as they did later on, he was as rude as he knew how to be, for this part of the enterprise he guarded as his own from the start.

One is compelled to think sometimes that Hammerstein really did not enjoy prosperity. Perhaps it bored him: when he had it, he was always doing something to bring it to an abrupt end. Relations deteriorated sharply all during 1894, in spite of great and continuing success for the music hall. By the end of the year there was no disguising it any longer: Hammerstein's days were numbered.

The actual gage of battle was a young lady who called herself Mlle di Dio and aspired to sing in the manner of a French *chanteuse*. She had, in the course of her lawful occasions, aroused the devotion of a champagne salesman named George Kessler, who represented one of the important French firms. Mr. Kessler wished Mlle di Dio to sing at Koster and Bial's Music Hall, but Hammerstein refused to engage her. Kessler then went to the partners, and Koster insisted to Hammerstein that Mlle di Dio be booked. Hammerstein still refused. The row between the partners then was epic; Mlle di Dio was booked for the next week in spite of anything Hammerstein could say or do.

On the night of her first appearance Hammerstein took a box next to Kessler's. Kessler had, in fact, taken a large number of boxes and filled them with persons who could be depended upon to applaud Mlle di Dio. The moment the young lady came out and began to sing, Hammerstein stood up and hissed. He hissed loud and long; the whole audience turned toward him rather than toward the performer. His mighty silk hat, pointed imperial beard, and Prince Albert coat were a uniform known to all in that audience. No doubt the cigar waved in the air as he hissed. Everybody knew that he was Oscar Hammerstein and that he was the general director of this theater. Laughter broke out.

4. *Oscar Avenged*

Mr. Kessler, the champagne salesman, was righteously indignant and assailed Hammerstein as soon as he could catch his breath. They adjourned to the corridor behind the boxes and fought—briefly, but enough to get themselves ejected from the theater by the ushers. In the street outside they resumed their fisticuffs, were arrested by the police, and were taken to the Jefferson Market Police Station. Here Koster and Bial made haste to bail out the champagne salesman, leaving their partner, Hammerstein, in his cell. Friends came along and released him, too, a little later.

The case was dismissed in the police court, but it provided the crisis that caused Hammerstein's departure from Koster and Bial's. The hissing of Mlle di Dio by her own theater manager struck the newspapers as funny, and they printed full accounts of it not only in New York but throughout the country and even in Europe. The incident attracted more attention to Hammerstein than he had ever received before, and made his partners, in effect, the butt of an international joke. Koster and Bial had good reason to feel aggrieved and persecuted.

They were to feel still more so, as Hammerstein brought to bear every legal device his lawyers could muster. He tried by application to the Attorney General of New York State to get Koster and Bial removed from the corporation for misconduct. When this failed, he brought an action for damages to himself and a cancelation of the contract he had with them. A concurrent action asked for a receivership and an injunction to keep them from interfering with him. While this was being tried, he also attempted to get them adjudged in contempt of court for refusing him permission to inspect the ticket sale at the theater.

The case of Hammerstein vs. Koster and Bial dragged on for many days and brought a good deal of unwelcome publicity from the amused and quizzical press—unwelcome, that is, to Koster and Bial; Hammerstein neither then nor afterward minded how much was printed in the newspapers about his affairs. At last his harassed partners, out of sheer exhaustion and bewilderment, made a settlement out of court, and it was greatly to Hammerstein's advantage: he obtained $375,000 in cash and a mortgage of $300,000 on the theater he had built.

As he was leaving the lawyers' offices he said: "When I get through with you, everybody will forget there ever was a Koster and Bial's. I will build a house the like of which has never been seen in the whole world."

He did. He built a group of theaters so ambitious, and presented variety programs of such lavishness and originality, as to extinguish any previous achievement in the field by Koster and Bial or anybody else. He captured the top variety acts away from his former partners, no matter what the cost, and before very long he captured their audience, too.

His new theater had not finished its second year when Koster and Bial's Music Hall had closed, the partners were out of business, and Bial was dead—of helpless anger or a broken heart, or possibly both. Whether it was because they had pointedly left him in jail while bailing out the wine salesman, or because—and this is more likely—they had crossed him and put upon the stage of his theater an artist he did not want, this was an instance in which the normally forgiving Oscar could not forgive, but made good his threat and drove them to the wall.

Before his theater had ended its third year, he was asking the court for permission to retrieve the last few hundred dollars he had in the world from under the pillow of his cot in a little room of the vast Olympia. He had ruined his former partners and bankrupted himself.

But in the meantime he had become Mr. Hammerstein of Times Square.

X

Mr. Hammerstein of Times Square

It is possible to make out a good case for the thesis that Oscar Hammerstein created Times Square. Writers on the American theater have said so often enough, and it is clear that he was the first to see how strategically the streets (Broadway, Seventh Avenue, Forty-second and Forty-third and Forty-fourth streets) came together in that place. The extravagant theaters he was now to build there attracted great crowds to the area and helped to make it the hub of the theatrical wheel. It is the fact that within ten years after Hammerstein began his prodigal ventures there, twelve theaters were built in Forty-second Street and twenty-five within the immediate neighborhood of the first Hammerstein house. Property values rose sharply, and although all of this development cannot be attributed to Hammerstein alone, there is not much doubt that he played an appreciable part in it.

At the time of his leaving it, Thirty-fourth Street was still the theater center, and a good many of the playhouses were even farther downtown, toward Madison Square. Hammerstein's answer to such geographical considerations was that people would come to Forty-fourth Street if they had a good reason for doing so. "My theater will make a place for itself," he said, "because I will give the public what they have never had before."

83

1. Four Theaters in One

Even before his triumphant settlement with Koster and Bial, Hammerstein had taken an option on the property on the east side of Broadway, between Forty-fourth and Forty-fifth streets, once occupied by the 71st Regiment Armory, which had been destroyed by fire. He now purchased not only this property but two adjacent houses, one on Forty-fourth Street and one on Forty-fifth Street, tore down the houses, and opened up the whole huge stretch of land for excavation and building.

With these three purchases he acquired a front of 203 feet on Broadway, 154 feet on Forty-fifth Street, and 101 feet on Forty-fourth. Here was room for a theater larger than any in existence; Hammerstein announced on March 14 that he would build not one but four related and connected theaters. The excavations began in early April, but so much blasting was required that the foundations were not actually completed until the middle of June. It was a race against time, for, with his customary assurance, he had announced November 15 as the date of the opening.

As usual, he had the McElfatrick firm file the plans and obtain the building permits, but the whole idea of the structure and all its distinctive details were the products of his drawing board, altered from time to time as the building progressed. The Olympia, as he named it, was an immense project. Brought to completion by an army of workmen that autumn, it comprised a vast music hall, larger than any other in the world; a concert hall of "noble design and ample proportions"; a theater on unique lines for comic opera, burlesque, and light entertainment; and an Oriental café, a smoking room, a billiard room, lounging rooms, and cloakrooms.

The Olympia Music Hall alone seated 2,800 persons. It was separated by a ten-foot alley from the Concert Hall, and this again by a ten-foot alley from the theater, which was called the Lyric. Music Hall, Concert Hall, and Lyric Theatre were completed by the huge Roof Garden, glassed in and heated for winter, cooled for summer, where still another form of entertainment was to be provided. All this was augmented by ample room for the bar, restaurant, and promenade, none of which was permitted to the legitimate theaters of New York at that time under the licensing laws.

2. The Fabulous Olympia

Aside from the architectural and engineering effort involved in such an unprecedented design, Hammerstein was busy all summer long with his programs. He had been trapped at the Manhattan without a program and did not intend to let it happen again: he had agents scouring Europe for variety acts for months before the Olympia opened. Even at the Manhattan he had paid the highest salaries to music-hall entertainers. Now he was prepared to go beyond all limits then known. He was able to book Anton Seidl for concerts in his Concert Hall and a musical show called *Excelsior, Jr.* for his Lyric Theatre, but the vast Music Hall would demand an endless supply of variety acts and he wanted the best to be found in all the capitals.

From all of his agents in Europe, who numbered ten at one time, Hammerstein obtained a collection of variety acts which would fill his Music Hall for months to come—acrobats and trapeze performers from Berlin, dancers from Spain, comedians and singers from London and Paris. The sums paid were so large that they amounted practically to bribes. It was Hammerstein himself who afterward complained about "competitive bidding" by managers for variety acts. He ascribed a good part of his later troubles at the Olympia to these tactics, which he had been among the first to introduce.

Seeking a particularly bright jewel to crown the opening of his new theater, he tried to get Emma Calvé. She had had a glittering success with both press and public the previous season, her first in New York, in *Cavalleria Rusticana* and *Carmen*, but had not returned because her fees at the Metropolitan were too small. She considered Hammerstein's invitation merely, it appears, because he offered such fantastic sums, but eventually she returned to the Metropolitan instead, with the largest fee of any opera star of the time. Hammerstein believed that he had helped to boost Calvé's opera fee, a sensation of the day, and perhaps he had. A decade later she did sing for him in an opera house of his own, and after still another decade she made a tour of the United States in vaudeville, thus fulfilling both of his wishes, though not both for him and at wide intervals of time.

Failing to get Calvé, he succeeded in getting the Parisian goddess of the *café chantant*, Yvette Guilbert. He did not get her, however, for the opening. As it turned out, it did not matter in the least who was on the opening bill. The entertainment was hardly noticed. The object of New York's wild curiosity was the group of theaters and the crowd that surged through it.

The Olympia opened its doors November 25, 1895, in a manner befitting a theater that was to fill New York with clamor for the next year and more.The extraordinary policy was to admit the public to all of these various entertainments for fifty cents, and in consequence the audiences tended to rove about from one theater to the next. The opening night was such a mob scene as has seldom been witnessed. Curiosity had been aroused by all the details of the building and its decoration—in which Arthur Hammerstein, now twenty-three and expert at plastering, modeling, and all the kindred arts, had a decisive hand. Hammerstein had installed all sorts of special devices of his own invention (he took out thirty-eight patents at this time), and they had all been well advertised. The air was "changed every three and a half minutes," for example. A thousand men had worked night and day to finish the structure. It had the largest and most expensive chandelier ever made in America. And so on.

Arthur Hammerstein remembers that the two elevators installed at the Olympia came from the Otis Company. There were at the time only two elevator companies in New York. He asked his father: "Why Otis? Their bid was much higher than the A.B.C."

Hammerstein replied: "I don't intend to pay for it, anyway, and the Otis Company can better stand the loss."

There were actually seats for six thousand persons in all three of the halls on the ground floor, but ten thousand tickets were sold on the opening night and thousands more would-be customers stormed the doors in an effort to get in without tickets. The police had a difficult time and so did the crowd. It was ten o'clock, according to the press, before any semblance of order came out of all this.

There was, moreover, paint. It is a recurring Hammerstein story: he always opened his theaters before the paint was dry. On this occasion there was paint of all colors on the decorous black backs of the patrons. The *Times* said: "Mr. Hammerstein took his share of it, and a safe statement is that nine-tenths of the men who strolled around Olympia carried home samples of it on their backs." De Lancey Nicoll and Elihu Root "rubbed the walls in the balcony promenade a few times and made a combination of yellow, red and blue."

Having sunk everything he possessed in the Olympia, Hammerstein had negotiated a mortgage of $960,000 with the New York Life Insurance Company to clear off his indebtedness. Now he was free, at least for a while, to play at omnipotence in this fantastic realm, and he made the most of it. For himself he reserved one room over the Music Hall entrance, where he had his workshop, his piano, and a cot. There he spent many nights not only working at inventions but composing the musical indiscretions (ballet and opera) that were to do so much to ruin the theater.

3. The Goddess of the Café Chantant

On December 13, 1895, Yvette Guilbert landed in New York with an outburst of publicity in all the press. Her fame had spread to all countries by now. Very few stage artists have evoked the interest of writers and painters as did Guilbert. A great deal had already been written about her even in the United States, and sketches of her extraordinary head had been seen. Hammerstein knew, without having heard her, that this was something unique in the field and that it would arouse New York's curiosity to the utmost. Even at $4,000 a week she had hesitated. She was, as she always said, a "bad sailor," and in addition she had received even more extravagant offers to sing in St. Petersburg. It may also be, as Hammerstein suspected, that his enemies (among whom he counted Koster and Bial as the chief) had spread rumors about his "irresponsibility," as they called it, and French artists are traditionally afraid of not getting their money. At all events, Guilbert had delayed until Hammerstein had to open without her.

Now, on December 17, Hammerstein at last had the honor of presenting her in her American debut, and a very remarkable one it was. Huneker said of the event:

"The audience at the Olympia last night endorsed the opinion of Europe that Yvette Guilbert is the most original and the most artistic music hall singer ever seen upon the public stage, by this generation at least. The salvos of the applause which greeted her from every nook and corner of the packed house encouraged her and she sang the principal songs of her repertoire with the artistic vein and excellence which have made her reputation.

"When Mlle Guilbert was singing Jules Jouy's tragic tale of the gutter, 'La Pierreuse,' one could have heard a pin drop in the auditorium, usually so noisy. The woman magnetized her audience completely. A hushed attention followed each song and when, here and there, noisy revellers in the house broke the almost oppressive silence, they were speedily rebuked by impatient hisses. Yvette Guilbert has captured New York as she has captured all the cities of Europe."

It was on the occasion of the debut of Guilbert that Acton Davies, critic of the New York *Evening Sun* and at that time an important personage, was offended by some muddle about the seats reserved for him and took out his spleen in sarcasms against Hammerstein. Hammerstein read them, was angry, and ordered that Davies be excluded from the theater in future. Charles Dillingham, afterward a successful manager, was press agent for the Olympia. "I'm press agent, Mr. Hammerstein," he said, "I'm not your bouncer." Hammerstein was ready. "I'll be my own bouncer," he said. And his reputation for belligerency was such that Dillingham knew he meant physical violence; he found means of warning Acton Davies from coming to the theater.

New York's appetite for the songs of Guilbert was such that her four weeks' engagement nowhere near exhausted it, in spite of the Olympia's enormous seating capacity. The engagement was extended for another four weeks. There probably were hundreds or perhaps thousands of New Yorkers who went to hear her again and again: she was that kind of performer, as many still living must remember. She accomplished magical effects with facial expression and some sparing gestures, but most of all by means of her voice. She seemed to have neither breath nor range, but she could be heard in every part of the theater, and her voice, such as it was, could be darkened or lightened at will, could convey chilling horror as easily as a young girl's naïve grace. She was called a *diseuse*, and, if I am not mistaken, the word was invented by her, but she was also a *chanteuse* of the most extraordinary kind because her means were impregnated with musical and not simply dramatic values.

Hammerstein was taking in $15,000 a week during Guilbert's engagement, and at the time, especially at fifty cents a ticket, the sum was enormous. In spite of this, he grew tired of her for a variety of reasons, one of which may have been the jealousy he so often displayed toward a star or a company that belonged to him. His fierce passion for czardom, for absolute autocracy over his own realm, which came up again and again through his career, operated not only against well-wishers who would have brought him financial advantage (such as the Clarence Mackays in later days), but against even a stage artist or musician who claimed too much allegiance from the public within his own bailiwick. Some of his quarrels with Mary Garden were of this nature, as was his final unfortunate break with the conductor Cleofonte Campanini.

In the case of Guilbert he had another reason for making trouble. He had spent a great many sleepless nights composing a grand dramatic ballet on the Faust subject. He called it *Marguerite* and took it very seriously indeed. It demanded so much of the program that it could not be produced while Guilbert was there. Moreover, Hammerstein was aware that his ballet could not get sufficient attention unless it were made the principal part of the spectacle.

He deliberately provoked a quarrel with Mlle Guilbert in order to get her to abbreviate her contract. It meant little to her: she was in demand throughout the world. She terminated her contract after the seventh week and returned to Paris. Hammerstein produced his ballet *Marguerite* and kept it on the bill in spite of its immediate and unrelieved failure with press and public. Receipts at the Music Hall dropped from $15,000 to $4,000 a week.

4. Headliners, Censorship, and Teddy Roosevelt

Business might have continued bad indefinitely but for a happy discovery of Hammerstein's. The variety acts were good: the first of a long line of Tiller Girls (precision chorus) came from England this winter, and the comedian Sam Bernard had his beginnings at the same time. But the Music Hall lacked the one principal element, afterward called the "headliner" in vaudeville, without which no large public could be enticed into the house. Hammerstein found his headliner in Barcelona in the person of a quick-change artist, clown, and imitator called Fregoli, whose Parisian manager was happy to sign a contract.

Fregoli made his American debut on May 11, 1896, and from then on until the Music Hall closed on June 15 for the summer the money rolled into the coffers. After June 15 Hammerstein moved Fregoli and his company of twenty-five up to the Roof Garden, which he cooled by a system of waterfalls, and the money continued to roll in.

All of his enterprises were in operation this season, and if it had not been for his obstinacy about the ballet *Marguerite*, he would have done well indeed. His Concert Hall was popular above all on Sundays; the Lyric Theatre housed *Excelsior, Jr.* until March 28, and followed it with *The Strange Adventures of Miss Brown*. The Harlem theaters were operating a full season from September to June. At the Harlem Opera House there were numerous notable offerings, including, among others, Lillian Russell in *The American Beauty*; Mansfield in *Beau Brummel, Jekyll and Hyde*, and (for the first time) *Arms and the Man*; Ada Rehan in Shakespeare repertoire; Mrs. Leslie Carter in *Zaza*; and William Faversham in *Lord and Lady Algy*.

During the summer the indefatigable Oscar was writing a new opera called *Santa Maria*, which he designed for production at the Music Hall the following season. To accomplish this he began to form a permanent light-opera company around the soprano Camille d'Arville. His adventures in composition never seemed to teach him anything at this period, either about his own gifts in that direction or the public's taste.

While he was preparing *Santa Maria*, he arranged a program of "operatic tableaux" to open his Music Hall season, based on scenes from *La Sonnambula, Tannhäuser, Faust*, and *Lohengrin*. The curtain rose on a scene from the opera, and after the tableau had been sufficiently appreciated by the audience, the singer burst into song. Between these tableaux there were "Living Pictures," frankly composed for the beauty of the human form, without singing: these touched a degree of nudity never before seen in a New York theater, and there was a tremendous uproar.

No doubt Hammerstein had foreseen all this. In any case, he took full advantage of it by means of polemics in the press about censorship. The public flocked to see his "Living Pictures," whether they cared anything for the interludes of opera or not. The altercation grew very hot and finally Theodore Roosevelt, then Commissioner of Police for New York, was obliged to visit the Music Hall himself to see whether an outrage upon decency had been committed.

Roosevelt discovered that one of the "Living Pictures" was copied from a painting that hung in the library of his own home, and said so in a statement to the press. He regarded the whole act as "artistic," and quite evidently enjoyed it. The clamor died down.

Santa Maria was produced September 14, 1896, with Camille d'Arville and James T. Powers in the cast. Edna May, whom *The Belle of New York* made famous on both sides of the ocean not long afterward, was in the chorus. The failure of the work was not quite so overwhelming as that of *Marguerite*, perhaps because Hammerstein had spent a great deal of money on its production. He had an orchestra of fifty-five in the pit, for example, which was about twice the size of the usual musical-comedy orchestra. His principals were expensive, his costumes and settings lavish. (An odd touch in the decor, which Arthur recalled, was a scene made of papier-mâché, with peaks like mountains, covered with tinfoil. By the end of the first week the foil began to turn black and had to be refreshed regularly with paint.)

The critics saw redeeming features in *Santa Maria*, and for a few days there was some hope that it might attract a public. That hope was vain, and in the end—after a more than fair trial—it brought its author, composer, and producer less than ten per cent of the actual cash he had spent on it. In his rage at the failure of his opera, Oscar accused his sons Willie and Arthur of standing outside the theater and stopping would-be patrons from buying tickets.

During this winter the Roof Garden, now heated and rechristened the Winter Garden, was opened for a stage entertainment in cabaret style, with the patrons seated at tables for food and drink, and dancing until two in the morning. *Santa Maria* was moved to the Lyric Theatre at a continuing loss, but the Music Hall housed a popular extravaganza called *Evangeline*. Oscar acquired a new sort of renown by making rules of propriety for his Winter Garden—keeping out Tenderloin characters, for instance —and his *bal champêtre* in the Winter Garden was regulated so as to be "both gay and proper," showing "the bright side of Parisian life."

One of his discoveries that season was the Cherry Sisters, a trio of midwestern ladies whose efforts, even in Iowa and Nebraska, were considered uproariously funny through their painstaking ineptitude. They were Addie, Lizzie, and Jessie, and they did imitations, sang songs, and committed recitations of such works as "Curfew Shall Not Ring Tonight." Perhaps this had all been done quite seriously in the small towns of the Mississippi Valley, but by the time Oscar got through with it even the Cherry Sisters themselves must have known that they were funny.

He read of them by chance in a newspaper and guessed that they must present the particular kind of awfulness which sometimes delights a New York audience. He did not know where they were, but he sent Al Aarons, his stage manager, to Chicago to find them. Aarons found them and brought them back at a wage of $100 a week for all three, with their railroad and hotel expenses.

They made their debut November 28, dressed in red calico and filled with assurance. Arthur and Willie Hammerstein stood in corners of the gallery and threw vegetables and fish at the stage, which was protected by a net. The audience was childishly pleased by this exercise, and henceforth the Cherry Sisters were regularly pelted with harmless missiles which, of course, never reached them. The act was, for its moment, a hilarious success.

Two events of the winter gave Hammerstein ideas for sketches that were much appreciated at the time. One was the "Seeley dinner": Herbert Barnum Seeley, a nephew of P. T. Barnum, gave a bachelor dinner at Sherry's for the approaching wedding of his brother and invited some fifty "gentlemen of established social position," as Seeley was rich but "led a muted existence on the outer fringes of the social citadel." In order to get his "fifty gentlemen of established social position" to accept his invitations, he gave them broad hints to the effect that the entertainment offered them would be something out of the ordinary. This, from a Barnum, sounded good: all fifty gentlemen accepted.

Mr. Hammerstein of Times Square

The unfortunate Seeley was not clever: he dickered with one variety agent and then, declaring his terms too high, went to another to book his entertainers. The aggrieved agent who had been passed over waited until the night of the dinner and then went to the police, complaining that obscene orgies were taking place in a private room at Sherry's. One of the agent's friends, a vaudeville actor, complained tearfully that his own daughter was being forced into total nudity to perform her contracted dance. Captain Chapman of the Tenderloin area—a personage known to all New York—raided Sherry's with six policemen in uniform, found nothing amiss, and issued a stern warning to Seeley and his guests against any obscenity or indecency in their further revels.

This admonition was taken seriously by Little Egypt, the principal dancer of the evening. She was the lady, possibly Egyptian, who had introduced Arab dancing (known as "hoochee-koochee") at the Chicago World's Fair, and she is said to have had remarkable control of the abdominal muscles. She had already danced once before the police captain's raid, wearing an open Zouave jacket and a pair of lace drawers. It had been her intention to divest herself of these for her second dance, but after Captain Chapman's visit she retained her chaste garments and did not, in fact, dance on the table at all.

This affair was recorded in the press from the Atlantic to the Pacific—at first in veiled references, then in more and more accusing tones, and finally in every detail after Little Egypt issued her statement.

The "Seeley dinner" was the sensation of the hour, and every one of the "fifty gentlemen of established social position" had the pleasure of seeing his name in print many times over. Hammerstein decided to reproduce the whole affair on the stage of the Olympia, and engaged his son Arthur to write the skit with James Thornton. He made contracts with every performer who had appeared at the real dinner—Little Egypt and a number of others—and provided a carefully recognizable caricature of Captain Chapman in the actor who dominated the scene. (This kind of thing became common in revues much later on, first in Paris and then in London and New York, but it was a novelty in 1897.) *The Seeley Dinner* was apparently very funny to its audiences, and the Music Hall was filled by it for two months.

5. A Panic and a Ball

Another event of the day which provided revue material was the Bradley Martin ball on February 10, 1897.

This celebrated entertainment, to which 1,200 invitations were issued, took place in the midst of a terrible depression (the panic of 1896, which extended through the winter). There were great unemployment and downright starvation in the land. Mrs. Bradley Martin was a disciple of the social mentor Ward McAllister, who had long operated as prime minister for the queen of New York, Mrs. Astor. She had accepted his doctrine that the cure for all social problems was a ball. It would create business and "alleviate the hardships of the poor." She decided upon a ball in the costumes that might have been worn at Versailles for presentation to Louis XV.

Both in England and in the United States the newspapers devoted considerable space to the Bradley Martin ball even before it took place. Something about it horrified clergymen, editors, and a large part of the public; it seemed to exemplify "the heartless extravagance of the rich" in a time of nation-wide suffering. There were reports that as much as $250,000 was being spent upon the evening. Mrs. Martin's bill at the Waldorf was actually $9,000, which paid not only for the rooms and music, but for sixty-one cases of champagne and a large quantity of liquor: it could certainly not be done today. Nevertheless, the country rang with it, and so much was made of it that the Bradley Martins decided to live in England for a while.

Hammerstein saw his opportunity and produced a long revue extravaganza called *The Bradley-Radley Ball*, words and music both by himself. To get it on the boards he had to close *The Seeley Dinner;* this piece was still filling the house, but the anxiety to hear and see his own work was too much for his acumen. For *The Bradley-Radley Ball* he tore out some rows of seats in the Music Hall, so as to permit tables for drinking; smoking was to be permitted for the first time; the Concert Hall was done over as a promenade for the Music Hall patrons. *The Bradley-Radley Ball* opened March 7 and closed (with the theater) in early June.

Just at this period both Hammerstein and his son Arthur were arrested, by Theodore Roosevelt's order, for operating a dance hall in the Roof Garden at the Olympia. The objection was made not because of any indecency in the entertainment, but because of the employment of a notorious character called Chuck Connors, the "Mayor of the Bowery," who danced with a girl known as "The Rag."

Arthur had already had his troubles with Connors, who was so irresponsible that he had to be fetched to the theater each night. On one occasion he was found asleep on the roof of his tenement dwelling, in the rain. By all accounts, the performance must have been something like an *apache* dance, and New Yorkers, with their well-known predilection for low life in high surroundings, crowded in to see it.

Roosevelt, the Police Commissioner, went to see it himself and something about its social incongruity shocked him as the nudes of the preceding autumn had not. He ordered the arrests, from which Hammerstein extracted every ounce of publicity possible. The proceedings were dropped, but not until Roosevelt had been made to feel rather foolish. It must have been obvious that his true objection to the presence of "the Mayor of the Bowery" was instinctive and social, a remnant of his upper-class background.

One of the innovations of the summer on the Roof Garden was the introduction of Isham's Octaroons, a company made up entirely of Negro singers and dancers. No Negro show had yet been seen in a Broadway theater, although thirty and forty years later such productions were to become an almost standard element in any season. "Negro comedy," as it was called, had been restricted to individual white performers in blackface paint. Hammerstein's originality, in this as in so many other things, did not arise from principles but from the persistent attempt to provide novelty for his public—to "give the people what they have never had before."

6. Descent to Earth

Whatever he did—and it must be conceded that he tried practically everything—Hammerstein's fortunes at the Olympia declined with a steady downward zig-zag. Sometimes he had weeks of handsome receipts for one theater and losses on another; sometimes all the theaters did well; but the whole tendency of the enterprise was toward less and less profit even when it was not toward more and more loss.

Hammerstein blamed other managers for the heights to which salaries had risen for leading variety performers, but, as we have seen, he was himself as much responsible as anybody for this condition. His own obstinate whims, against which his sons Arthur and Willie and his loyal lieutenants, such as Aarons and Dillingham, could not prevail, contributed more to the decline than anything else. He spent far more on productions of his own composition than was necessary, and kept them on the stage for weeks after the public had plainly indicated its unwillingness to hear or see them. This was true especially of *Marguerite* and *Santa Maria*, to which he was to add, in his last season at the Olympia, a musical playlet called *Very Little Faust and Much Marguerite*, and at the very end, in the theater's last month, another called *War Bubbles*.

During his period as director at Koster and Bial's he had had a running feud with Carver B. Clive, a press agent who had been with Koster and Bial before they came to the Manhattan. Clive, who quarreled with Hammerstein over office space, signs, and other matters of temporary importance, used to call him a "cantankerous crackpot." The expression caught the ear of theater people, traveled about, and was much used of Hammerstein during these years. No disinterested reader of the story could fail to see in many cases how the expression fitted his behavior, most of all when his temperament dictated courses to his own disadvantage.

There was a case very much in point during the 1897–1898 season, Hammerstein's last, at the Lyric Theatre in the Olympia. Here he had installed an operetta from Paris called *La Poupée*, with Anna Held as its star, opening October 21. Mlle Held was to become much more famous later under the management of Florenz Ziegfeld, but she was already a favorite and her natural endowments suited her ideally for *La Poupée*, which accordingly was playing to crowded houses.

At this point Hammerstein became fitfully enamored of a fat girl named Alice Rose, who had a pretty voice. His weakness for fat girls with pretty voices was already known and was to become better known thereafter. It is possible that his own smallness made him susceptible to big women. At all events, egged on by Alice

Rose, he decided to pick some sort of quarrel with Anna Held and give her part in the operetta to his new friend. Miss Rose was without any physical suitability for *La Poupée*, but the quarrel was duly engineered, Mlle Held flew into a rage and canceled her contract, and Miss Rose got the part. The audience for *La Poupée* disappeared overnight.

Once during this period of playing *La Poupée* to empty houses Arthur Hammerstein remarked to his father that it was a pity he had not saved the net curtain that had been used to protect the Cherry Sisters; it might come in handy for Miss Alice Rose. Oscar threw an inkwell at him.

Nothing thereafter succeeded at the Lyric and very little at the Music Hall. Dan Leno, idol of the music halls in London, was brought over and failed. Throughout the winter of 1897–1898 Hammerstein was in a perpetual struggle to borrow money, to make money speculatively, or to get it by any means in his power. His taxes on the Olympia were unpaid and he was threatened with suits not only by the city but by the New York Life Insurance Company, which was entitled to foreclose when the taxes were not paid. He continued to pay his artists and all workmen in the theater, by hook or by crook, but he knew that when his *War Bubbles* came to production in May (words and music by himself) it would have to make a phenomenal success or he would lose the theater for good. It failed at once, with great thoroughness, and the Olympia closed June 8, 1898.

Just at the end of his tether, Hammerstein wrote one of those scribbled notes which used to be legendary in the theater district. He was not one for letter-writing and kept no secretary. The president of the New York Life Insurance Company, Mr. John A. McCall, wrote to him to ask that a representative of the company be put into his office to help run the theater financially, so that the interest payments and taxes could be paid as they fell due. Hammerstein replied:

"I am in receipt of your letter, which is now before me, and in a few minutes it will be behind me. Respectfully yours, Oscar Hammerstein."

The New York Life Insurance Company foreclosed the mortgage, and the Olympia was sold at auction on June 29 for $967,-400. Hammerstein had put everything he possessed into the Olympia to keep it going, and now he was penniless—the theaters in Harlem, his house in 120th Street, everything had gone. The receiver for the Olympia obtained a writ from the court denying Hammerstein access to the premises.

Hammerstein's debacle with the Olympia was, in all probability, the most complete he ever suffered; it left him literally with no money even for food. His son Arthur had saved and hidden away $700, of which he now gave his father $500, and Oscar used it almost all up in paying small leftover bills. Everything had been swept away now, and for most men it would have been the end of a career. Oscar was just over fifty. There seemed no likelihood that his fortunes, which had risen so high, would ever take such an upward sweep again.

Hammerstein was not dismayed. On the contrary, he displayed a certain perverse pride in the dramatic severity of his misfortune, proclaiming by his demeanor that even his disasters were not mediocre. Meeting a friend on Broadway, he proffered a cigar.

"I have lost all my theaters, my home, and everything else," he said. "My fortune consists of two cigars. I will share it with you."

Before long an episode gave him the opportunity to make the state of his fortunes dramatically public, and characteristically he made the most of it. The press seized upon another good Hammerstein story and reported it with lively sympathy. He had hidden $400 under his pillow in the little room at the Olympia which served him for workshop, music studio, and bedroom. Forbidden by the courts to trespass on these premises, he nevertheless climbed a fire escape one night and attempted to enter his own room to obtain the $400, which was all he personally owned. He was caught, arrested, and charged with contempt of court. To the kindly judge who heard the case he made a sort of oration, not devoid of self-pity, which nevertheless did contain the facts of his disaster.

"You Honor," he said, "I have lost over one million dollars in my efforts to entertain the New York public. Thirty-six years of labor have gone for nought. A stranger is in possession of all its fruits. Your Honor, you can hardly realize the tension under which a music-hall manager such as I have been must do his work. He has to plunge into enterprises with every fiber of his brain on the alert. Through years of unremitting labor I had acquired over one million dollars. I put it into a great amusement palace. Now a strange being has the right to say to me: 'Get out! If you dare to touch a pin in this building I will have you arrested!' He has taken possession of my thirty-six years of labor."

The judge ordered the $400 given back to Hammerstein, and the contempt charge was dismissed.

Yet through these very days, when it might have seemed that his active career was over, Hammerstein was already dreaming of a new theater at the heart of what is now Times Square, on the corner of Seventh Avenue and Forty-second Street. Walking with his friend the comedian Louis Harrison up Broadway from his hotel (the old Vendôme at Forty-first Street), he pointed to the site and said: "You see those old shacks and stables? That, Louis, is the finest site in New York for a theater. I am going to build one there, and I have only ten cents in my pocket. . . . I am going down to Wall Street, and I am coming back in a couple of hours and buy that property and build a beautiful theater."

He got into a cable car and spent half of his ten cents on a journey to Wall Street.

XI

A Hammerstein Miracle

HE BUILDING of the Victoria Theatre was a dazzling piece of legerdemain on Hammerstein's part because it was done from nothing—and not only from nothing, but from that worse-than-nothing that consists in being "in disgrace with fortune and men's eyes." Hammerstein had not only lost his theaters and all he owned, but had been publicly characterized as "irresponsible," unable to operate his business or pay his taxes or obtain public support for his centers of amusement. It was not a situation that would make persons with money to lend eager to invest in any scheme of his. And yet he opened the Victoria in March, 1899, less than a year after his shipwreck at the Olympia.

1. Out of Thin Air, a New Theater

His mind had dwelt upon those unused lots at Seventh Avenue and Forty-second Street for a long time. He had been looking at the property for a year or so, but his preoccupation with the Olympia had made it impossible for him to try new ventures. Now he investigated the status of the property—covered by small run-down buildings and a stable—with auspicious results. It was part of an estate belonging to several heirs who were in disagreement among themselves: that was why it had remained so long relatively disused and abandoned. He was told to go to Albany to see an administrator, who might be able to help him.

At this period it is quite possible that Hammerstein borrowed small sums from his numerous friends, although this was never his habit. His own resources were the ones he had always had: his nimble brain, his clever fingers, his instinct of genius. The instinct for Times Square was an instinct of genius; if he had been able to buy it all, he would in time have made scores of millions.

At this nadir of his fortune, meanwhile, he turned again to invention, and several small gadgets brought him in a little money as a result. We know of one, a device for extending and shortening men's suspenders so that they could be made of washable linen instead of the prevailing elastic. This probably made a great deal of money for somebody else afterward, but Oscar sold it— after vain endeavors at higher game—for $300. A patented inkwell had less luck. Then he thought once more of the cigar trade, in which he had made all his money in earlier days, and found what he needed. This happy development came afterward: when he went to Albany to see the administrator of the Times Square estate that interested him, he had no money to offer at all.

He was in Albany only one day. What his powers of persuasion were we have heard from many who knew him. He encountered flat opposition at first: it was too commonly known that he was "irresponsible." But he persisted, and was able to go back to New York the same day with a twenty-year lease on the corner property in Forty-second Street. For this lease he had paid down no money whatever.

Moreover, the lease was extremely advantageous. He was to pay $18,000 a year for the ground lease, with an option for another twenty years at an increase of six per cent of whatever revaluation might be necessary. He was free of the taxes; the owners were responsible for those. A similar lease came shortly afterward for the lot adjoining his projected Victoria Theatre: here he was to build the Republic Theatre, afterward called the Belasco, on a ground lease of $5,000 a year for twenty years with an increase of six per cent of the new valuation at the end of that time.

In his fever to get started on the new undertaking, he now brought off a valuable invention that he at first thought might earn him as much as $100,000 with royalties besides. It was a machine for splitting and making useful the stems of the tobacco leaf, hitherto thrown away as waste. The machine was good; he knew it was good; he knew that it would bring a fortune to somebody. But his need for cash was so great that after prolonged negotiation he sold it finally for $25,000 down and no royalties.

Still, $25,000 was a great deal of money to Hammerstein at the time, and its real value in labor, materials, and other commodities was a great deal more than it would be today. The gold dollar in 1898–1899 was no longer five times more valuable than the paper dollar of today, perhaps, but it had not sagged much below that: the deflation which accompanied and followed the panic of 1896–1897 maintained its purchasing power.

Hammerstein began to build the Victoria Theatre in the summer of 1898 and publicly promised to open it in March, 1899. One of his theatrical friends bet him "a suit of clothes" that it would be nearer March, 1900, before he opened its doors; this was one bet he won and collected, for he wore the "suit of clothes" on his opening night.

2. The Good Fairy on the Trolley Car

The Victoria Theatre was built as cheaply as possible. Every bit of old brick and lumber from the buildings torn down on the site was put to use. Instead of paying good money to cart the rubbish away and dump it, Hammerstein used it all to fill in the hollow spaces between floors or in walls. He haunted auctions and the sales yards of house-wreckers to obtain whatever he needed for the fittings of the house.

Even so, long before the building was completed, his money was spent. He had gone into debt as far as he was able to the various furnishers of material, contractors, and other firms, and he could not obtain a mortgage on the building until, as in his previous experiences, the roof was on. Again he faced the final leap necessary for the completion of the house, and faced it with no money, as usual.

There ensued an episode almost too good to be true, but Hammerstein told it often in later years as one of the proofs that his entire life had been "a romance." A contractor to whom he owed money had told him that morning that he would work no more without payment, but that if Hammerstein could pay him $2,000 on account, he would put the roof on the building.

All his life Oscar had been a devotee of the streetcar, the trolley car, the cable car. He often rode the trolley car merely to think. On this occasion he happened to sit beside a girl who recognized him and spoke to him.

"I was in the chorus of *Santa Maria*," she said. "You were very good to me."

He replied that times had changed; they fell into talk; more to relieve himself than for any other reason, he told of how he had built a new theater and could not complete it unless he could get a mortgage, and could not get the mortgage unless the roof was put on, and could not put the roof on it without $2,000 in cash.

The girl promptly offered to give him the $2,000 and led him by the hand to the Garfield Bank at Twenty-third Street and Broadway, where she drew out the money and put it into his hands. He returned at once to Forty-second Street and gave it to the contractor.

In telling the story years later Hammerstein said: "It shows that if opportunity does not come knocking at your door, you may be sitting beside her in a streetcar."

Now Hammerstein was in business again. He bought a vanload of red plush from a fire-insurance company for fifty dollars and then fought with the company over who was to pay the three-dollar charge for cartage to the Victoria. He bought carpets at twenty-five cents a yard from a trans-Atlantic liner that was being retired from service, and fittings wherever he could get them, junk shop or not.

He had a bout of fisticuffs with the Irishman Gilly Moore, who owned the livery stable that now had to be torn down. Then he took a liking to the man, and the row ended, as his rows so often did, in an amiable lunch across the street. He kept Gilly Moore's hay barn, again on whim, for years afterward and used to retire to it as a sort of hideaway when the theater itself was oppressive to him. During the building of the theater he advised his son Arthur to watch Gilly Moore's tactics in selling horses: the Irishman would parade a horse on Broadway until a prospective buyer appeared, and then a competitive buyer—Gilly's employee—would inevitably appear to run the price up.

Hammerstein had put Arthur to work on the theater, and the final decorative scheme—in white and gold, with electric lights inside the theater, with Oscar's red plush in the commodious lounging rooms—was mainly Arthur's work.

"The reason the coloring was white and gold," said Arthur, "was that we had no money for paint—the 'white' was only the unpainted plaster. We covered the supporting beams with cast cornices, which I made in my shop, and high-lighted the ornament with gilt. We modeled the cornices with a leaf encircling a hole for electric light bulbs to be inserted, thereby eliminating the expense of electrical fixtures."

The pattern for the Victoria was, Arthur said, the Folies-Bergère in Paris. The orchestra seats, all secondhand, were forever breaking down, and were often held up by beer boxes supplied by Harry Mock, who ran the bar. When Willie later managed the theater, he told his father that all the chairs ought to be gone over and new castings supplied where necessary.

"The public considers this theater a night of slumming," Hammerstein said. "If it's too nice, they won't come. Leave the chairs alone."

3. Broadway's Hero of the Hour

The opening night of the Victoria, on March 2, 1899, was probably the great personal triumph of Hammerstein's life, as far as the New York public was concerned. The Manhattan Opera afterward was the fulfillment of a life's ambition, and its opening was for him a solemn moment. But in these few months New York had created a special drama all its own about Oscar Hammerstein. His fall from high estate and his sudden, spectacular resumption of activity made such a story as is loved particularly by the New York theater. The city was swept by an immense curiosity about the new house, and by a wave of warm personal regard for Hammerstein himself. He was Broadway's hero of the hour.

As much as a hundred dollars a seat was paid for the opening night of the Victoria, out of curiosity and also out of fervent admiration for Hammerstein. He had fallen and risen again with such dizzy speed; he was the success story of America not once, but several times; he was the immigrant boy who conquered Broadway and could not be discouraged by the blows of fate. The account given by Alan Dale in the New York *American* on the following day reveals the state of mind:

"Everybody conceivable and inconceivable came. Such a thing as standing room became an impossibility. The boxes bulged with graciously bedecked women. The orchestra stalls were billows of men and women.

"The Victoria, at a bird's-eye view, looks like a big tinkling pearl—all white and gold with the opals of electricity studding it in profusion. It was very much *en fête*. Gorgeous carpets, splendid lounges and all the ultra-elegance the metropolis loves were to be seen everywhere. Hammerstein has profited by his experience with the lost Olympia. There is an abundance of lounging room. In the new Victoria you can 'loaf' if you like, in any clothes you like. You are not jostled by families. There is room for the elbows. And on the first balcony is a promenade very suggestive of the big promenade at the London Empire. Very gorgeous and spacious is this promenade. I should say that it would become the favorite lounging place of New York. There is nothing like it in this metropolis. For, after all, in a city like this there are good folks who don't want seats, who are not hankering for an entertainment, parcelled off rigorously into acts, who prefer to smoke and talk, and laugh, and shake away dull care.

"There is everything at the new Victoria—comfortable orchestra seats, if you want them—more lounging room, if you are in a lounging humor. It is a very vast improvement on the Olympia.

"I really don't know, however, why I am writing all this. It surely can't be for the benefit of those who weren't there—you can't tell me there was anybody anywhere else. . . . A holiday-making crowd out to enjoy a new toy. The suffocating rush at the back of the house refused to be suffocated. It talked Hammerstein—that irrepressible manager had made a hit by his very misfortunes and the plucky way in which he endured them.

"New York's a pretty good place to make a hit in. If there's a kinder, more appreciative and more encouraging city anywhere, tell me where it is. Oscar was the hero of the night. I don't believe there was one spark of humanity present that didn't wish him godspeed from the very base of the ventricles. They clamored for his speech before it came. The roar of approval must have been heard at the Battery. It was a red letter night, with very red letters. The enthusiasm will cling to the house for many days to come.

"The attraction? Let me see, what was it? Hammerstein! Yes, of course, Hammerstein: but there was a little something called 'A Reign of Error' (I don't know why) introduced by the Rogers Brothers. They indulged in their accustomed repartee. It was a light, frothy, unpremeditated sort of entertainment in which specialty-laden people came on the stage, unloaded themselves and went away again. There was Ada Lewis, always a delightful artist, who gave us a 'dopy' girl and a tough 'lydy,' Miss Georgia Caine, who tried the Vesta Tilley act, George F. Marion, who did a 'dago' specialty, there was Maude Raymond, a noisy young woman, and a Cyril Scott sort of young man named Farr, who sang a good song called 'Long Ago in Alcala' very nicely indeed. There were a number of others on the bill. The show rattled along deliriously, and any poor wretch who tried to criticize it got lost in the tangle.

"A Victoria Festival March was composed for the occasion by Mr. Hammerstein, who probably wrote it while he was watching his workmen toying with girders. Nothing will ever stop Hammerstein from composing. I believe he is a sort of automatic arrangement. He will probably write marches for all the new theaters that he builds and let no man pull them asunder. Yes, it was a large, thick and well-groomed night, and everybody had his money's worth. Vive Hammerstein and Vive his new Victoria! May he continue building and composing and adding to the gayety of this particular nation."

Hammerstein's appearance before the curtain at a quarter past ten that night brought an ovation of great volume indeed, but also of a most particular quality: the crowd cheered not only his theater and his entertainment (which they seem to have taken rather absent-mindedly) but his own courage and bounce, his resilient leap into the air after blows that would have kept most men down forever. He valued it. "I believe I shall carry the memory of this night with me to my grave," he told them.

A Hammerstein Miracle

4. Up on the Paradise Roof

The Victoria operated as a theater for musical comedies, extravaganzas, and straight plays. Under this regime Oscar produced nothing of his own except innumerable marches, waltzes, and other short pieces to be played by the orchestra before or after the performance or between the acts. (There were said to have been about two hundred of these, but nobody knows exactly.) He booked into his theater productions of other managers, who in every case guaranteed his operating expenses; if their productions made a profit, he was entitled to a percentage of the gross receipts. Under this system he could not actually lose money and often made it.

The musical comedies and other light entertainments at the Victoria are of little or no interest at this late day. In the autumn there was usually a farce musical to show the talents of the Rogers Brothers, favored comedians of the moment. There was one musical play by John Philip Sousa, a failure, and there were several in which well-known singers or comedians took part (Edna Wallace, Marguerite Sylva, and others).

The most successful production at the Victoria during its four years as a legitimate theater—before it became a vaudeville house in 1904—was, however, of the most serious character: a dramatization of Tolstoy's *Resurrection*, played by Blanche Walsh. This gloomy play enthralled New Yorkers and ran for a year and a half (1902–1903), bringing a net profit of more than $100,000 into Oscar's pocket. Incidentally, this play, in an operatic setting by Franco Alfano, provided Mary Garden with her last creation before retirement.

Hammerstein busied himself in 1900 with the building of the Republic Theatre next door to the Victoria, with a small seating capacity and a small foyer, both departures for him. He wanted it not only to house plays, but also because its roof, continuous with that of the Victoria, would give him space for a huge roof garden where he could produce entertainments after his liking and sell food and drink. He spent much time and money on his roof garden, but they were well repaid: the Paradise Garden, as he called it, was an immediate and continuing success, even though he opened its operation with an operetta of his own, mixed with vaudeville acts.

The Republic opened September 27, 1900, with a play called *Sag Harbor*, with and by James A. Herne. The cast included Lionel Barrymore, William Hodge, and Chrystal Herne, all of great weight on Broadway afterward. The house had its ups and downs, and Hammerstein's interest in a theater for plays alone was, in any case, limited: he disposed of it by lease to David Belasco in 1901. Belasco made his own alterations and reopened it as the Belasco Theatre, with Mrs. Leslie Carter in *Dubarry* as his first play.

Out of sheer whim, on his Paradise Roof, Hammerstein now installed a "Swiss Farm" in one corner, with a live cow and live ducks and a live goat and a costumed dairymaid, a showman's reminiscence of the Petit Trianon high above New York. There was also a friendly monkey, which, when petted by the women, was trained to reach up under their skirts, producing shrieks from the ladies and laughter from the whole male audience.

The roof garden caught on; it was crowded all summer long when the theaters were closed. Eating, drinking, and smoking were perhaps as much a part of the entertainment as anything that went on on the stage, but there were also a considerable number of popular variety acts playing there every year. Hammerstein introduced the anomaly known as "singing waiters" there. The establishment became so legendary that no visitor from elsewhere in the United States counted a trip to New York complete without an evening on the Paradise Roof. A great many of the patrons for *Resurrection* adjourned to the roof when that solemn drama was over: a little relaxation was in order after Tolstoy.

The musical shows booked into the Victoria were by no means all successes. During the performance of one very poor offering, which Hammerstein himself disliked, a drunken man was being ejected from the theater by the ushers. Hammerstein came over to see what was the matter.

"I'm not drunk," the man said. "I paid my money and I want to see the show."

Hammerstein laughed. "You must be drunk if you want to see this show," he said.

One evening when Hammerstein was handing out quarter-dollars to newsboys, as was his custom, on the sidewalk in front of his theater, a man came up to him with a complaint. This man had pestered the box office for seats when there were none to be had for weeks in advance.

"Mr. Hammerstein, I've been insulted by your ticket-seller at the box office," he said.

"By the blond or the dark fellow?" Hammerstein asked.

"The blond," said the indignant customer.

"It's good it wasn't the dark fellow or he'd have punched you right in the nose," said Hammerstein.

XII

The Gold Mine of Vaudeville

THE GAMBLER in Hammerstein now seems to have gone into retirement. He wanted money, as much money as he could get. But he wanted to be sure of it. His terrible catastrophe at the Olympia had cured him of the Micawberish expectation that "something" would turn up. And it seems evident from what followed that his plans for the production of opera must by now have been nearly ripe.

Casting about for a way to put the Victoria on the soundest possible money-making basis, his mind turned back to his halcyon year at Koster and Bial's. There the money had rolled in. All he had to do was spend it. Since the old Manhattan had been sold to make way for Macy's department store in 1901, no physical trace of that experience was left, but its bright dollar sign remained in Hammerstein's memory. In its glow he saw that the Victoria, too, could be transformed into a vaudeville theater selling food and drink. He swiftly made the necessary alterations in its auditorium.

1. The New Victoria

The Victoria Theatre of Varieties, as he renamed it, opened on February 8, 1904, and from the outset it was a gold mine. Through a good many of the coming years it was to bring in $4,000 a week

The Gold Mine of Vaudeville

net profit for Hammerstein. With such earnings, and no income tax, it was inevitable that he would before long bring his dream of grand opera into being. As we know, Hammerstein never had any use for money except to spend it. His lifelong fixation upon opera made it quite clear where the money would go.

He had arranged for himself two rooms on the balcony of the Victoria, an office and a bedroom-living-room, with one window on the alley. Here he spent many solitary hours drawing up plans and, a great part of the time, playing the piano. His numerous compositions and inventions during the 1900's were all evolved there. (Just at this period he invented a kind of vacuum cleaner, a forerunner of the present-day implement.) He ate little and drank nothing. To almost any observer it must have been apparent that this was a man with a fixed idea.

He would not have been able to materialize his dreams, in all probability, except for the devotion and the varied capacities of his sons Arthur and William. Arthur had gone into business for himself as a building contractor and was doing very well when his father called him to do the redecoration of the Victoria. (Incidentally, one of Arthur's painters painted over the wall in Hammerstein's office on which the "old man" had the habit of doing all his bookkeeping in pencil.) Arthur was afterward to assume the responsibility of the box office and innumerable other tasks at the Manhattan Opera. He had inherited his father's inventive talent and a great deal of his liking for music, although in the direction of operetta rather than opera.

Willie was a born theater man, especially for vaudeville and for the various stunts, either in publicity or in performance, associated with vaudeville. His father had used him with good results at the Columbus Theatre in Harlem. It was Willie who was destined to make the Victoria the most successful variety theater ever known in New York, and to produce the flow of gold which made Hammerstein's opera possible. It must have been disheartening to both of these sons to see the rich rewards of all their efforts swallowed up by a passion they did not share. Neither of them had more than a faint liking for opera, and neither could follow their father into the mysteries of his obsession. They did not fail him, however, in the coming years, and it was they who made it possible for the old man to enact his dream before the whole world.

2. The Great Nut House

The Victoria as a "theatre of varieties" had no rival in New York or anywhere else. It booked not only the well-known variety acts and those of European success, but also curiosities of such a wide range that they make the latter-day reader think of P. T. Barnum. Willie Hammerstein was without fatigue, remorse, or embarrassment in his search for oddities, and he succeeded so well that the vaudeville authority Douglas Gilbert, in his book *American Vaudeville* in 1940, called the Victoria "the great nut vaudeville house of New York." The public's avidity to see persons notorious for whatever reason provided excuse enough for booking bridge jumpers and stunt flyers, divorcees, channel swimmers, and record-breakers of any kind; whether or not they had stage talent was irrelevant. Willie's policy brought a huge public thronging to the Victoria and kept the theater operating profitably every week in the year, all the year round, from 1904 until it closed its doors in 1915.

Hardly anybody nowadays would be interested in the two-headed, double-rumped, and upside-down freaks that Oscar Hammerstein—or, in reality, Willie—introduced to New York at the Victoria Theatre. They all had their day in the public press, particularly what was called the "yellow press" (an expression that is no longer so distinctive). Oscar himself had a profound contempt for them, even when he paid them $2,000 or $3,000 a week. One lady, who had been acquitted of murdering her husband, played a week under these conditions and asked him for another week. "No, madam," he said, "not unless you shoot another man."

The popularity of Hammerstein's freakish attractions brought him numerous applicants for the honor (and wages) of an appearance at the Victoria. One man made his way into Oscar's office and offered to commit suicide on the stage. Hammerstein's reply: "That might be all right, but what would you do for an encore?"

Barnum and Bailey's circus also provided many successful turns at the Victoria, and by an arrangement between Hammerstein and James A. Bailey, the circus manager, it was possible to get them for less than any vaudeville house would have had to pay. Bailey could sign them to long-term contracts and turn them over to Hammerstein when the circus season ended.

The Gold Mine of Vaudeville

Celebrated entertainers also graced the Victoria's stage. No first-class variety theater could do without them, and the Victoria's list of stars is long and brilliant. Nora Bayes and Al Shean made their first great successes there; both were to have long careers, the latter in that "Gallagher and Shean" act which was to be the bane of any person possessing either of those names in years to come.

Weber and Fields, Marie Dressler, Bert Williams, Houdini, John Bunny, Buster Keaton, Eva Tanguay; Charlie Chaplin, still young, new, and not yet famous; all the famous prizefighters of the day, including Jim Corbett, Jack Johnson, and Jess Willard—all of them came to the Victoria, along with Don the Talking Dog, the Georgia Minstrels, and many forgotten notables of the trapeze and the bicycle. Hammerstein was the first to introduce in vaudeville a version of the present-day newsreel, known as "Vitagraph News," forerunner of that film colossus which was one day to make vaudeville itself obsolete. He was also the first to exhibit trained fleas in a show. This was in the Paradise Roof Garden atop the Victoria.

Meanwhile the Paradise Roof had changed its venue. In the summer of 1904 it transferred its artistic loyalty from Switzerland to Holland, represented by windmill, rustic bridge, and ruined castle. Hammerstein's famous cow, which by now had lived so long on the roof that it might have pined away at a lower altitude, was effectively fitted into this landscape, and was milked every night by an electrical milking machine, an immense curiosity, tended by a pretty Dutch dairymaid. "What more do you want on a hot night?" Hammerstein asked.

On one occasion in March, 1905, Oscar himself trod the boards in one of the Victoria's entertainments. It arose out of a casual joke: Lew Dockstader, whose minstrel show was about to open, complained of how hard it was to get a good "end man." Hammerstein asked if he would do; Dockstader said he could name his own terms.

It was only for one night, but it was thoroughly advertised all over the Broadway district and there was a capacity crowd to see Oscar make his debut. He was at the height of his popularity as a Broadway "character," and nobody in New York was permitted to be unaware of his hat, his cigar, his clothing, his beard, and his style of humor. "The One, the Only, the Original Oscar Hammerstein" was to make a "Debut Extraordinary," as the handbills said.

He came out to tremendous applause, sang a song, made a few jokes, and recited a monologue. According to the press, there was a fifteen-minute demonstration afterward and it was difficult for the rest of the show to proceed. Whether he was good, bad, or indifferent, New York liked him and wished to make that fact plain beyond question.

3. Press Agentry, Hammerstein Style

The show at the Victoria ran from 1:45 to 6:00 in the afternoon and from 7:45 to midnight. People came and went as they pleased during this time, and there was much anxiety among the variety artists to get themselves placed in the middle or just after the middle of the show, when a fairly stationary audience might be assumed. Tickets were only a dollar, and in the very crowded weeks there was a lively business done in the street by speculators. One of these, Morris Gest, who afterward became a producer and an importer of productions (he brought Reinhardt's *Miracle* to America), started as a ticket speculator in front of the Victoria. He came to some kind of arrangement with Willie Hammerstein and afterward joined the staff of the theater. Hammerstein himself never wanted to discourage or oppose the ticket speculators because he thought their presence in the street indicated the success of the house.

Through the mad years of its existence the Victoria steadily delivered $200,000 a year and sometimes more as net profit for Hammerstein. The means by which such huge profits were acquired from a moderate-sized theater at low prices were numerous, but there is little doubt that publicity came high in the list. Hammerstein had a natural aptitude for supplying the newspapers with material that interested their readers: he was always "good copy." By this time everything he did was chronicled, and he occupied more space in the papers than any other man of the time—as has been said—except Théodore Roosevelt. Much of this was natural, spontaneous: he was always picturesque and frequently witty. His bouts with the law were numerous and he had a certain zest for any kind of contest, particularly lawsuits. He did not mind being arrested for infringing the building laws or the law against Sunday performances in a theater. This law, a serious threat to the Victoria's profits, he neatly circumvented by suppressing some few vaudeville acts and calling the others "sacred concerts."

But aside from the natural fact of his own personality, which generated myth and legend, there was also a brilliant inventiveness that enabled him, time and again, to impose a publicity story on the newspapers without their recognizing it for what it was. Some of these were straight hoaxes. Others could be considered exploitation.

There was a girl from Colorado, pretty and with vocal ambitions but no great talent, who tried out for the Victoria. Hammerstein told her that if she could become a newspaper celebrity in some manner, he would give her a week at the Victoria. He suggested that she might dress as a cowgirl and ride through Broadway to Times Square and there, when a crowd had collected, sing to the public until the police arrested her. She followed his instructions, with results that were splashed over the newspapers for days: she was a "poor girl from Colorado" who had no way of getting on in the theater because she was too virtuous and modest for the hardhearted managers. She played the Victoria the following week to crowded houses: Hammerstein was not a "hardhearted manager."

Such "press-agent stunts" were child's play to Hammerstein. In time the newspapers grew wary of this kind of trick, but Oscar's stunts were usually too good to be ignored. In addition to all these elements in an unrivaled publicity campaign lasting for years, there was also the genuine newsworthiness that marked Hammerstein and all his projects, particularly the Victoria. Stories were always actually *happening* there. On one occasion a snake-charmer was bitten by one of her own snakes and the Negro prizefighter Jack Johnson, also on the program, sucked the venom out of her arm. Like the escape of the bear on the Paradise Roof, when Hammerstein himself was the hero, this was not a press-agent stunt. It simply happened.

4. *Willie*

The value of publicity to a variety theater like the Victoria was that it could bring crowded houses for entertainment which, of itself, commanded no high price and might otherwise go unnoticed.

Willie Hammerstein in particular had an uncanny talent for digging up acts that cost next to nothing and yet—by means of publicity—filled the house. One of these, not in the Victoria but in its roof garden, was a Negro girl called "Sober Sue." Prizes were offered to anybody who could make her laugh, and some of the most celebrated comedians of the day tried—for nothing—to bring about this result. She never laughed—for the simple reason that her face muscles were paralyzed—but she became such a curiosity for all New York that the roof was thronged for many weeks. The girl was paid $20 a week and no doubt brought more profit to the house than many celebrated entertainers at $1,000 or $2,000 a week.

By such devices the Victoria became a perennial sensation and a nearly inexhaustible source of income for Hammerstein. Behind the theater's success lay an extraordinary collaboration, and an extraordinary relationship, between Oscar and his son Willie. So much money in the coffers was, as might be expected, a grave temptation to Hammerstein. He could not have it without spending it. And so from early 1904 he left the Victoria more and more to Willie.

Willie was by now a taciturn, quiet man, without his father's spectacular color and bounce but with a great deal of the same genius for showmanship. The relationship between them was that of an absolute sovereign with his prime minister. Willie did an immense amount of work for which he was responsible to his father and to nobody else. His devotion to his father never wavered at any time, even in dark days, and when he made some new discovery in the vaudeville field, which was often, he approached the sovereign in a tentative and deprecatory way.

Very often it was Oscar who, by some turn of phrase or suggestion of showmanship, turned Willie's discoveries into gold on Broadway. Willie found on one occasion a lady who rode the bicycle none too well and sang at the same time, also none too well; her distinction was that she did so in a one-piece bathing suit. Oscar said: "Bill her as the 'Bathing Beauty' and she'll be all right." The phrase was new; the bathing suit itself, although decorous by modern standards, was also new; the lady was successful.

Willie's talent was providential for Hammerstein because the Old Man's mind was turning more and more toward the central aim of his life, the production of opera. He never lost hold of the reins at the Victoria; Willie came to him about everything of any importance; and all through this period a number of the most remarkable outbursts of publicity—some of them sheer hoaxes—which helped to fill the Victoria Theatre were inventions of the Old Man's.

Thus, he filled the press with stories about a disappearing actress or performer (in one case it was May Yohe, owner of the Hope Diamond) who afterward was "found" somewhere just in time to make an appearance at the Victoria. The press of the day either had not yet penetrated the nature of these publicity hoaxes, even when the same trick was repeated at only a year's interval, or else it was willing to be fooled by Oscar, while the curiosity of the public responded as always.

With all these successes the Victoria and its Paradise Roof had a great lead over any competitor in its own area, and the lead was made official by an agreement among the principal vaudeville managers. Under this agreement Hammerstein had the field to himself north of Thirtieth Street and south of Ninety-sixth Street in mid-New York.

It was a maneuver of great skill and highly recompensed; it seems that the chief reason why the competing managements (Keith, Proctor and Tony Pastor) were willing to surrender such a central territory was their fear that Hammerstein might combine with one or the other of them. In theory, Hammerstein would have overwhelmed the whole vaudeville business if he had combined with one of the rival chains; in practice, we are entitled to suspect, he never could have worked with any of them, for he always had to be monarch in his own realm. However, their fear was enough to produce the zoning arrangement under which the Victoria prospered exceedingly for ten years and more.

Oscar did not need to worry about the Victoria with Willie there. However rapacious the demands of opera in the next few years, Willie wrung out of the Victoria all that Oscar asked. A cartoon of the time represented a truck as drawing up every evening at the box-office of the Victoria to load up with currency; the same truck arrived at the Manhattan Opera soon afterward and disgorged the lot. This may not have been strictly accurate, but it was the essential truth.

XIII

"The Largest Theater
in the World"

Hammerstein was spending a good deal of his time walking the streets, looking for a likely piece of property. The Pennsylvania Station was then going up, and its grandiose lines convinced him that Thirty-fourth Street would soon become a great thoroughfare of the city, a center like the Times Square he had already done so much to create. He acquired a plot of ground in that street, west of Eighth Avenue, on which he was determined to build the largest of all his theaters. In fact, his announced intention was to build nothing less than "the largest theater in the world."

In this he was reacting in characteristic Hammerstein fashion to a stupendous project that had just been announced by a pair of showmen great in another field. The partners Thompson and Dundy had built a fortune out of country fairs and carnivals, and had capped their success with Luna Park in Coney Island. These stalwarts, with substantial backing from rich investors, proposed to create the New York Hippodrome on Sixth Avenue to house immense entertainments, half circus and half extravaganza, the like of which had not been seen in New York before. To Hammerstein this was clearly a challenge. He in turn undertook to outdo them with a theater larger than theirs or anyone's, anywhere, to be called the Drury Lane, in which he also would stage immense and variegated spectacles.

1. *The Wily Deceiver*

We are entitled to wonder why he engaged in this transparent charade. Surely he had opera in mind from the very beginning of the enterprise. All of his life points in that direction, and he was now fifty-six years old. Yet as he searched for and bought a site, and began to draw up plans for yet another theater, no word of opera seems to have crossed his lips. Instead, he echoed the Thompson and Dundy plans for the Hippodrome, boasting only that his theater would be even larger and his spectacles even more prodigal.

I believe that this minor deception was principally aimed at Willie and Arthur. It could hardly have been suspected at the time, but it seems clear enough in retrospect that he was a little afraid of his two capable sons. Arthur and Willie, as we have seen, were devoted to their father, deferential to him in all respects, and afraid of him. Apparently he felt something of the same diffidence toward them. It was no secret that they considered his obsession with opera a weakness and even a misfortune in so great a man, that they were in dread of every move of his that might lead to opera as a certain step toward costly failure. Arthur, at least, repeatedly tried to dissuade him from such moves, but never succeeded. He since expressed his remorse for these efforts, seeing in retrospect that opera was from the first his father's inescapable mission. It is hard to see why he should feel remorse, however, for, once the die was cast, Arthur was as selflessly dedicated to making a success of his father's dream as though it were his own.

Thus, it seems probable that all of Oscar's talk at this time about the Drury Lane Theatre and its "super-spectacles," all of his palaver about rivalry with the Hippodrome, was put forth to deceive these two devoted sons, to allay their anxiety and forestall their disapproval for as long as possible.

They were not in the least deceived. They were constantly aware that opera was the fatal magnet for their father, and they suspected from the start that the great new theater would turn out to be a house for operatic productions. Hammerstein had been playing opera music to himself more and more for the past year, going over the piano scores of a large number of works, making himself thoroughly familiar with them. As this took place in his rooms at the Victoria, it was no secret from Willie and Arthur. Although they did their best to discourage any idea of an opera venture whenever opportunity offered, both must have felt what Arthur later avowed: that with their father some sort of pre-ordained fate made their opposition useless.

It was, as we think it over now, an oddity in human relationships. The sons had hardly been permitted to know their father while they were growing up, and the father had apparently been only half aware of his sons. And yet as they came to maturity, these sons supplied a loyal though bewildered lieutenancy, without which he could not have brought to fruition his lifelong dream.

Most men would have found it quite enough to be engaged in constructing "the largest theater in the world." Hammerstein's passion for building was not so easily satiated. He found another piece of land in Forty-second Street which seemed to him ideal for a theater, and here he proceeded to build another small house along the lines of his Republic—that is, with limited foyer space and small seating capacity. This he leased to the comedian Lew Fields, who had frequently appeared at the Victoria in the famous team of Weber and Fields. Hammerstein promised to have the new house ready for an opening on December 1, 1904, as The Lew M. Fields Theatre. There were the usual difficulties with the building authorities—Hammerstein never built a theater without them —and one in particular concerned the size of the marquee he was extending from the entrance of the theater to the curbstone. He was arrested several times for refusal to obey the authorities, but he fought it through somehow and got his marquee by having the work done at night. The theater, Hammerstein's eighth, actually opened on December 5, 1904, only five days late, with Victor Herbert's operetta *It Happened in Nordland*, starring Fields at the head of an extremely expensive cast that included Marie Cahill, Pauline Frederick, and Bessie Clayton.

The particular distinction of this theater, afterward called Wallack's, was that it contained an automatic fire-fighting apparatus of Hammerstein's own invention. He showed it to the Building and Fire Department officials on Thanksgiving Day, 1904. It consisted in the use of the gridiron to carry water from two 5,000-gallon tanks on the roof of the house, all controlled by one chain from backstage. It was the only theater at the time in New York or anywhere else equipped in such fashion against the danger of fire.

2. The Die Is Cast for Opera

The strain on Hammerstein during 1904 was great in every way, and one of his rare illnesses was a result. He had been architect and builder, inventor and designer for two new theaters at the same time. His finances, in spite of the flood of gold from the Victoria, were strained to the utmost. He was probably suffering from an inner conflict over whether or not to cast the final die for opera. At all events, he fell unconscious in the street during that summer and was taken to a hospital for a month's enforced rest. It seems to have been a case of exhaustion, nothing more, and he resumed his astounding routine of work immediately afterward, but it should have been a warning that even his remarkable endowment of nervous and physical energy was not without limit. He resented any attempt to dictate to him in any manner, and this resentment extended even to doctors. He would go his own way. "I lead a life of great simplicity," he said. "I eat little and drink nothing and smoke only twenty-five cigars a day."

Toward the end of this year he avowed his intentions to his sons Willie and Arthur. Arthur had been doing very well in the contracting business for plastering and bricklaying, accumulating not only money but considerable experience with practical building problems. Hammerstein had called Arthur from this business to build the Victoria. He now sent for him once more and asked him to undertake the completion of the "largest theater in the world," no longer to be that, and no longer to be called the Drury Lane Theatre, but, boldly and simply: The Manhattan Opera House.

Arthur's acceptance of this offer changed the whole of his own life and led him—after the Manhattan Opera was no more—into a long career as a producer of operettas, including some of the most successful of modern times. He had grave misgivings about opera, which he never even really liked. His brother Willie shared his feelings. However, neither of them could quite withstand the imperious will and the persuasive powers of their father.

From now on Willie's role was to continue the flow of profit from the Victoria Theatre. Arthur was to build the Manhattan Opera House, but this was only the first step. When it was almost completed, his father brought him into the organization as principal lieutenant. His bricklaying days, to his regret, were over, and he remained in the theater thereafter.

The Victoria was now called upon to produce the absolute limit in profit, and under Willie's administration it did so. Every dollar Hammerstein got from it went into a fund or pool for the production of opera, and with it such other gains as came his way, including still another new invention, a "bunching" machine for the cigar-makers.

3. Meanwhile, the Metropolitan

Hammerstein was now openly driving ahead with his plans for the theater in Thirty-fourth Street which was to be his crowning achievement, an opera house in which he would present his own company in his own productions, and it seems worth while at this point to see what had been happening in the opera world of New York meanwhile.

The opera world of New York could only mean the Metropolitan Opera House. The Metropolitan was Hammerstein's poltergeist. He never had less than one eye and one ear on it; he heard what he could and was conscious even of what he could not hear. His monumental resentment of its methods and significance, even of its very existence, was to color all the rest of his life. It happened— and this may well have contributed to his enmity—that during his spectacular success at the Olympia and his equally spectacular failure the Metropolitan had enjoyed a flowering of what has often been called "the golden age of opera."

This began with the joint directorship of Maurice Grau and Henry Abbey in the season of 1891–1892, and continued through Grau's sole tenure, after Abbey's death, until 1903. The partners began by restoring the Metropolitan's international status, after years of opera only in German, and continued, with little interruption, to build a company without parallel.

There were about a dozen really great singers alive at the time, and the Metropolitan seemed to have them all. The company was thoroughly international: Eames and Nordica were Americans, Melba was Australian, Calvé French, the De Reszkes Polish, and Lilli Lehmann—back once more at the Metropolitan—was German. Marcella Sembrich, of Polish birth and Italian training, had made her debut in Athens.

Grau leaned heavily on London, and during these years the Metropolitan and Covent Garden companies came to be almost identical. Whole productions were moved from one house to the other, with casts intact. The Metropolitan company gave a season at the Auditorium Theatre in Chicago either before or after the New York season, and occasional performances also in Philadelphia, so that in effect the same company played in London, New York, Chicago, and Philadelphia. Individually the singers were attached to various leading opera houses of Europe—the Paris Opéra, the Opéra-Comique, the resident companies in Berlin or Vienna or Milan. But the London-New York-Chicago seasons alone united them, in a galaxy which even then was perceived to be literally unequaled.

With the addition of Ernestine Schumann-Heink in 1898, these great artists together crowned the last years of the nineteenth century with performances that have not had their like, either before or since. Two performances of *Tristan und Isolde* during that period, with Lehmann and the De Reszkes, have remained famous in operatic lore. The one on the afternoon of January 7, 1899, was regarded by Lehmann herself as "the ideal *Tristan* performance of my life." The critic W. J. Henderson, of the *Times* and later the *Sun*, who lived to the age of eighty-two, was accustomed to refer to it as the best in his long experience.

With the turn of the century the golden age was already fading. Grau was ailing, and at the same time the deficiencies of his method were becoming apparent. He had always concentrated on principal singers to the comparative neglect of chorus, orchestra, and settings, and he had been lax about rehearsals with the principals besides. Now that some of the most magical of these artists —Lehmann, the De Reszkes, and at times both Calvé and Melba— were absent, performances were meeting increasing complaints. By the end of 1901 the *Times* was rebuking the Metropolitan for "bad scenery in most of the operas, a poor chorus, a wretched ballet, a mediocre orchestra, and general laxity and carelessness in all departments."

In the spring of 1903 Grau retired. To succeed him, one faction within the opera board wanted Walter Damrosch and another wanted Heinrich Conried. Since his matinee-idol days and Hammerstein's last brush with him, Conried had successfully managed the Irving Place Theatre, presenting well-known German actors and actresses in plays that New York was not to see in English for years.

4. An Old Enemy, a New Opportunity

Conried won the post at the Metropolitan. This, as we can well imagine, irked Hammerstein more than most of the events of the day. He had entertained a cordial detestation for Conried since their early association and its climax in a violent quarrel. Conried had also been stage director for the pirated *Cavalleria Rusticana* that robbed Oscar of the clear honor, for which he had paid, of being the first to produce it. He never forgave Conreid for these and other misdeeds that rankled in his usually forgiving memory: there must have been, we are bound to conjecture, some personal clashes besides those we know of, for there is not the slightest doubt that Hammerstein had an animus against Conried which the known circumstances of their past association and potential rivalry could not have occasioned.

Hammerstein was capable of quick and tempestuous angers, but not of bearing a grudge (except in the one instance of Koster and Bial), and he was generous without stint, without display, and with little regard for his own financial situation. Once, in the early days of the Victoria when that theater's continuing success was not yet a certainty, he tore up an envelope containing $10,000 worth of I.O.U.'s, out of a distaste for collecting money from people in difficulty. An associate on the *Tobacco Journal*, years before, who had borrowed $3,000 in a time of need, came with a check for the full amount at a time when Hammerstein was himself in trouble, and Hammerstein refused to accept payment, insisting that the money had been a gift, not a loan. This man's family told the story with affectionate gratitude for years afterward. Hammerstein forgave an absconding cashier and, some years later, was paying the man's hospital bills as the man himself lay dying. Oscar could quarrel with an artist in a manner that would lead an onlooker to believe mortal enmity must be the result, and two days later all would have been forgotten.

What, therefore, he had against Conried we must imagine for ourselves. It was something more than the arrogance and bad behavior of the young matinee idol Conried had once been. It was more than the jealousy of one opera manager for another. No doubt Hammerstein felt, when Conried's appointment to the Metropolitan was announced, that this was a brilliant example of fate's perverseness and injustice. Conried had no musical knowledge, and Hammerstein, for all his amateurishness, had a great deal. He might with some justice have felt that the directorship of the Metropolitan should by rights have come to him—except that he could never have endured domination by a board of financiers. If the directorship had gone to Walter Damrosch his feelings would have been far different, for Damrosch was a conductor and composer. We may suppose that Conried's reign at the Metropolitan was one more reason, added to far deeper and more potent ones, for Hammerstein's determination to give battle to that institution on the full, extravagant scale of first-class international opera.

What it cost Hammerstein to enjoy complete autocracy in his own opera house, without a board or even a backer, can be seen by a glance at Conried's personal fortunes. Like many managers of established opera houses before him, Conried was in the business to make what he could out of it. According to Irving Kolodin in *The Story of the Metropolitan Opera*, in the five years from 1903 to 1908 when he retired before the incoming Gatti-Casazza, his income was close to $400,000. He was paid an annual salary of $20,000, and he garnered almost as much in addition each year by his "benefit" and gala performances, in which singers felt obliged to appear without fee. He also made a profit on his original investment of $75,000 in the company when on his retirement William Kissam Vanderbilt bought his interest for $90,000.

Conried inherited from Grau two commitments that were to stand him in good stead: a contract with Enrico Caruso, to be fulfilled in New York at the end of 1903, and an option with Geraldine Farrar, at this time idolized in Berlin. Caruso had just made his phenomenal success at Covent Garden in the summer of 1903, and was bound in due course to do the same thing in America. Moreover, the resources of the Metropolitan, although not what they had been only a few years before, were still formidable. Conried's period of management was nevertheless one of the most inglorious, judging by the unending complaint of the press. One of the reasons, of course, was Hammerstein's competition.

Conried's opening season was distinguished by his production of *Parsifal*. Wagner had regarded the opera as a "sacred festival" drama and wished it to remain as the particular consecration of Bayreuth. Now he was twenty years dead and his wishes, in the absence of effective international copyright laws, were no longer binding. The Metropolitan had once before been dissuaded from this particular piracy by Lilli Lehmann. On this occasion Frau Cosima Wagner appealed to the German Emperor and sought an injunction in the courts of New York State, without avail. Repercussions in the press and the protests of the clergy stirred up a lively interest, and for his *première* performance, on Christmas Eve, 1903, Conried was able to fill the Metropolitan at ten dollars an orchestra seat. *Parsifal* was repeated for ten more performances during the season, to packed houses, and when Conried chose it for his "benefit" that April he enjoyed a personal profit, from this "sacred" drama, of about $10,000.

It has often been said that Conried could have brought into the Metropolitan at this time the very singers and the very works with which Hammerstein was to have such resplendent success. He had an option on the services of Luisa Tetrazzini and allowed it to lapse. Most of the modern French works that Hammerstein presented a few years later were available, almost all of them in the office of the Paris agent Gabriel Astruc. Mary Garden had become famous overnight, on April 13, 1900, when she sang Louise at the Opéra-Comique, and her performance in *Pelléas et Mélisande* in Paris in 1902 had been fully reported in America as in other countries. Gatti-Casazza in his memoirs has suggested that Conried ought to have bought the American rights to all the new French works whether he produced them or not—merely as a preemptive maneuver—and the implication is that the same might have been done with singers. The truth seems to be that Conried was making money by using the same singers, settings, and scores that had done duty before, and he saw no reason for varying his program. It was, as it happened, Hammerstein's golden opportunity.

There was thus plenty of reason for Hammerstein to be dream-

"The Largest Theater in the World"

ing of opera again. So far as we know, he had never stopped, and the doldrums into which the Metropolitan had fallen under the aegis of his old enemy Conried must have been a most powerful encouragement. *Parsifal* was the sensation of two seasons and then retired to its present status. Except for Caruso—a big exception—nothing new of any enduring merit had happened at the Metropolitan since the great seasons of Grau.

Hammerstein was getting ready.

XIV

At Last, the Manhattan Opera House

Hammerstein as an architect was distinguished above all for the acoustical results he achieved. We have already observed that he built for the ear, and I have hazarded the supposition that he, like many other lovers of music, had music running in his head at practically all times. All of his theaters could hold musical sound beautifully, but Oscar himself seems never to have given any precise explanation of how he did it. He experimented with various woods, of course, and with various designs. Arthur, who carried out his father's specifications, tells us that beneath the hardwood floor of the orchestra pit there was first put down a layer of broken glass one and one-half feet deep, the whole length and width of the pit. Overhead, as a sounding-board, was a hollow hung ceiling, elliptical in shape, which followed the contour of the top of the proscenium arch. The outside of this hollow ceiling was edged with a hollow plaster beam about eighteen inches square. Beyond these interesting details, we have no explanation of the principles upon which Oscar operated. Perhaps some of his success was luck, but when we find the same effects obtaining in nine or ten theaters we are obliged to conclude that he had a special talent for this kind of architecture.

At Last, the Manhattan Opera House

1. Something New in Opera Houses

In the case of the Manhattan Opera House there may have been an element of chance, arising from the fact that he wanted it to be quite different from the Metropolitan. As the Metropolitan is cavernous and deep, he wanted the Manhattan to be soft and broad, and it so happened that this shape produced acoustical results of the first order. Above all—and this he could not possibly have known when he built it—the Manhattan was suited to those delicate and subtle works that have to be seen in detail as well as heard. Such a masterpiece as *Pelléas et Mélisande* is lost on three-quarters of the audience at the Metropolitan, but it was at home in the Manhattan. *Le Jongleur de Notre Dame*, a much lesser work but memorable in its performance, could hardly have made its impression at all in the Metropolitan. To the audience, the singers at the Metropolitan seem very far away, and most of the details of action are difficult to follow in that house. The Manhattan had almost exactly the same seating capacity, but the audience seemed closer together and nearer to the stage. Every newspaper in New York commented upon this fact in the opening days of Hammerstein's first season.

There are a number of opera theaters in the United States which have exceptional acoustical qualities and are able, in spite of great size, to create an impression of intimacy in works where it is necessary. One is the Academy of Music in Philadelphia, which, by accident or design, has an almost miraculous clarity of sound. Another was the Auditorium in Chicago, which by its broad, open structure and shell-like receptivity seemed to bring the whole audience and stage into a closer relationship. It may have been something akin to the Philadelphia Academy and the Chicago Auditorium which Hammerstein set out to design in his Manhattan Opera. Or he may simply have been trying to make it as different as possible from the Metropolitan. At all events, he succeeded not only in that endeavor, but in the larger purpose of creating a theater where an opera audience could really share in the experience of the stage.

Some of his experimentation was questioned then and still is. The stage of the Manhattan was of cement, for instance, and a certain fluidity of movement which is possible on wood could not be achieved on cement. (Mary Garden told me this.) The Lexington, Hammerstein's last New York theater, was superior in this respect and also had a fabulous acoustical quality. But from the point of view of the audience, the Manhattan was something quite new in that it seemed much smaller than it really was, and the stage appeared to be closer. The accounts written of its early days speak of the "warmth" of the house and its embracing quality. Instead of having a wall of boxes and balconies straight up and down, as at the Metropolitan, it opened out in a gradual and circular movement which seemed to get everybody in, so that no part of the house was outside the magical arc. Hammerstein's designs were responsible for the effect, of course, although most of the actual building was accomplished under the direction of his son Arthur.

There is no doubt at all that Hammerstein studied the Metropolitan architecturally, just as he studied its repertoire and methods. He wanted to profit by the Metropolitan's mistakes, and he was shrewd enough to know what they were.

The Manhattan Opera House was actually completed, as all the newspapers of the day inform us, about one hour before the curtain rose on its first performance. Apparently the paint was, as usual with Hammerstein, still wet in many places. There was never enough time for Hammerstein: he seems to have made his dates purposely difficult to meet, perhaps with the notion that if he did not, there would be some doubt of getting the job done at all.

Originally he entertained the idea that he could give opera at fairly reasonable prices—opera for the masses. He discovered very early that this would not be possible if he used internationally known singers, all of whom demanded large fees, and if the chorus and orchestra were to be kept up to standard. The fiendish expense of opera production was by no means unknown to Hammerstein, but he had never until now embarked on the really big enterprise of a full international company. He learned, to his sorrow, how expensive rehearsals can be and how necessary they are, and it is immensely to his credit that he gave his principal conductor, Cleofonte Campanini, all the rehearsal time he demanded during the first three seasons.

At Last, the Manhattan Opera House

2. *A Shower of 1,000-Franc Notes*

Leaving the actual building of the house more and more to Arthur, the Old Man set himself throughout 1905 to the task of organizing his company. He wanted, of course, some internationally famous singers to counterbalance the Metropolitan's Caruso and Sembrich.

The most famous singer in the world was undoubtedly Nellie Melba, and Hammerstein determined to get her at almost any cost. Aside from Caruso, the reigning tenor of the Italian opera houses was Alessandro Bonci, who had never yet been heard in the United States. Maurice Renaud was an idol at the Paris Opéra; he was a baritone of the grand style, a Don Giovanni beyond compare at the time. The Metropolitan had held a contract with him and had allowed it to lapse, paying him damages, and thus he too had not yet been heard in New York. Charles Dalmorès, then young and very handsome, was at the beginning of his renown as a dramatic tenor in French and Italian operas. The sumptuous basso of Vittorio Arimondi, the buffo skills of Charles Gilibert, and the imposing contralto of Eleanora de Cisneros were all available. De Cisneros (born Eleanor Broadfoot) had been heard briefly at the Metropolitan in small parts; her subsequent career had been in Europe. Mary Garden was the queen of the Opéra-Comique in Paris, and although Hammerstein was unable to get her to America for his first season, there is no doubt that he had her in mind from the beginning. He went to Europe to sign contracts with these and other singers.

It is impossible not to tell the Melba story, although it is equally impossible to guarantee its veracity. It appears that Mme Melba had no wish to come to the United States at all, and no particular desire to associate herself with a new opera company in any case. Mr. Hammerstein went to see her at the Grand Hotel in Paris, where she was living during engagements at the Opéra. He could not prevail upon her. Melba was immensely successful and rich; large fees did not dazzle her any more; she was in demand in every opera house in the world, from St. Petersburg to Buenos Aires. Her silvery tones were still at their loveliest, and there was a cloud of legend about her. Her romance with Philippe d'Orléans,

131

pretender to the throne of France, may have been partly responsible for her reluctance to revisit America, as it was also responsible for much of her contemporary legend.

For whatever reasons, Hammerstein failed utterly. The legend is that in his last interview, in her sitting room at the hotel, he accepted her decision with a bow and then, taking a wad of thousand-franc banknotes from his coat pocket, he opened it out fanwise and threw it into the air. The banknotes fell all over the room. Mme Melba stared at him in utter amazement. He bowed again and left. As he walked down the corridor he was pursued by the sound of Melba's helpless laughter, apparently a highly robust noise. She signed the contract the next day.

The most decisive of Hammerstein's acts in the formation of his company was the engagement of Cleofonte Campanini as principal conductor. This remarkable animator and inspirer of great operatic performances was the younger brother of the heroic tenor Italo Campanini and was married to Eva Tetrazzini, elder sister of Luisa. Hammerstein had made an effort to get the services of Arturo Toscanini, then chief conductor at La Scala in Milan, but without success. Toscanini at that time was much too wedded to the Scala to think of America; and when he finally came over, it was to join the Metropolitan as part of an arrangement including Giulio Gatti-Casazza as general manager.

Campanini, older than Toscanini, had worked in his youth at the Metropolitan, but in his maturity had not yet appeared in the United States. He was an indefatigable worker who could rehearse all day every day and conduct practically every night. His command of all the forces—orchestra, chorus, and principals—was of an electrical kind which New York had not so far experienced. For a new opera company containing many artists who had never sung together it was all-important to have a conductor of this quality, and Hammerstein recognized it so amply that he gave Campanini practically unlimited authority over every detail of performance. As the Metropolitan had nothing of similar caliber—Arturo Vigna, its chief Italian conductor, was a listless time-beater—Hammerstein began with a formidable advantage. Campanini's prestige in the opera houses of Europe was also useful, as many singers who were otherwise timorous about the new enterprise were reassured by his presence.

Another element in Hammerstein's company for which he was

personally responsible was his chorus. He recruited it from the young people of the New York voice studios, for the most part, adding experienced choristers from Italy just as the season was about to begin. His chorus had youth, looks, voices, and ambition. It is seldom that one reads such praise as the New York music critics lavished upon this chorus, so often the least regarded part of opera production.

In this particular season the choristers were making news at the Metropolitan in a wage dispute with Conried; they went on strike and the Metropolitan was without a chorus for a few days. Hammerstein wanted no difficulties of that sort, and when his American chorus asked for half-pay for the three weeks of pre-seasonal rehearsal, he gave it to them at once.

In the staff assembled through 1905 to deal with the administration of the new opera company there were some notable figures. William J. Guard, the press agent of the Manhattan, made a place for himself in New York life then and for many years afterward when he went to the Metropolitan. "Billy" Guard he was called, and he was both amiable and astute; Hammerstein often had occasion to be grateful for his high professional skill. There was no need to persuade the papers to write about Hammerstein—he was now and had been for years eminently newsworthy—but there were often times when manipulation of the news became necessary. The subscription department and box office in general were in the hands of Lyle Andrews, another Hammerstein stalwart.

Arthur Hammerstein, having built the theater, was now pressed into service by his father as a sort of general aide-de-camp ("my four years of opera torture," he called it) and learned how to face the innumerable difficulties of the impresario. Jacques Coini, a stage director of great talent, was imported from Brussels to see to the staging of the operas, and Hammerstein's old friend Mme Freisinger, who had worked with him on earlier productions, undertook to supply all the costumes. When Hammerstein went to her he was without ready cash—the building of the theater had taken all he possessed—so the good lady invested $20,000 of her own money in the materials she needed to dress the repertoire.

Oscar Hammerstein I

3. One Man against the Metropolitan

Hammerstein's plans aroused intense curiosity in the press and public. This was not only because of his picturesque personality, but because the actual enterprise was so daring, so hazardous, so improbable. One man alone, without financial backing other than the profits of his vaudeville theater, was undertaking to rival the entrenched and highly organized Metropolitan Opera.

Hammerstein was owner, builder, and architect of his own theater, producer, director, everything rolled into one. There was something intensely appealing about his valor, his high spirits, his unquenchable optimism. He seemed to know and care so little about the powers of New York society and finance, the great Astor-Morgan combination upon which he was making war. As we read the press of 1906 we come across constant expressions of the admiration and wonder with which the writers—W. J. Henderson, Richard Aldrich, and the rest—watched his course. They all knew, probably a good deal more accurately than he did, what he was up against, what forces would almost inevitably combine to crush him. The favorable attitude of the press was a result of this admiration, and Hammerstein made use of it abundantly. Almost every day he would give forth some kind of statement, divulging his projects piecemeal so that each separate item got its full value in the newspapers.

In some of these statements he was playing the press as a fisherman plays a big fish. All through 1905–1906 there were statements of one sort or another about the De Reszke brothers. Mr. Hammerstein was "negotiating" with them; Mr. Hammerstein "hoped" to get Jean de Reszke out of retirement; Mr. Hammerstein was going to bring Édouard de Reszke back in any case. The fact seems to be that there never was any question of Jean de Reszke returning to the stage or to America. Hammerstein did have an option on the services of Édouard de Reszke, but sacrificed it when he heard the basso sing a concert in Paris; the voice was no longer equal to the needs of opera. Whatever the truth of the matter, the name of the De Reszke brothers was always good for a newspaper story, and Hammerstein used it for that purpose. The same was true of Melba and, to a lesser degree, of Bonci.

134

At Last, the Manhattan Opera House

Hammerstein joined battle almost at once over *La Bohème*, and for Melba's sake. Her Mimi was famous, the great success of all her later career, and Hammerstein "positively announced" it a number of times although the publishing house of Ricordi in Milan retorted that the Metropolitan had exclusive rights to it.

The right and wrong of the matter cannot be determined exactly. Certainly Hammerstein thought he had a verbal agreement with George Maxwell, Ricordi's New York representative, covering all the Puccini operas. He was also convinced that it was not the Ricordi firm but the Metropolitan and Conried who tried to do him out of these works. He had originally announced *Madama Butterfly*, then new, and afterward *La Bohème: Bohème* was at one time scheduled as his opening-night opera. Ricordi went to court and Hammerstein had to forgo his *Bohème* for a while.

In this, as in numerous other difficulties he encountered in 1905–1906, he was always inclined to see the hairy hand of Heinrich Conried. There were persistent stories that singers had been warned against appearing in Hammerstein's company; that some artists had been told they would never be paid; that a sort of whispering campaign was going on, emanating from Conried, to discredit Hammerstein and discourage any prospective member of his company.

It may all have been true and it may partly have been imagined; Hammerstein was always more than ready to believe ill of Conried. However, with Campanini at his side and Melba definitely contracted for ten performances, Hammerstein could overcome the whispering campaign easily enough. His major difficulties came not from slander or ill-will but from the sheer physical necessities of preparing an opera season from scratch, with not a dress or a stage set or a trombone ready to hand.

The hours of work Hammerstein put in during this period of preparation were prodigious. He is said to have been active as many as twenty hours out of the twenty-four, and there was hardly a detail of the preparation which did not require and receive his close personal attention. He had deliberately chosen to challenge the Metropolitan, and even invited conflicts in repertoire, singers, and dates. He went so far as to set his opening for the same night as the Metropolitan's, and postponed it only because he was not ready.

He might have sidestepped some of the conflict if he had wished to do so. For example, he need not have given his performances on the same nights as the Metropolitan: Tuesdays and Thursdays, when no operas were performed at the Metropolitan, would presumably have released a large public to Hammerstein if he had produced on those days. But he chose to run in direct opposition to the older opera house, giving his performances at the same time as theirs: Mondays, Wednesdays, Fridays, and two on Saturdays. His announced reason for not utilizing Tuesdays and Thursdays was that these nights were required for rehearsal. It is not easy to understand why he could not have rehearsed on Mondays and performed on Tuesdays, and his statements on the subject are not convincing. To my way of thinking, he really *wanted* the direct conflict with the other opera house. It appealed to his combative spirits; it was a large part of his fun.

Similarly, he might have avoided a good many other elements of rivalry. *Aïda*, for example, is an opera peculiarly suited to the Metropolitan's architecture, acoustics, and style. It might quite reasonably have been left to the Metropolitan while Hammerstein devoted his energies to something else. But no: he could not leave it alone, but must challenge the direct comparison by producing his own *Aïda*. The sharper the conflict, the better he liked it. So he would pit Bonci against Caruso, Melba against Sembrich, in an all-out "opera war" in which somebody was bound to get rather badly hurt.

After the arrival of Mary Garden, it is true, Hammerstein's repertoire did begin to differentiate itself more markedly from that of the Metropolitan. Hammerstein brought whole productions for her from Paris. This, however, was in the second season. In his first season and during the year of preparation for it, Hammerstein had not really found his bearings, operatically speaking, and his sovereign desire to fight with the Metropolitan seems to have been the determinant of all his choices.

As he explained it himself, his task at the beginning was to build a sort of standard repertoire which would thereafter remain as the base of the operation. While he was still in the early stages of this process, working with singers who were often strangers to one another, he had to give a great deal of rehearsal time to the bread-and-butter operas, the ever familiar *Aïda, Faust, Carmen,* and *Rigoletto*. Hammerstein's fame does not rest on those productions —except possibly *Carmen*—but, like all opera managers, he thought he could not run a season without them. It is no doubt true that the bread-and-butter works are necessary and basic if there is but one opera house in a city, but when there are two running at the same time, it is hardly imperative for them to duplicate their efforts. Or so it would seem to the onlooker, and in retrospect: at the time, and to Oscar Hammerstein, it was different. He wanted a full-fledged "international opera" season in flat opposition to the Metropolitan, and this was the way he went about it.

4. A Man in a Hurry

The characteristic of Hammerstein in opera as in all his other theater enterprises was, to begin with, haste. He was always in a hurry, always jumping ahead of himself. Most men undertaking to create a new opera company would have taken two or three years, at least, to do what Hammerstein did in one. The simple physical labor involved in a production of *Aïda*, for example, is immense: costumes, scenery, chorus, ballet, orchestra. In Hammerstein's case, nothing was ready-made; everything had to be created. Nowadays at the Metropolitan there are two hundred and fifty persons on stage during the triumphal scene of *Aïda*. Hammerstein did not run to quite such display, but he aimed at it.

Where everything and everybody is new and time is short, there must be a general feeling of shakiness through the whole period of preparation. It is not surprising, therefore, that substitutions had to be made from time to time, and that postponements took place; the fact of the matter is that Hammerstein started his first season without knowing how it was going to end.

An opera season ought to be, and usually is, planned with the utmost exactitude a full year in advance. The girl who is going to sing a small part in *Carmen* on a given date in April a year from now is assigned to the part already; there are many shake-ups and breakdowns in the course of a season, but on paper, at least, it is plotted to the inch. Nothing has ever been devised to take care of such contingencies as sudden illnesses except having two or three singers for each part, and even then there may be last-minute difficulties of the most hair-raising nature. A New York winter is sometimes hard on delicate throats, and nobody—not even a conductor—is free from physical hazards.

Hammerstein's immense daring at the outset, in forming a company that had virtually no available substitutes for leading parts, was rewarded by exceptional luck. He got through the first season with hardly any of the mishaps his improvisation had invited. True, Maurice Renaud had a period of hoarseness after his first arrival in New York, but otherwise it seems that all the Hammerstein singers were immune to the misfortunes of weather and bronchial disturbance. During the very same period, numerous substitutions and changes were forced on the Metropolitan by the illnesses of singers—including both Caruso and Sembrich, healthy performers if ever there were such. It seems to have been Hammerstein's luck at its high tide—which, like his luck at its low tide, was phenomenal.

For, with all his strenuous work, his employment of skilled agents in Europe, his own tour there, and his twenty-hour-a-day schedule, he ended his preparation with a company dangerously close to minimum level. He had exactly one dramatic soprano, Mme Russ, for all the heavy parts in Italian opera; he had, until the advent of Melba later on, just one coloratura, Mlle Regina Pinkert; and throughout the season he had only one leading dramatic contralto, Mme de Cisneros. His lyric tenor was Bonci, with no replacement. His Italian dramatic tenor was Amadeo Bassi, with no replacement. His French tenor was Dalmorès, with no replacement. He was a little better off in baritones (Renaud for a short time, Ancona for the season, Sammarco later, Seveilhac throughout), but his only basso for leading parts was Vittorio Arimondi in both Italian and French.

Even adding the mezzo-soprano Bressler-Gianoli for a long series of performances as *Carmen*, the limitations of such a company are manifest. It would tax anybody's ingenuity even to contrive a repertoire to fit this array of artists, and quite obviously Hammerstein would be obliged sometimes to ask them to sing in successive performances (as he did) or even twice in one day (as he did). The loyalty of the company to the impresario was shown by the fact that these heavy demands were all met, sometimes to the vocal discomfort of the singer.

We may be sure that Hammerstein knew what risks he was running, and took them deliberately because of his limited treasury. He had been piling up money for the Manhattan Opera House and its company as fast as he could, but the theater itself was costing a fortune and every principal singer was to receive a substantial fee. Mme Melba's contract demanded that she be paid before the curtain rose on any of her performances—paid in cash. This was not so unusual as it might be today. Sarah Bernhardt operated on the same principle for years, as did others who could enforce it.

Hammerstein's desire for well-rehearsed performances with fresh direction, costumes, and sets, his employment of the perfectionist Campanini, his anxiety to see that the theater itself was adequate and appropriately decorated, were all heavy drains upon the available resources. He had not the slightest chance of getting through his season at all unless he could bring in enough money at the box office to pay for the running expenses after the start was made. Even with all the earnings from the Victoria Theatre his finances were precarious throughout, and he knew in advance that they would be.

He was trusting to luck, of course, and to himself—to his energizing faculty, his own form of creation. It is small wonder that many in New York called him a "madman" during 1905–1906, and that his success in completing his first season—merely in completing it, regardless of profit—was regarded as one of the wonders of the time.

While Oscar went to Europe and concentrated on the formation of his company, the theater was steadily going up under Arthur's direction. As it neared completion there were long articles about it in the press, describing the "modern French" style (it was Louis XIV) and its red, buff, and gold decorations. Arthur was at his wits' end to get the house finished in time, particularly as his father had actually announced the opening night to coincide with that of the Metropolitan on November 26, 1906. This date could not be kept, and the opening night of the Manhattan was then announced for Monday, December 3, 1906, one week later. Even so, as we have seen, the theater was not pronounced finished until about one hour before curtain time, and not all the paint was yet dry.

This means that the rehearsals took place while the workmen were still busy in the house. Campanini rehearsed the orchestra diligently at times when it would have been difficult for anybody else to hear them, such was the pounding of hammers; he started his rehearsals at a time when the stage could not be used at all. When the stage in whole or in part could be used, full rehearsals with orchestra, chorus, and principals were held while the workmen and decorators were still operating. The pandemonium must have been extreme. All nerves were on edge, all tempers frayed. At this period—and, it is said, on the very day of the opening—while Oscar Hammerstein was in an aisle watching the rehearsal, a reporter from one of the New York papers came to him and asked him to hear a certain American baritone.

"He's going to be the greatest of all American baritones some day," the reporter said.

"I can wait," said Hammerstein.

5. In the Enemy Camp

The Metropolitan Opera approached the season of 1906–1907 under certain handicaps. Conried was ill. Caruso had been arrested in the monkey house of the Central Park Zoo, one week before the opening of the season, on the charge of annoying a lady. On the other hand, the opening-night opera, *Roméo et Juliette*, offered the debut in the United States of Miss Geraldine Farrar, an American girl of twenty-four who had already won great popularity in Berlin as well as the admiration of the German Crown Prince.

At the next performance Caruso made his first appearance of the season in *La Bohème*, with Mme Sembrich and Scotti. There is much evidence that he was extremely nervous and afraid of his audience until, at the end of Rodolfo's narrative, there was tumultuous applause. From then on the episode of the monkey house at the Zoo was forgotten, so far as the opera and its public were concerned.

Farrar's debut was a success, on the whole; Caruso was an idol, as always; and Sembrich had "never sung better." Vigna, the Italian conductor, was chided a bit, but nowhere near so sharply as he was to be later after New York had heard Campanini. There were interesting new productions announced—the first *Madama Butterfly* and the first *Salome*. There was a visit from Puccini in prospect; there was a German repertoire with casts that Hammerstein could not touch.

And yet he had one advantage over the established company. New York was more than a little tired of the Metropolitan. This was not true of New York society, which owned the boxes (the "Diamond Horseshoe") and went to the opera without regard to what was presented or how. It was, however, true of most of the critics, whose tone in reviewing Metropolitan productions was often captious in the extreme. It was true of a large public besides, as Hammerstein proved.

There was, therefore, some basis for his confidence. He may have overestimated his own strength, but it was in his nature to do so, and luck was on his side. There were wonders quite beyond Hammerstein's control, such as the vocal supremacy of Nellie Melba at the age of forty-six. It is certain that Hammerstein engaged Melba for her fame; how was he to know that she would sing for him better than she had ever sung before? These and other elements of good fortune were to attend him. Among such elements the Metropolitan's general debility in organization, its lack of true ensemble, its inferior conductors, and its old-fashioned style in production were to be counted. Moreover, nobody could have foreseen that one of Conried's greatest cards in the game, his production of Richard Strauss's *Salome*, would have to be withdrawn because of moral objections after a single performance.

Pitching the established Metropolitan against the new and untried Manhattan, we may see that for the latter (in spite of great excellences that will be noted later) it was essentially a gamble that came off, a leap in the dark which landed well. In 1906 and early 1907 Conried was in the habit of referring to "the so-called opera house in Thirty-fourth Street." By the season's end he was engaged in a scramble to get singers away from Hammerstein and to keep his own. The alteration in the Metropolitan's own tone tells the story.

6. Eve of Battle

The press campaign for some months before the opening of the Manhattan was incessant, and grew to a high pitch before the first curtain went up. Hammerstein himself gave interviews and statements in a steady flow, also contributing articles to the press from time to time. In one of these, two days before his opening, he said substantially what he said on the first night: "To the public of New York, to those who love the arts and to those who love effort and achievement of any sort, I dedicate the Manhattan Opera House" (*Evening Telegram*, December 1, 1906).

The special talents of William J. Guard were also at work. There were a great many stories about singers, and some of them bear the mark of the skilled press agent. "Hammerstein's Lost Tenor" was one headline: it referred to Amadeo Bassi, "last heard of in Buenos Aires." The arrival of Bonci and a score of other singers produced more of the same. They got to New York on November 18, and there were stories of various kinds: one that Mme Giacomini, a minor mezzo-soprano, was suing her landlord at an Italian boardinghouse for her opera costumes. (The dire suggestion of conspiracy to hurt Hammerstein?)

One of the oddest of these inventions was to the effect that Caruso had challenged Bonci to a duel. No amount of denial could keep this from the front pages for at least a day. Another story claimed that Eleanora de Cisneros narrowly escaped injury to herself and her wardrobe in a collision of ships en route to America.

From time to time in the final week—and actually on the final day—Hammerstein was interviewed in the midst of carpenters and painters while rehearsals were progressing. There were recurrent stories about *La Bohème*, which Hammerstein steadily asserted he was going to produce in spite of any opposition, and which he eventually did produce. The tone of all this press agitation was favorable in the sense that it gave full weight to Hammerstein's difficulties while feeding a public curiosity which had grown steadily through the months.

Then, at last, the house and its company were ready—ready in a sense; ready enough to keep the date Hammerstein had fixed for himself and for the public. In the language of a headline in the New York *American* (December 3, 1906): "Last Workmen to Leave New Manhattan as Arrival of Audience Begins." This was, as it happens, simply true.

XV

The Opening Night

THE ACTUAL OPENING of Hammerstein's opera house aroused the interest of the whole United States. The opera was *I Puritani*, almost forgotten in America; but if it had been *Puss-in-Boots*, it would have made no difference to the public. The throngs that made their way to Eighth Avenue and Thirty-fourth Street—an outlandish region to many of them —were eager, above all, to see the theater, to see Oscar, and to see the rest of the audience. The fame of Bonci had indeed preceeded him, and there were no doubt many who came for him, but by and large it was an audience of curosity.

1. Not Even Standing Room

Every seat in the huge auditorium (there were 3,100) was sold, and the standing room behind the last rows was packed to suffocation. There were also crowds outside who could not get in. Although this huge audience had started to gather in good time, neither the traffic police nor Hammerstein's house staff was fully prepared to deal with such a crush. It proved impossible to get the "automobiles and wagonettes" through Thirty-fourth Street in any reasonable order and time.

The long, slow procession stretched all the way from Fifth Avenue, moving an inch at a time. There was but one entrance for the public to the Manhattan Opera House (there are three at the Metropolitan), and this fact added to the confusion. It was, on the whole, a good-humored crowd, and no actual quarrels or casualties were reported, but the whole press the next day gave an account of the mob scene and advised Hammerstein to take steps in future to deal with it. No such scene, as a matter of fact, ever occurred again, although the house was often filled to capacity; not only did Hammerstein learn how to deal with it, but the public that turned out simply to stare, not to enter the theater at all, was never again like this.

Hammerstein, at the peak of his form, watched the crowds and the crowds watched him. He was in all parts of the house; he was with the conductor, the stage director, the singers, the box office; he was resplendent in silk hat and cigar, lit or unlit, as millions of Americans were now accustomed to view him.

It became necessary, as he saw quite early in the evening, to hold the curtain. There was unparalleled confusion in the seating of the ticket-holders even after they had obtained entrance to the theater. The ushers were not sufficiently familiar with the house, and the general hysteria of the opening night did nothing to help them. The muddles were innumerable and the house had nowhere near settled down or even found itself at eight o'clock, although the crowd had already formed at half past seven. One of the difficulties was the dense formation of standing-room ticket-holders all around the periphery of the bowl, through whom it was almost impossible to penetrate.

Hammerstein therefore held the curtain for half an hour. By that time some semblance of order had come into the house, although the audience was still struggling in during the first act and there were still crowds outside, unable to obtain admission. The first outburst of enthusiasm came when Cleofonte Campanini came to the conductor's podium and raised his baton. New York did not know him, but enough curiosity about him had been aroused already to ensure a reception.

Receptions, "ovations," and the like were the order of the evening, as so often on first nights. There was one of a slightly erroneous nature when Mario Ancona, the baritone, made his entrance. This big, fat baritone, the owner of a superb natural voice, bore no resemblance to the tiny, elegant tenor Bonci. And yet somewhere in the gallery cries of "Viva Bonci!" arose and had to be hushed by the more knowing members of the audience.

The fact was that in that huge audience hardly anybody had heard *I Puritani* before, and the plot, if it can be called a plot, was unknown. It had been produced in New York decades earlier; Patti had sung it there in her day, and so had Sembrich, who had made her world debut as Elvira in Athens; but by now it was new again. The difficulty in producing the opera did not reside in the music for the coloratura soprano, but in the tenor's part, which, having been written for Rubini, had a range beyond the capacity of all but the rarest voices. This was, of course, why Hammerstein chose it, or acquiesced in it, as a debut for Bonci: he was probably the only tenor of the century who could have sung it at all without transposing a great deal of the music.

2. The Duel of Tenors

I Puritani was an opera that Caruso had dropped from his repertoire early in his career; he did not have the required kind of voice. Bonci did. Thus, it showed up not only Bonci's advantages, but Caruso's disadvantages, if such they were.

The comparison of Bonci to Caruso would have been, in any case, a primary component of Hammerstein's season: it filled many, many columns of newsprint during the next few months. From this distance in time it seems a little foolish to have concocted a rivalry between voices that were fundamentally so different. Bonci had a perfectly produced high tenor voice of the utmost beauty and used it with the utmost elegance of style. His breathing was phenomenal and his taste beyond criticism. As the New York *Times* remarked some months later, "There never was an Italian singer with a finer style than Bonci."

Caruso's voice was, even then, much more robust, and he committed errors of taste and judgment in practically every performance. He had, however, a luscious tone that penetrated to every part of the house, his middle and lower voice surpassed that of almost any other tenor, and—when he did not force them—his high notes, up to C, were as clear as a golden trumpet. His appeal to the widest public had already been confirmed, and it remained sure to the very end. It is possible that the constant comparison of his errors with Bonci's perfection may have irritated him, but he had all possible revenges: the public never lost its predilection for him, his phonograph records were extraordinary and have survived, his fortune was great, and he will be remembered. Bonci, except by specialists, is already forgotten.

At the Manhattan's first night the purely operatic interest of the audience, aside from its curiosity about the theater itself and Oscar Hammerstein, was nevertheless centered upon Bonci and the inescapable comparison. He was received with great applause at his entrance. Many in the audience may have heard him in Europe, but the reception was due most of all to the general excitement of a first night, an "opera war," and a "duel of tenors." As the evening went on and he had greater opportunities to display his extraordinary vocalism, the applause rose to great heights. Reading between the lines, one may be permitted to guess that he was not quite so perfect in this performance as in some later in the season, but nothing could disturb the violin-like purity of his delivery, especially in the upper part of the voice. The reviews on the following day paid full tribute to all his qualities, although most of them pointed out that the sensuous (or "luscious" or "resplendent") beauty of Caruso's tone was not his.

On the same night Caruso and Sembrich were singing *Marta* at the Metropolitan, a revival, and in spite of the mob scene at the Manhattan the older house was also full. New York's appetite for opera had risen—perhaps with its population, perhaps with the influx of European immigrants in recent years—to the point where it seemed possible for two opera companies to exist.

The rest of the cast of *I Puritani* was not so warmly reviewed as Bonci. The Elvira was Mlle Regina Pinkert, now making her first appearance in the United States. She was only twenty-four, had made her debut at La Scala in Milan at seventeen, and was singing in the opera company at Kiev, in the Ukraine, when Hammerstein's agents found and engaged her. She apparently had a good command of flowery, light music, although she was not a sensational coloratura by any means. The men besides Bonci were Mario Ancona, whose opulent baritone had been heard at the Metropolitan ten years before, and Vittorio Arimondi, a commanding basso.

The reviewers were struck, from the very first, by Campanini's conducting. He had been working under difficulties, as we have seen, and yet he animated and controlled the entire performance in a way New York had not known in works of this kind. There were rough spots—which under such conditions could not have been avoided—but the impression made by Campanini was deep from the very beginning. It grew steadily deeper all through this and succeeding seasons until it forced the Metropolitan to bring Toscanini to America as the only possible counterattack.

Another element of Hammerstein's strength which has already been mentioned was his youthful and good-looking chorus, every member of which had been picked and trained to sing accurately and as if they belonged to the drama. The New York *World* spoke of their "volume, resonanace, quality, precision of tone, accuracy of intonation and boldness of attack." Other accounts complimented their appearance. In this and succeeding performances the chorus seems to have been a constant surprise to the critics. No doubt the Metropolitan's chorus, at fifteen dollars a week and no pay for pre-season rehearsals, had deteriorated so badly that a fresh collection of young people with good voices was startling to hear and to behold.

3. Oscar Takes His Bows

And Hammerstein—! After the second act, Bonci, now fully recovered from his severe first-act stage fright, drew Oscar onto the stage to take bows with the singers. As the newspapers later remarked, Hammerstein seemed more nervous even than Bonci. He tried to depart by a door that had not been made to open—the kind of contretemps which delights an audience.

Again at the final curtain he was brought out for bow after bow. At last, in response to the audience's clamor, he stepped forward to make his little speech. This time, apparently, he was not nervous in the least. If he had not planned to make this speech, at this moment when he looked out at his admiring first-night audience he seems to have known precisely what he wished to tell them. He proposed to make it perfectly clear that he, and he alone, had created this institution.

"Ladies and gentlemen," he began, when the audience had quieted to hear him, "I am very much gratified. There is a sensation of pride and of fear."

There was a burst of appreciative laughter, the first of several. He went on, in part:

"I can only say that this is an effort toward the furtherance of industry and music. I am compelled to add that I am the only one who has created this institution. I have had no assistance, financially or morally. The burden has all been upon me and the responsibility is all mine. I have no board of directors, nobody to tell me what I should and should not do. (*Laughter*)

"I have concluded in my years of decline—for you can see that I am already out of my boyhood days—that if I can aid with that which I have earned honestly—can aid the cause of music—it would be something I could look back upon with what you call pride. I have never expected to make a dollar out of this enterprise.

"Many people endow libraries (*Voice from the gallery: 'One on Carnegie!'*) and hospitals: but I have yet to see one who has endowed opera. When the curtain falls tonight it is the beginning of a series of trials—nothing else.

"The ensemble which surrounds this institution is so large and is composed of so many celebrities of music that every opera for the next three or four weeks is experimental, and depends for success or failure on this audience and this city (*Applause and cheers*)."

In Proscenium Box 13, listening to this, were Mr. and Mrs. Otto Kahn of the Metropolitan's board of directors. With their party was Mr. Eliot Gregory, also a director of the Metropolitan. Other members of the Metropolitan forces were scattered through the audience, including a number of singers. How they reacted to Hammerstein's pointed thrusts is not known, but Hammerstein's attitude toward society patrons of opera was abundantly clear even without the implications of his little curtain speech. It was apparent in the very design of his theater.

Hammerstein must have decided, even before he built his opera house, even while he was worrying over the blueprints for the theater, that he would ignore the support or non-support of high society. He had boxes—forty of them—but they were arranged, like the rest of the theater, for their relationship to the stage and not to one another. The New York *Times* of the day after says, in a special "social" story apart from the news story and the review of the opera:

"While the world of fashion went to the Metropolitan and applauded Sembrich and the famous quartet in *Marta*, the musical people found their way to the Manhattan Opera House to hear Bonci, the famous tenor, and the other new singers. It is evident that Mr. Hammerstein is not catering for the Metropolitan element.

"The auditorium is designed for seeing and hearing, but not for the display of jewels and gowns. Still, the first-night audience at the Manhattan was quite representative, and there were many notable and prominent people present, although at the Metropolitan not one of the parterre boxes was empty, and the audience there was as brilliant as on the opening night a week ago.

"So far there was no defection from the time-honored list of the Metropolitan subscribers."

There then follows a very long list of "exceptions"—persons belonging to New York society who had undertaken the hazardous journey to Eighth Avenue and Thirty-fourth Street to hear opera. The society reporter further states: "On matters sartorial the first night audience followed a go-as-you-please style of dressing. Not only were the standees clad, as are many of the same class of genuine music-lovers at the Metropolitan, in white cotton blouses and plaid walking-skirts topped by serviceable but non-ornamental headgear, but they wore these in many of the orchestra as well as gallery seats, removing, of course, the view-obstructing chapeaux, while next to them sat women in the most gorgeous of highly colored or white dinner and evening dresses, wearing lofty aigrettes and quantities of pearls, diamonds and other precious gems. The display of jewels was indeed a very handsome one."

This candid chronicler remarks that the house was so built that the occupants of the first tier of boxes, the equivalent of the Metropolitan's "Diamond Horseshoe," could not be seen except from the other boxes and the front of the orchestra. The rest of the house had a "splendid view of the stage" but not of the inmates of these boxes. "It seemed the aim of the management last evening to make as little of the social feature of the opening as possible." One of the signs of this aim was that "the intermissions were short."

All this may seem trivial detail, but nobody acquainted with the problems of opera in the United States could deny that the support of fashionable society is of great financial importance. Oscar Hammerstein had at this time no acquaintance with, and no use for, persons in high society. He undoubtedly thought that their influence had laid a dead hand on the Metropolitan, turning it into something more like a horse show or a garden party than an institution for the performance of operatic music. It is not conceivable that he could have built his house in this precise way, with a noticeable disregard for the boxholders' desire to display their jewels, if he had not considered the entire situation and taken his decision. Later on, as we shall see, he was not at all receptive to advances from persons of wealth and position, and in at least one case—that of Mr. and Mrs. Clarence Mackay—he indulged in a quarrel for which we have difficulty finding a reason. Probably he associated all of New York society with the Metropolitan; and as he had quite consciously chosen to give battle to the Metropolitan in every possible domain, his disregard for society was a part of the whole, or an inevitable concomitant.

His greatness and his courage were shown in this as much as in the larger purpose. If he intended to revivify opera in New York, to shake it loose from dead tradition and routine, as he clearly did intend, then to emancipate it from the bondage of high society was a definite part of the enterprise.

He was to gain and suffer from this. There were times in the next few weeks when he had to face half-empty orchestra seats and boxes. The galleries were filled from the beginning, but no great opera house can continue—unless it is heavily subsidized—on the patronage of those who pay least for their tickets. Yet his courage in trying brought him considerable reward in the esteem of the public and the critics—so much so that we find the press actually scolding the public on some occasions for ingratitude in not supporting Hammerstein more fully.

And with this growth of esteem for his endeavor, as was inevitable, his opera house did actually become fashionable. Not, of course, with the Morgan-Vanderbilt-Astor clans who, among them, owned most of the Metropolitan boxes as well as the house itself and had a great vested interest in loyalty to the old establishment; but with the numerous younger members of New York society who began to realize his aim and to appreciate it.

When Melba arrived, this process became obvious: at her performances society was out in force. Later on, with Mary Garden, a new element of fashionable support was added—that of the seekers after novelty, the intellectual snobs, those who wished to know and discuss the latest in all things. Certain of her admirers among the critics (Huneker, Van Vechten, and others) created for Garden a kind of cult which drew heavily from the ranks of New York society. Thus Hammerstein, without courting it and even, as we have seen, by ignoring it, did obtain a great deal of support after a while from the ranks of the rich and grand, and particularly from their youth. Perhaps he always knew that this, too, would come.

At all events, when he had finished his remarks before the curtain on the opening night, there could be no doubt in anyone's mind that Hammerstein meant to maintain his opera house without a Diamond Horseshoe, or go down trying.

4. After the Night of Nights

Having said what he had to say, Oscar left the stage. For a long time the audience continued to call for him, but he did not come out again.

For Hammerstein this was a very solemn moment, nothing less than the coronation of a lifetime. Probably it should not surprise us that after audience and performers were gone, the lights out, and the theater locked up for the night, he rode alone in a streetcar to Forty-second Street, ate an oyster stew at Childs, and went to his two rooms on the Victoria's balcony and to bed. That he celebrated his triumph thus, we are told by those who should know —those who can remember or have heard the story from those who could remember the great night.

It is quite consonant with all the rest of his character that he should have stuck to his streetcar, his Childs restaurant, and his lonely chambers on this night of nights. His reflections, we may suppose, were of grim but undeniable satisfaction. He had "done it"—one of the headlines of the next day (New York *Journal*) quotes him as crying out: "I did it!" when the curtain fell on *I Puritani*. He had done it against every imaginable form of opposition, in which he counted the devious and unrelenting hostility of Heinrich Conried; he had done it against the wishes of his own sons, who were nevertheless aiding him to the limit; he had done it, most of all, by himself.

He must also have been a prey to considerable anxiety for the future, for his ability to get through the program he had designed. Nights such as this opening, when $12,000 came into the coffers, would be rare. Much was to be done if a whole season of opera was to come into being, and he had some weeks—a month, in fact —before he could count on the saving presence of Melba, if Melba could save. He had already been forced to postpone the performance of *Don Giovanni*, scheduled as his second opera (on Wednesday), because it required more preparation than he had been able to give it. He knew as well as anybody else that he was walking on eggshells as far as his company was concerned: he did not have enough principal singers to carry on unless everything worked his way.

These anxieties he may have felt, must have felt, and yet he never showed them when he was face to face with the press or the public. All was bland confidence, smiling enjoyment. Perhaps he wanted to be alone so that he could keep his worries to himself and show the world a face only of triumph. Melba relates in her memoirs that she had really decided to sing for him when she saw him dining alone at the Armenonville restaurant in Paris: she was "sorry for him." Perhaps to Mme Melba dining alone in a public restaurant was pathos itself, but to Hammerstein it was practically the rule of his life.

At all events, when he woke up the next day (or, if we may guess at the truth, before he went to bed that night) he must have known by the morning newspapers how eminently he had succeeded. All the headlines proclaimed it. "New Opera House Opens, Scores Decided Success," said the New York *World*. "Manhattan Opera House Big Success," declared the *Evening Telegram*. "Triumph for Hammerstein Grand Opera," shouted the *Journal*. "New Opera House Opened with Star Spangled Banner: Hammerstein Seen in Blaze of Glory," crowed the New York *American*. The New York *Times* headline was more modest—"Oscar Hammerstein's First Night of Opera"—but the review that accompanied the news story was highly laudatory.

For a man of almost sixty who had aimed at this result through innumerable vicissitudes for many years, the contemplation of the newspapers on December 4 must have been a wondrous pleasure.

The Opening Night

To have produced an opera unnoticed would not at all have given the same result. Ludwig of Bavaria was capable of producing opera for the sake of the opera, whether anybody else cared or not, and whether anybody else listened; Hammerstein, true to his showman's calling, wanted all the fanfare he could get. He needed it in order to sell tickets in future, but he also wanted it for itself; it gave him, personally, a sense of achievement and a reconciliation with fate. The many reporters who visited him on December 4 found a smiling, urbane, and happy Hammerstein, sure of himself, his company, and his future. He was tired, yes, he admitted that; he had a toothache, yes; but (as one paper narrates) when he was addressed as "Mr. Impresario" his toothache disappeared.

He certainly knew, having read the newspapers with the utmost thoroughness, that Mlle Pinkert, his one and only coloratura, had not been a success. Until Melba arrived he would have to depend on her for the soprano parts in all the operas in which Bonci sang. Pinkert's reviews were not downright bad, but they were not by any means good enough for the occasion. They also contained a note of condescension which is, in all criticism, the most galling element. The young Polish soprano knew no English (her communications were in Italian), but she must have known the truth through the many obliging friends who work in an opera house. What Oscar had to do to restore her to good spirits we do not know. We do know, from many instances, that he was extraordinarily good at smoothing down ruffled feathers and had some kind of special genius for dealing with singers.

In this very week—his first—a crisis of magnitude arose over the hoarseness of Maurice Renaud. Renaud did not want to make his American debut when he was not in good voice. He had been one of the most difficult of all singers for Hammerstein to obtain, and his contract, covering every contingency possible or impossible, covered forty-eight legal pages. Hammerstein's immediate task, on the very day after the triumphal opening, was to persuade Renaud to make his American debut on the next night (Wednesday) in *Rigoletto* even if a rest became necessary afterward. In this, too, he succeeded.

And on that very day—the papers having been signed and filed the day before—New York learned that Hammerstein had no intention of giving up *La Bohème*. In the United States Circuit Court, where G. Ricordi of Milan had brought suit to restrain him from producing *La Bohème*, on the ground that Conried owned the exclusive rights to it by contract, Hammerstein declared that his own oral contract of the preceding March was valid and could be proved. He thus served notice that he fully intended to proceed with his plans—and, perhaps, thumbed his nose once more at Conried.

XVI

Some Anxious Weeks— and Melba

HAMMERSTEIN'S WORDS about "the beginning of a series of trials" were all too literally true. For about three weeks he had them in sufficient number to keep even his indefatigable spirit fully occupied.

For his second performance his chief worry was Renaud and his obstinate throat condition. Renaud was, next to Bonci, the principal European celebrity to be introduced to New York in the early part of the season. Fees in those days were always exaggerated in the press, and Renaud's was usually given as $1,600. Judging by the final Hammerstein-Kahn contract, in which his fee is given as $1,000, I should think that his fee in 1906–1907 was about $750 for each performance, possibly $800.

1. A Crucial Sore Throat

Renaud's contract had been drawn up with a multitude of precautions to protect the singer. There were stipulations of all sorts, such as that his valet was to have an outside cabin on the steamer coming and going, and that a carriage was to be provided for him for all rehearsals. Hammerstein himself revealed these facts in an interview printed the following week. He had treated Renaud with every consideration, and the result was that when the baritone felt his voice to be in improper condition for his first performance, he asked Hammerstein to deduct his fee. Hammerstein did not do so.

We do not know how Hammerstein "coaxed" (his own word) this famous singer to sing before he thought himself quite ready. We only know that he did so. Renaud made his American debut as Rigoletto on Wednesday, December 5, 1906, with a resounding success. Hammerstein did two special things for him. First, he caused an announcement to be made from the stage, between the first and second acts, to the effect that M. Renaud was suffering from hoarseness and asked that this fact be considered. Second, Renaud was allowed to rest indefinitely after this performance until he felt himself perfectly well and confident.

We all know the nervousness of singers, even the greatest of them, about their throats. Caruso's letters to his wife are full of anxiety over his throat. In this case, however, Renaud could have omitted the announcement of his illness and nobody would have been the wiser. Every critic in New York reviewed him glowingly, and most of them said that they never would have known he was hoarse if he had not announced it. He was a "singing actor," as the later phrase had it, rather than a simple exponent of vocalism: his artistry was greater than his natural voice. He seems to have been an artist of such consummate skill, power, and conviction that he could not be resisted.

Nevertheless, the loss of Renaud from subsequent casts for the next twelve days was uncomfortable for Hammerstein. He was obliged to substitute Mario Ancona, whom (as we shall see later) he never really liked, and who was in any case an old story to New York, having been for years at the Metropolitan. Ancona had a rich voice, but as an artist he was, by all accounts, never in Renaud's class. And besides all that, Hammerstein had banked heavily on Renaud to give luster to his casts, and in those early weeks they needed it. Renaud was not able to appear again until December 17.

This first performance of *Rigoletto* afforded, aside from Renaud's debut, a better opportunity to judge Bonci's powers. The diminutive tenor did not sing many of the same roles as Caruso;

the Duke in *Rigoletto* was one. On this occasion, with no stage fright and the assurance that he had been well received—buoyed up, as well, by Renaud's presence, as all first-rate artists are by each other—he greatly deepened the impression he had made on the first night. Some critics had found his exquisite singing in *I Puritani* "lacking in warmth": they did not find it so in *Rigoletto*. When he sang *"La donna è mobile,"* it was impossible to restrain the audience, and Campanini, who as a rule was inflexibly opposed to encores, had to give in and repeat the air.

Mlle Pinkert's reviews were mixed and none of them exceptionally good. When Hammerstein looked back over this first season of his, it must have afforded him some ironic amusement to reflect that the Polish soprano, only twenty-four years old, gave some critics the impression of having lost "the bloom of youth" from her voice—a thing that was never said of Nellie Melba, almost twice her age.

2. In the Audience, Certain Stars

There were several interesting details of a non-musical character about the night of Hammerstein's second opera. For one thing, Geraldine Farrar was present in a box with Mr. and Mrs. Walter Damrosch. For another, Mme Sembrich and her husband, Professor Stengel, occupied a stage box opposite them. We have no evidence that Conried disliked having his singers (and board directors!) present at the opposing house, but he cannot have been too greatly pleased.

Another operatic event took place on the same night. Mlle Lina Cavalieri, once of the Folies-Bergère, made her debut at the Metropolitan in the title role of *Fedora*, with Caruso and Scotti. The new opera was not well received and the new soprano was praised more for her looks than for her singing, but she was to play quite a part in Hammerstein's activities later on. Cavalieri was then and remained for many years a woman of the most exceptional loveliness, yet her operatic career seems to have been a deviation rather than a fulfillment: she began in the Folies-Bergère and finished her public career as the director of a beauty shop in Paris. The havoc that she was to create among younger members of the ruling families at the Metropolitan, the Astors and the Vanderbilts, was yet to come; it was a part of the long and complicated "opera war."

As his third performance Hammerstein had chosen *Faust*, for the debut of Charles Dalmorès.

This celebrated French tenor was at the time thirty-four years old, tall and handsome, the possessor of a powerful voice of fine quality, and qualified both as musician and actor. He had been trained in the conservatories of Nancy, Lyon, and Paris, but originally he was a player of the violoncello and the French horn. Indeed, he was at first refused for the Paris Conservatoire on the ground that he was "too good a musician to waste his time in becoming a mediocre singer." After his debut in 1899 in Rouen he sang at La Monnaie in Brussels and had been for the two preceding seasons at Covent Garden in London. His renown was yet to come: in fact, it was in his long series of performances with Mary Garden that he became really famous. At this time he was not known in New York, even by reputation, except to a few. He had been one of the first singers Hammerstein had engaged on his trip to Europe some months before—thus indicating, along with Renaud, the direction in which Hammerstein's mind was turning.

The soprano for this performance was Pauline Donalda, a Canadian girl of twenty-three who had also been singing with success at Covent Garden. She had a particularly appealing presence, it seems, and a fresh young voice; she was better received than any other of Hammerstein's sopranos until the arrival of Melba.

The *Faust* performance was not well attended. It was what the papers called a "light house," particularly in the orchestra and boxes, although from there on to the ceiling the tickets were all sold. Dalmorès and Donalda were equally unknown; Renaud had been obliged to cancel his appearance; Arimondi as Méphistophélès was not a drawing-card. Hammerstein must have reflected on that night that his "series of trials" was on its way.

And yet the reviews of the performance as a whole were good, and the *Times* remarked that those who were present had a very good time indeed. Again the chorus came in for praise: "What a chorus!" the *Times* critic, Richard Aldrich, exclaimed, and devoted an entire paragraph to the subject. In every performance through this early period the chorus, the orchestra, and Campanini drew the admiration of the critics, whatever they said of the principals. The chorus, orchestra, and conductor at the Metropolitan were seldom mentioned.

Campanini was a tired man at the end of that week. He conducted not only the first three evening performances, all-important for the initial effect of the new venture, but also the repetition of *I Puritani* at Saturday's matinee (December 8). To open his Saturday-night series at popular prices Hammerstein had nothing ready except a repetition of *Faust*, with Jean Altschewsky instead of Dalmorès. Arimondi had to sing Méphistophélès, Donalda Marguerite, and Seveilhac Valentin, on two successive nights. The conductor at the "pop" performance was Leandro Campanari, one of Campanini's two assistants. To sing difficult operatic parts on two nights running is a strain on any voice, but Hammerstein was forced to demand it; he had no alternative.

On that Friday night of the first week, when he was offering *Faust* to a "light house," an almost equally "light house" gathered at the Metropolitan for the *première* of *La Damnation de Faust*, with Farrar, Rousselière, and Plançon.

Hammerstein ended his first week in expansive and even exultant mood. Reading the quotations from his various interviews, one gets the impression that he was probably startled to find that he had gone through the week without disaster. He laughed at the idea that an occasional poor house might discourage him. You cannot expect a mob every night, was the gist of his argument: wait until you see my *Carmen* and my *Aïda!*

3. The Edge of Disaster

During his second week, still handicapped by the absence of Renaud, and with only the Renaud operas rehearsed and prepared, Hammerstein must have gone through a great deal more anxiety than he would allow to be seen. The operas of the week were *Rigoletto, Don Giovanni, Carmen, Don Giovanni* at the Saturday matinee, and for the popular-priced Saturday night another *Carmen*. This was running perilously near the edge of breakdown. He could not make Ancona sing in every performance, and the French baritone Seveilhac was not of the first quality; yet these were the only baritones he had to sing the Renaud parts, and he had no other operas ready. He has himself related how he amazed Mme Bressler-Gianoli, the Swiss mezzo-soprano, by asking her to sing on two successive nights; she had "never heard of such a thing." But in this poverty-stricken week she did.

He got through this one, too, thanks to Bonci and to that same Swiss mezzo. Bonci sang three times—Monday, Wednesday, and Saturday matinee—with uniform success. His Don Ottavio in *Don Giovanni*, always one of his very finest achievements, was praised to the skies. It was not so with his companions. Donalda (Zerlina) was always reviewed kindly, even sweetly—she must have been a very pretty girl—but not in the tone used of great singers. Mme Giannina Russ, who made her debut as Donna Anna on the Wednesday night, was adjudged rough and unsuited to Mozart's music. Ancona was acceptable in this, as in everything else, because of his voice, but he was in no sense a true substitute for Renaud. Charles Gilibert, the French buffo, did very well with Leporello, and Campanini was increasingly praised, but the entire press by this time had made up its mind that Hammerstein's casts were weak on the side of the women.

This statement was to be repeated constantly throughout December until it must have set Hammerstein's teeth on edge. Every day he must have prayed for Melba, but he could not have been sure of anything about her, contract or no contract, until she had actually sailed from Europe on December 22. Nothing could prevent her from having an illness, real or imaginary, and a doctor's certificate is accepted in all opera houses, even up to curtain time, as a legal basis for abrogation of contract.

There was one amazing stroke of luck—if it was luck—in this second week. The Swiss mezzo-soprano Bressler-Gianoli made a stunning success in *Carmen*, one of the greatest ever known in New York. Her conception of the role was totally different from Calvé's and yet it cohered as a really powerful and integrated character, a dramatic and musical creation. Her voice was rather dark and she sang all the music as written, with none of the transpositions or substituted notes common among sopranos who try that part. She made no effort to look different from the other cigarette girls—indeed, the *Times* remarked that of the entire factory she was the shabbiest—but she seems to have been some sort of tornado on the stage, a force of nature. She had actually sung Carmen some years before in New York, with an organization called the New Orleans French Opera, which quickly disbanded. This had been more or less forgotten; few thought of it when Hammerstein brought her back. The impact of her performance now, with Dalmorès as Don José and Campanini conducting at the peak of his natural ferocity, seems to have been something New York had never experienced before.

The success of this *Carmen* was a godsend to Hammerstein. He may have expected it (he said he did), but as an experienced showman he also knew that it is impossible to be certain of your public until it has spoken. Bressler-Gianoli's Carmen drew larger houses at every repetition until it became that joy of managers, a certain and inevitable sell-out every time it was announced. The usual Micaëla in this long run of *Carmen* was Donalda; at first the Toreador was Ancona, but Renaud after his recovery took it for some performances, Seveilhac for others.

Aside from the *Carmen*, nothing very providential happened to Hammerstein during the remaining two weeks of December. His *Aïda* was ready in the third week and was performed on Wednesday, December 19, and at the following Saturday matinee. It was not at all well received, except in the top galleries, and yet, oddly enough, it became a popular production and was repeated often, drawing larger houses each time. Some of this was due to the imposing contralto Eleanora de Cisneros, who made her debut as Amneris, but some credit must also have gone to the soprano Giannina Russ as Aïda, although she was not admired by the critics. The tenor Amadeo Bassi (the "lost tenor" of the press-agent stories) also made his debut in this production.

The other operas of the third and fourth weeks were chiefly repetitions, the only new ones offered being *Lucia di Lammermoor* and *Il Trovatore*, both of which Campanini left to his assistant Tanara. The chief justifications for *Il Trovatore* were apparently De Cisneros and Dalmorès (Mme Russ was still "rough"). *Lucia* had two performances with the unlucky Mlle Pinkert in the title role, but from the reviews one might have thought the opera had been written for Bonci.

Maurice Renaud, back in voice again, returned on December 17 in *Don Giovanni* with brilliant results. From then on until the end of his season he was the delight of the critics and a great favorite with the public.

4. And Finally Melba

Melba's arrival at the end of December gave the whole Manhattan company new life. It was surrounded by considerable excitement in the press and among her innumerable friends and admirers—an excitement that needed no stimulation from the press agent. Melba by this time was a dominant figure in opera everywhere, and the curiosity over her return to America was great. On her last visit, in 1904, she had been in the midst of a long illness; after only one performance at the Metropolitan (in *La Bohème*) she had been obliged to cancel all other engagements. Hammerstein must have thought: *Thank God she's here! Now I wonder what she'll do on the stage!*

She was, as a personality, one of the most arguable of all prima donnas. The Melba stories, both in her favor and against her, are almost without number. There can be little doubt that her enormous popularity throughout the world had to some extent gone to her head; she was human, after all, and such fortune comes to very few creatures in this life. If she liked a certain kind of toast, as she did, it was promptly named after her (and has since been commercialized everywhere); if she liked a certain combination of peach and ice cream, the same thing happened; there were flowers and perfumes and all sorts of objects which bore her name or were associated with her. Her particular kind of fame, so pervasive and unlocalized, transcended opera and even the theater itself, becoming a part of the general consciousness. She was, as they say, a household word, and more literally than could be said of almost anybody else in her time.

Whether she was really as imperious, demanding, grandiose, and unreasonable as some of the stories would indicate can hardly be ascertained now. There are stories to prove that she was, certainly, but there are just as many to prove that she was not. She was extremely kind when her heart was moved, and the available evidence is that Hammerstein had in some way moved her heart. She had no other reason for revisiting New York: she could have made just as much or more money in any of the great opera houses of Europe, and her American fame was already well established. We are led to the conclusion that she liked and admired what he was doing (his "pluck," as she called it) and actually wanted to help him. She would not do so, of course, without a whacking big fee, for she was an excellent businesswoman; but, after all, fees had presented no problem to Melba for some years past.

She certainly had some prima-donna habits, such as taking bows alone. There is a story to the effect that the first time John McCormack sang with her at Covent Garden and started out to take a bow, she said to him: "In this house nobody takes bows with Melba." As she practically owned Covent Garden, this is probably true. We also know that conductors were intimidated by her, but this, after all, was at least in part their fault. It is related that in this first season at the Manhattan Campanini stopped her in the middle of a rehearsal to correct a tempo and do the passage over again. She stared at him in unaffected amazement. It probably had not happened to her in years. But without protest she went back and did it over in his way.

With all her business acumen, she was certainly both kind and generous. Numbers of young singers were aided by her, and she was a great giver of presents. In this Manhattan season she sold her autographs, which were in great demand, and sent all the proceeds to a home for blind children on Long Island. In Australia, where she was a sort of uncrowned queen—audiences in theaters rose when she entered as a member of the public—her beneficence is well remembered.

Still, she was a prima donna, the greatest of her time, and the Manhattan company was put on its toes by her mere presence. It is good for such a company to be put on its toes: the evidence is that all performances, not only the ones in which she appeared, improved after her arrival.

5. Prima Donna to the Rescue

Melba sang for the first time on Wednesday, January 2, in *La Traviata*, with Bassi and Ancona, Campanini conducting. The house was packed to the walls and many who tried could not get in at all. Hammerstein was saved indeed: for not only did she shed the glamour of her presence on the huge crowd, but she sang as she had not sung in years, if ever.

It was, by all authoritative accounts, a voice unlike any other except, perhaps, that of Adelina Patti some decades earlier. It was pure and "silvery" (that word is constantly used) with a perfectly equalized range from the B-flat below middle C to the F above high C. The breath control, phrasing, and modulations were all beyond criticism. The only debate at the time (and one sees it even in the sedate pages of *Grove's Dictionary of Music and Musicians*) was as to how much of this was art and how much nature. It is indeed a tribute to Melba that nobody could really tell where nature ended and art began. She had had only one year of "master" training, with Mathilde Marchesi in Paris, teacher also of Calvé and Eames. After that she had made a series of phenomenal debuts: at La Monnaie in Brussels (October 12, 1887) as Gilda; at Covent Garden, London (1887), as Lucia; at the Opéra in Paris (1889) as Ophélie.

Now she was approaching her forty-sixth birthday, at the very least. Richard Aldrich in the *Times*, after remarking upon her illness on her last trip to America, found her still in possession of all those marvelous qualities of pure vocalism which had so often been admired here in other years. "Her voice has its old-time lusciousness and purity, its exquisite smoothness and fullness; it is poured out with all spontaneity and freedom. Mme Melba's singing of the music of Violetta was a delight from beginning to end."

It was Melba's evening, of course, but the critics were also delighted by some other aspects of the production. For one thing, Hammerstein had decided to do it in the décor and costumes of 1848, which is what the drama demands (can one imagine the dramatic situation of *La Dame aux Camélias* in any other period?). Nowadays this would occasion no remark, but audiences in New York and elsewhere had been accustomed for years to seeing the work dressed in a seventeenth-century style that, although thoroughly false, was supposed to take the curse off the old prejudice against opera "in modern dress." By this time 1848 was no longer "modern," but the habit of anachronism had persisted until Hammerstein did away with it.

Campanini's conducting, no doubt because of Melba, had some extra electricity that night; the chorus was superb in its two scenes; Ancona was well received, as usual; only Bassi, the tenor, was not equal to the rest of the company. Aldrich remarks upon his "mouselike and querulous style," and the other critics were equally unappreciative of his efforts. Hammerstein, however, had taken the choice that almost any impresario would have taken on this occasion. He did not want to do anything that could take away from the effulgence of Melba as the center of the evening. This is the obvious reasoning, aside from money considerations, that would lead him to put his secondary tenor and baritone with her instead of Bonci and Renaud. It could also very well be that these singers, particularly Bonci, did not care much about being mere adjuncts to Melba's debut. Such is the way of opera houses.

The success of Melba in this season surpassed anything she had ever done in America before. Every time she sang, the house was filled to its uttermost limits. She had been engaged for ten performances and she remained for fifteen; she was supposed to sing once a week and in several weeks she sang twice. There seems to have been no end to her kindness, her benevolence, her indulgence, in this particular year. Considering how sharp she could be, and had been, with other managers, it is only possible to conclude that she liked Hammerstein as much as she said she did. Moreover, no human being, not even a Melba, can be quite insensible to the atmosphere in which she was doing her work, an atmosphere that called out the very best she had to give and made her glow with special satisfaction.

This atmosphere requires a little explanation. She was not only "saving Hammerstein from disaster," as the standard reference books have it, but she was, in Hammerstein's house, the *prima donna assoluta*. There was literally no other woman in the company who came within planetary distance of her accomplishment, popularity, and fame. According to my reading of Mme Melba's character, this in itself was a situation that supplied great satisfactions. In almost any other company there would have been a few other luminaries, but in the Manhattan, for this one season, Melba was alone. This, plus the feeling that she was really needed, really wanted, and that the public was responding as never before, put her into the angelic mood in which she not only sang better, but felt better and behaved better than at any time in years. She said it herself, and I think she knew.

All of her succeeding performances were greeted rapturously by the largest audiences that the house could accommodate, and with actually mounting enthusiasm by the critics. For her second performance, the week after her first, Hammerstein gave her Bonci and Renaud with Campanini for a performance of *Rigoletto*. It was expensive and delicate casting. Usually Melba's name alone was carried in capital letters in the advertisements, but for this evening (Friday, January 11, 1907) all three were so displayed: MELBA, BONCI, RENAUD.

Rigoletto, a masterpiece easy to victimize by routine treatment, was brought to life by a superlative performance under Campanini's sovereign control. Every one of the principals sang and acted better than before. Melba was supreme; Bonci "added a volume of luscious tone which surprised even his warmest admirers"; Renaud "sang and acted with a power that carried all before him" (New York *Times*). The presence of three such artists in one cast usually has the effect of keying each of them to a higher pitch of achievement, as it did in this case—and as it did with Campanini himself. The *Times* declared that this was "the best production of *Rigoletto* seen in New York for many years."

Pleasant reading for Caruso, Sembrich, and Conried!

On that very evening, as it happened, Conried was introducing one of his novelties at the Metropolitan: a revival of Meyerbeer's *Africaine*, in Italian as *L'Africana*, with Fremstad and Caruso. It was very coldly reviewed by the critics and had to be dropped. Even Caruso could not save it. The music was too high for Fremstad and the rest of the cast was indifferent, but the worst element, according to the press, was the crude and patchy conducting of Arturo Vigna. This unfortunate man had done quite well at the Metropolitan up to now, but he could not stand the constant comparison with Campanini. As a result, Conried was already attempting to make advances to Toscanini in Milan (as is shown in Gatti-Casazza's memoirs). The Metropolitan, which had been so haughty toward "the so-called opera house in Thirty-fourth Street," was beginning to feel the breeze.

Melba, we may be sure, knew more about this than any of us could know today. She saw the Metropolitan growing agitated, she read its bad reviews, she saw the immense crowds she attracted to the Manhattan, and, although we have no positive knowledge of any real grudge she had against the Metropolitan, she must at least have felt gratified at the effects of her own power—gratified or amazed.

For the astonishing fact is that from now on all the performances at the Manhattan began to get good reviews and most of them to attract large houses—not only the "Melba nights"—and the Metropolitan, except for the *première* of *Butterfly* (February 11), had some notable mishaps. For example: on Friday, January 18, Hammerstein produced *Les Huguenots* (in Italian) with the same singers who had, most of them, failed to arouse much admiration earlier in the season, and it drew a huge house and excellent criticisms in the press. The same "distaff side" that had been found wanting before—Mme Russ and Mlle Pinkert—was now praised, quite possibly because they had actually improved, and another lady, Mme de Cisneros, had a decided success. And this was the very night when Conried was giving the *première* of Puccini's *Manon Lescaut* in the presence of the composer, with Cavalieri, Caruso, and Scotti singing. Where, the onlooker demanded, did so many operagoers come from? Had New York gone "opera mad"?

XVII

Opera War at Full Tilt

BY MID-JANUARY of Hammer-
stein's first season, as we have seen, the complacency of the Metropolitan was no longer unruffled. For the time, however, the war
between the opera houses was openly fought only by the chal-
lenger. The older house sat in apparent calm, although, if Hammerstein's accusations were not only the product of his angry im-
agining, subtle maneuvers were going on beneath the surface in
an effort to suppress the upstart. The first battle of the war was
apparently to be over whether or not Hammerstein was to succeed
in putting *La Bohème* on the Manhattan's stage for Mme Melba.

1. The Battle for La Bohème

The Puccini Question is murky now and was murky then. What
was the secret of the cabal that attempted to keep Hammerstein
from producing *La Bohème?* Was it, as Hammerstein firmly believed, a nefarious plot on Conried's part, an inimical maneuver
on the part of the Metropolitan? It may well have been. It cannot
be proved now. Certainly *La Bohème* had already been produced
all over the world, and by all sorts of companies, without a whim-
per out of the firm of Ricordi, which owned the rights. All they
asked was $150 a night for royalties. It had been played by travel-

ing opera companies in New York and more or less everywhere else in the United States. Hammerstein had an oral agreement with George Maxwell, the Ricordi representative in New York, dating from March, 1906, which would have permitted him to produce *La Bohème* and all the other Puccini works.

Now, suddenly, Ricordi had sought an injunction to keep Hammerstein from producing *La Bohème* on the ground that the Metropolitan owned the exclusive rights to that and all other Puccini operas in New York.

Hammerstein needed *La Bohème*—not only to give some slight flavor of modernity to his otherwise antique repertoire, but also because Mme Melba wanted it. In fact, Melba was just as determined to sing it as Hammerstein was to produce it. She had sung it everywhere else and she wanted to sing it at the Manhattan. Moreover, as her last appearance at the Metropolitan had been in *La Bohème* and had been badly marred by her illness, she undoubtedly wanted to show what she could do with it now. Any singer would have felt the same.

The Metropolitan, or at least Conried, took a hand in the matter directly by inviting Puccini to America for the *première* at this house of his latest work, *Madama Butterfly*, which was to take place February 11, with Farrar, Homer, Caruso, and Scotti in the cast. The composer arrived in New York on the liner *Kaiserin Augusta*, delayed by fog, on Friday, January 18, the night of the *première* of his *Manon Lescaut* at the Metropolitan. He got there just in time to hear and see the performance, which he professed to admire—although, from his parting remarks six weeks later, I doubt that he did. From that time onward he was treated as Metropolitan Opera property. He threw himself zealously into the preparation of *Madama Butterfly*, probably as a simple measure of self-defense against the ineptitudes of the conductor Arturo Vigna, but no doubt also for a substantial fee from Conried. And from the beginning to the end of his stay in America he was asked—in fact, almost every day—what he thought of the question of Hammerstein's production of *La Bohème*. From beginning to end he said he knew nothing whatever about it; it was a matter between Ricordi and Hammerstein.

Puccini was an honest man, as any reader of his letters must know. He would not have shied off so obstinately from this question if there had been any clear right and wrong involved—or, let us say, if he had not felt that there was something wrong somewhere. If, to put it crudely, Conried had bribed Ricordi to adopt the attitude that was adopted, I feel sure that Puccini had nothing to do with the business.

And the whole curious crisscross of interests, animosities, and fears which runs through this entire "opera war" was thereafter exhibited for weeks. Puccini did not want to offend either Ricordi or the Metropolitan; he equally did not wish to offend Hammerstein directly. How could he know which opera company would come out ahead? Cleofonte Campanini, threatened with a boycott from some of the Ricordi-controlled opera houses of Italy, could not or would not conduct *La Bohème* publicly, although he was willing to prepare it. Nobody was especially eager to offend Mme Melba, whose powers in several opera houses of the world were at that time very great, possibly as great as those of Ricordi. Her popularity in America was such it may have influenced even the courts; certainly it influenced the press. From the tone adopted by the press at the outset of this dispute, and confirmed steadily thereafter, Hammerstein must have had wide sympathy in his effort to put on *La Bohème*. As the press said more than once, he was only trying to do what many lesser companies had done before him, and the claim to exclusive rights by the Metropolitan, although probably valid, was a new arrangement, a new contract, hastily run up in the endeavor to do harm to Hammerstein.

Puccini had a "wonderful time" in America, and went sightseeing to Niagara as soon as his duties with *Madama Butterfly* were over. He worked hard on *Butterfly*, which then, as afterward, he considered his best opera. He obtained a good result, for the press in general held it to be the best production the Metropolitan had offered in Italian for a long time. He worked with orchestra, chorus, principals, and stage director, although he was unwilling to conduct this or any other opera. Arturo Vigna was the conductor, but, owing to Puccini's work, he turned in a far better performance than usual.

And the Puccini "wave" at the Metropolitan reached a great height that year, unquestionably because of the composer's visit and the effort to impress and please him. Four of his operas were in the repertoire and received twenty-one performances, more than those of any other composer. It would be a strange coincidence if this courtship of Puccini were not somehow connected with Conried's claim to exclusive rights for his works. In short, it looks as if Hammerstein may have been right in his suspicions, and that the Metropolitan management did in fact go to great lengths in the matter.

Ricordi's ace card was possession of the orchestral score of *La Bohème*, which had never been printed. The Milan firm took extraordinary precautions to see that no one of the existing manuscripts of the score (all of which were numbered and placed in various parts of the world) could possibly fall into Hammerstein's hands. The impresario made diligent search, through agents in the United States and elsewhere, and after much difficulty he came into possession of a mutilated orchestral score that had been used by a touring company from England some years before. Campanini knew the score so well, having memorized it and conducted it often, that he was able to supply the missing parts.

Thus Hammerstein proceeded with his plans and produced *La Bohème* on Friday, March 1, with Melba, Trentini, Bonci, Sammarco, Arimondi, and Gilibert. Fernando Tanara actually conducted the performance while Campanini sat in a box, but Campanini had rehearsed and prepared it in every detail.

The situation in court was that Ricordi's case for an injunction was pending and Hammerstein's answer had been given (as we have seen) on the eve of the Manhattan opening. As soon as Melba had had her three performances as Mimi and sailed away to Europe, Hammerstein voluntarily withdrew his opposition to the case and the court then granted the injunction. By this time it meant nothing; Hammerstein and Melba had had what they wanted, and by the next year almost anything might happen.

2. Score One for Hammerstein

Melba's brief repertoire made all the difference to Hammerstein. He could present her in operas that were already in production: *Lucia* (January 28) with Bonci, and *Faust* (February 8) with Dalmorès, along with repetitions of *La Traviata* and *Rigoletto*. These four constituted her list until the *Bohème* production, and it would be difficult to imagine reviews more favorable than those she received at each performance; yet in the *Bohème*, according to the New York *Times*, she "sang the music more beautifully than she has done anything else this season in New York."

That *Bohème*, Melba's and Hammerstein's victory, was full of surprises. For example, Emma Trentini, a lively soprano who reminded many persons of Fritzi Scheff, had a genuine personal success as Musetta. She had been in the company all season, singing small parts without any remarkable effect, and had even sung Micaëla in some of the numerous performances of *Carmen*. But Musetta was really her part, and she scored heavily, foreshadowing the time when she, like Scheff, would progress from opera to operetta. Bonci displayed a "full voice" in *La Bohème* as never before, and the new baritone Mario Sammarco made a great effect, as he did in everything.

Sammarco had appeared at the Manhattan for the first time on Friday, February 1, when *Cavalleria Rusticana* and *Pagliacci* were given to a full house with excellent critical response. He was one of the finest Italian baritones of the time, and Tonio was an ideal part for him; he repeated it a number of times during the rest of the year. He came when Hammerstein had been for two weeks at a low ebb in baritones, just as at the beginning of the season, with only Mario Ancona for everything, and Paul Seveilhac as a rather unsatisfactory second. Renaud had been obliged by other engagements to return to Europe after his *Don Giovanni* performance of January 16. He had made a deep impression in every role he sang, particularly in *Rigoletto* and *Don Giovanni*, but his unique performances in the French repertoire were still to come. After being so captious and difficult at the outset, he had become one of Hammerstein's pillars of strength, and his absence was felt.

Sammarco, however, in whatever he sang (*Pagliacci*, *Bohème*, *Rigoletto*, and one *Lucia* with Melba) was memorable in another style—the fresh and powerful Italian high baritone, youthful, resonant, and secure; until Ruffo came along some years later, there was nobody at the Metropolitan or elsewhere who could pour out this kind of tone as he did.

There were some disappointments, of course, but the complexion of everything in Hammerstein's project looked very rosy through February and March. Bonci's *Fra Diavolo*, which the critics thought "delightful," was sparsely attended by the public.

Bressler-Gianoli had to go away at the end of the fifteenth week, after having performed *Carmen* at least once and sometimes twice a week; her run of *Carmen* was one of the longest known in a single season. Dalmorès had a cold for a while and sang over it.

But, despite incidents of this sort, everything, including finance, looked better than Hammerstein had had any right to expect some months earlier. For one thing, he had obtained a loan of $400,000 from Frank Woolworth, founder of the Woolworth stores, with the Manhattan Opera House as security. This was to make sure of his coming season, although he already believed that the present season would end with some profit, however small.

Hammerstein negotiated this loan personally. He did not know Mr. Woolworth, but, hearing that he was interested in music and had often been at the Manhattan, he went to see him without preparation. He returned with a subscription to a box for every performance, and the loan of $400,000 in addition. We begin to understand what people meant when they called him "persuasive."

3. Supper with Two Prima Donnas

Melba's farewell for the season took place on Monday, March 25, in *La Bohème*. When the opera was over and bows had been taken, she appeared again to sing the Mad Scene from *Lucia*—a sort of extra caper more common in those days than now. After this, the stage was cleared and a caterer took over; it was Hammerstein's supper party for all the principals of the company and their wives or husbands. At that supper party (where they had *suprême de volaille Hammerstein* and ended with *pêche Melba*) Oscar must have felt expansive and more than a little incredulous. There he sat, surrounded by some of the finest singers and musicians in existence, with every likelihood of ending his season solvent, and with a substantial sum of money in the bank, thanks to Mr. Woolworth, toward next season's outlay. Needless to say, he had composed a piece for the occasion, a sort of potpourri called "Memories of the Manhattan Opera Season," which the orchestra dutifully played. He was the same magnificent Oscar, but this time his splendor was real. Moreover, he had Melba on his right and Calvé on his left.

173

Yes, Calvé.

Melba's departure would have left Hammerstein in precisely the same position as at the beginning of the season if he had not enlisted the services of another famous soprano. His "distaff side" had been a weakness, as he had good reason to remember; never again did he attempt to get through a season or any part of a season without prima-donna sopranos who could appeal to a large audience. He had learned that lesson so well that in future he tended in the other direction and supplied himself with such a wealth of prima donnas that it was difficult to carry out all their contracts. In this very month of March and even more in April, the papers were filled with stories of Hammerstein's contracts, signed or possible, with celebrated singers.

But now, with four more weeks to go and no Melba, he had been able to corral Emma Calvé to take over in her own repertoire of *Carmen, Cavalleria,* and *La Navarraise.* More than a decade before, he had wanted Calvé to sing for him in variety at the Olympia. Now he was achieving that ambition, too, but in a way that delighted him more.

We are not informed about the behavior of Mmes Melba and Calvé to each other on the occasion of that historic supper party. It must have been choice and rare, whether it was in the realm of cordiality or that of pinpricks. Both ladies were famous for their rudeness to rivals or other personages of equal rank in opera. A much younger singer, Mary Garden, endured some sizzling language from both of them when she had become, to their annoyance, an international prima donna. On one occasion when Garden and Melba sang at Windsor Castle after a state dinner for the King of Greece, Melba said to the court chamberlain, Lord Farquhar: "What a dreadful concert this would have been if I hadn't come!" Once Garden had supper at the Savoy in London with Calvé and others after a performance at Covent Garden. She was wearing a special perfume created for her. Mme Calvé sniffed the air and declared that she would have to change tables. "I shall not be able to eat, or I shall be sick," she said. These were the amenities of which we hear a good deal from those days. (Both incidents took place only a year or two after Hammerstein's Melba-Calvé supper.)

At all events, Melba departed and Calvé arrived. Melba's last performance was at the beginning of Hammerstein's seventeenth week; Calvé's first was two days later, Wednesday, March 27, in *Carmen*.

She, too, sang to a packed house and won excellent criticisms, although it is easy to see from the press that her voice was not what it had been a decade before. She was "less capricious in her singing and less unruly in her acting" than in her late years at the Metropolitan. She still was the center of the stage at all times, dressed the part "sumptuously," gave a "sensuous and wily" characterization, and held her audience enthralled. But there is no doubt that much of the bloom had been taken off her Carmen, the most famous of all, by the very different rendition given that same season by the relatively unknown Clotilde Bressler-Gianoli. Bressler-Gianoli's shabby, intense, earthy, and tempestuous Carmen had pleased both critics and public so much that Calvé's performance began to seem a bit stagy and, worst of all, old-fashioned. Of course she filled the house every time she sang it, and she sang it five times. In the eighteenth and twentieth weeks she sang it twice.

Her Santuzza in *Cavalleria Rusticana* came on the Saturday matinee in the seventeenth week (March 30), with Dalmorès as Turiddu; and Sammarco's Tonio illuminated the *Pagliacci* that went with it. It was repeated only once, although it, too, drew great crowds. Her *Navarraise*, given twice, was thought to be her best achievement (nearer to her temperament now than Carmen, the *Times* thought). Like *Cavalleria*, it was coupled with *Pagliacci*, which was good for almost endless repetitions because of the sensation Sammarco invariably created with the Prologue.

In all, Calvé gave nine performances in four weeks, and, although it took more care and thought than in her old reckless days, she was still able to subjugate an audience. The difference between Calvé and Melba was not one of age: Mme Melba was either three years older or three years younger than Mme Calvé, depending on which source one considers trustworthy. The *Encyclopædia Britannica* gives Calvé's birth date as 1858, but adds an interrogation, thus: 1858? Grove's Dictionary says she was born in 1864. If the truth were known, as it never really is about the ages of singers, they were probably just about the same age. They had both studied with Mme Marchesi and had had parallel careers, singing in all the same opera houses.

The difference was that Calvé's tremendously emotional voice, her impetuous temperament, and the abandon with which she squandered her great resources were the elements of a very great career but not of a very long one. Melba's instrumental style, which kept the abundant beauty of tone under control at all times, did not wear out either her throat or her temperament. She was never "carried away" by her own performances, and in her repertoire it was perhaps not desirable that she should be. As a result, Calvé left the operatic stage in 1910, when she was fifty (more or less), and Melba did not say farewell to Covent Garden until 1926.

It may be worth noticing that Calvé's beauty had, in spite of some gain in weight, endured better than her voice, whereas with Melba it was the opposite. The *Times* remarked of Melba's Marguerite that same season: "The years have told on Mme Melba's presence as they have not been able to tell upon her voice."

What Hammerstein had, therefore, in his two world-famous sopranos was one who had conserved her vocal resources and one who had not: Melba was at her very peak and Calvé was beginning to go, although even as she declined she remained one of the most interesting performers in the world.

Melba's farewell statement may be quoted in its brief entirety. It was issued the day before she sailed:

"I have never enjoyed any season in America so much as the one now closing. All through I have been in splendid health and spirits and I shall never forget the kindness with which I have been received. I am proud to have been associated with Mr. Hammerstein in his launching of New York's new opera house. What courage Mr. Hammerstein has shown and what wonders he has done! I think there must be something in the conditions of American life to encourage him, for I know of no opera manager in any city of the world who, single-handed and under circumstances of such difficulty and competition, would have risked his fortune in opera.

"His pluck appealed to me from the first, and I leave as I came, his loyal friend and admirer."

4. War in the Open

When the curtain fell after the last "popular-priced Saturday night" (another *Aïda*, of which there had been many), Oscar Hammerstein was no doubt happy and full of wonder that he had

176

actually won so great a battle. He did not, however, have much time to think it over. While the certified public accountants surveyed the books to see what really had happened, the "opera war" was in full tilt. It had started up in February, through the Puccini episode and others, and from now on it gained momentum all the time, with hardly even a lull in the summer. When Hammerstein and Conried went to Europe, their doings and utterances were reported from there, too. It was, without a doubt, an era of some madness, for which Hammerstein was largely responsible, but the public joined in with zest and the press could not have omitted the daily communiqués if they had wished to do so.

What the "opera war" meant was what all wars mean in the last analysis, a struggle for survival. Hammerstein had challenged from the very beginning. Then, from Melba's arrival, the storm began to gather. The Metropolitan had had a good deal of bad luck, it is true, including the expensive and superbly sung *première* of Strauss's *Salome* on January 20, which had to be dropped immediately on moral grounds. Hammerstein's successes were so numerous in the last half or three-quarters of his season that Conried could not keep up his pretense any longer. He accepted the challenge and went to work.

Both managers then began to make raids on each other, and a sort of double warfare ensued in which one part was above ground and reported in the press, the other subterranean and in some cases not known until years later. So far as the open warfare was concerned, Hammerstein was the more belligerent. In fact, his love of issuing statements, giving interviews, making plans public, would probably have flourished regardless of the stimulus it gave him to annoy Conried.

But in secret there were many activities that only came to light later. Thus, Conried made a determined effort to get Campanini for the Metropolitan and offered him a good deal more money than Hammerstein was paying. Campanini refused from the first and did not even tell Hammerstein: he had retained from his youthful experience a detestation of the Metropolitan and its methods, and in addition he was king at the Manhattan. Could anybody be king at the Metropolitan when every artistic effort was subject to the caprices (or the ignorance) of the Morgan-Astor-Vanderbilt directorate?

Thus he reasoned, and his loyalty to Hammerstein was constant until—with that fatality which dogged all his fortunes—Oscar himself destroyed it.

Bonci was another matter. Conried got him. It was very annoying to the Metropolitan to have its leading tenor constantly compared to Hammerstein's leading tenor, and the solution Conried found—costly though it was—seemed reasonable enough from some points of view: take Bonci, add him to Caruso, and the supply of Italian tenors is thereby exhausted. It was not, of course, true: there were other Italian tenors of the first rank, and Hammerstein had no trouble finding them.

Caruso's fee had been, in this 1906–1907 season just past, $1,440 for each of sixty-two performances. For the next season Conried was obliged to pay him $2,000 for each of sixty-eight performances. The jump in fee was due, of course, to Hammerstein. Just as Conried worked on Bonci, so Hammerstein worked on Caruso. We shall get to the Caruso story before long. At that time it was all supposedly secret, although the air was filled with rumors and some of them reached the press in one way or another.

5. Season's Accounting

Nearly every day, from the end of February onward, the newspapers carried some announcement, rumor, or speculation about the doings of the rival managers. Hammerstein (from the time he got the $400,000) erupted into statements about new works, conductors, and singers. Some things came to pass and some did not. He was going to produce Wagner with Hans Richter conducting: Cosima Wagner's hatred of the Metropolitan had made her exert her influence, said the press. Ernestine Schumann-Heink, later on, announced that she was "proud" to leave the Metropolitan for Hammerstein. Conried was going to bring Chaliapin from Europe and Hammerstein was going to bring Mary Garden (both of these were rumors long before they were facts).

Hammerstein's season ended April 19, Conried's a week earlier. Each had given twenty weeks of opera and each promised the same for next season. Hammerstein really did not have Mary Garden's signature to a contract when he began to use her name in March, 1907, for she refused to sign with an agent; she said: "If

Mr. Hammerstein wants to talk to me, he should come to Paris and do it." He did, however, have messages of such encouragement (from the French music publisher Durand to the American music publisher G. Schirmer) that he regarded this acquisition as certain. He did have a signed contract with Schumann-Heink, and it was announced on March 18 that he had signed the day before with the agent for Lillian Nordica. Mme Nordica had left the Metropolitan at the end of the preceding season (in a huff, it seems), but had refused to sign with Hammerstein because she felt unsure of his experiment. Now, on tour in the far west, she telegraphed that she, too, was "proud" to join him.

Mme Nordica's Metropolitan fee had been $1,250 for each of twenty performances, one of the highest received by any woman singer in the house (Eames's alone was a little higher). We do not know precisely what Hammerstein had to pay her, and there was, especially at this time, a tremendous lot of misrepresentation going on about the size of the fees in the "opera war," but it is safe to guess that Hammerstein must have paid $1,500 at least, perhaps $1,750.

He had already announced Melba and Calvé; now he had Nordica and Schumann-Heink as well, with a strong likelihood of Mary Garden. Instead of being "weak on the distaff side," he was going to be overloaded with prima donnas.

At the end of his season he had the task of dismissing a number of singers: that is, of refusing to renew his options on their services. To Ancona, whom he never really liked, he laid down severe conditions for possible renewal: he must lose thirty pounds, acquire a waistline, etc., etc. Hammerstein is supposed to have poked his forefinger at Ancona's protruding belly. "That is not fat," said the singer, "that is my chest." With Mlle Pinkert, the Polish coloratura, it was worse: she screamed, fainted, had assorted hysterics in Italian, and refused to accept her salary in dollars, although she had been doing so all year. (She wanted it in gold francs.)

The Bonci affair filled columns and columns of newsprint during the closing weeks of Hammerstein's season. The gist of it was that Conried simply bribed him away by paying $1,500 for each performance instead of $1,000, as Hammerstein's option provided for the tenor's second season. Bonci's contract was incredibly complicated and had so many peculiar clauses in it—about sums to be deposited in a bank in Florence; about Hammerstein as "an Italian citizen" (through his agent) and other legal fictions—that the clear option Oscar held for the next two years was shadowed. It was the kind of contract in which Clause S is carefully framed to cancel out Clause C, and Clause M to erase Clause F. Oscar went to court about it almost automatically—he loved going to court—but, aside from the pleasure of annoying Conried, he really did not care much about Bonci.

As he explained to the reporters when the story about Bonci's defection first appeared, there were other tenors. He showed them a contract signed just two weeks before with Giovanni Zenatello, the brilliant young Italian tenor who had been making great successes in Europe. This man, Hammerstein said, could sing anything, robust modern works as well as old lyric ones, and Bonci could sing only his own repertoire, all very old.

Bonci took refuge in his agents: he "knew nothing about the contracts." Conried confirmed the signature. The tenor was summoned to court on April 1 (all this time he was singing once or twice a week for Hammerstein) and endured some little embarrassment. In the end, he went to the Metropolitan and Hammerstein did not mourn, although, as he pointed out in a published letter, Bonci might have stayed in Europe a long time if he, Hammerstein, had not brought him to New York.

The certified public accountants showed that the first season of the Manhattan Opera had achieved a profit of $11,000. This is amazing in itself and Hammerstein had not expected even so much. However, Arthur Hammerstein is on record as believing that there was a profit of about $100,000, and Oscar Hammerstein himself said that his box office took in about $750,000 during the season. The whole system of bookkeeping and of money transfers was so peculiar, with that famous truck loading up currency at the Victoria Theatre and dumping it out at the Manhattan, that it would have been difficult for any expert to be sure. The main point is that he made some money, after lavish and often unexpected expenditures.

In the same season the Metropolitan lost $84,039.* Some of its productions had been destroyed in the San Francisco fire and had had to be replaced, but of course *all* of Hammerstein's were new in every particular, so this explanation does not explain. The sim-

*Kolodin: *The Story of the Metropolitan Opera*, p. 228.

plest reasoning leads us to conclude that both opera companies were under severe financial strain because of the competition, but that the Manhattan made a little money and the Metropolitan lost a respectable amount. It was the first time in a good many years that the Metropolitan had ended the season with a loss.

The war was on and the warrior was happy. Hammerstein's ebullience at the end of the season was the delight of the press. He talked not only of an opera house in Philadelphia—this was quite serious, and the *Times* reported that he had made a number of exploratory visits there—but also of Boston and Chicago, as well as of a number of other less likely cities from time to time. He talked of so many different kinds of new repertoire that it would have required a dozen opera houses to stage them all. The press took these improvisations with a grain of salt, but only one grain, and that a tentative one. It all sounded crazy, but who could tell? It had been equally crazy to think of a full opera season in opposition to the Metropolitan, and lo! Lo indeed! In the tone in which these grandiose imaginings were reported it is possible to detect skepticism, but skepticism tempered by the salutary reflection that the man who had already performed one impossibility might equally well perform others.

XVIII

The King in His Castle

AT THE FINAL PERFORMANCE of the season Hammerstein was once more drawn forth to make an entr'acte speech. The opera was *Aïda*, in which Mme Giannina Russ, once badly received, was now doing very well indeed, and on this evening Sammarco was making his only appearance as Amonasro this season.

Hammerstein came out at the end of the second act. The house he surveyed beyond the footlights was packed to the exits, exuberant and highly vocal in its approval. He was in every sense, at this, the successful end of his first season, the triumphant king in his castle, and it was in the tone of benevolent absolutism that he spoke.

1. Oscar vs. "Society"

This, as the press reported it, is what he said:

"I was not sure of my position when I stood on these boards five months ago, when I was starting an opera house without the aid of society. I found soon after that that there was no regular opera-going public, and I had to make one. In the first weeks sometimes there was not over $1,500 in the house, but I convinced the people that I was doing the right thing by them, that I had no commercial aim in view, and I made a public which wanted to hear grand opera sung in the best manner.

"Other men would have been discouraged by the lack of support but I was not, with the result that I am ending the season with the balance on the profit side.

"I am going abroad in a few weeks to engage artists to sing here next year—"

(Voice from the gallery: "Campanini!")

"Yes, Mr. Campanini is coming back. I want him most of all. I am going to spend all the money I have earned in an attempt to make this the most wonderful opera house in the world. Think of it: New York is the only city in the world that can support two opera houses of the first rank. The other one is certainly established (Laughter) and so is this one. (Applause) And the people who come here come for the opera. I want no others. I am not trying to establish a society clientele."

The Saturday-night audience to which he addressed these remarks had paid "popular prices"—three dollars for the best seat —to hear and see a production that, when Hammerstein first offered it, had been coldly received. There were few if any members of "New York society" in that audience.

But, whatever the audience, Hammerstein repeated this rejection of fashionable support at intervals afterward. What is more, his mind seems to have hardened so much that during the next season his son Arthur was actually afraid to tell him when evidence of strong support from society leaders began to appear.

Hammerstein's attitude was in the spirit of the time. The year 1907 was a panic year; the very rich, especially those of Wall Street, were not at all popular. The following year was a year of "hard times," although the Manhattan Opera showed no evidence of them. Moreover, it was the period of Theodore Roosevelt, the "trust-buster," who had just then been called a "humbug and a fakir" by a Congressional spokesman for the rich. Roosevelt's attack on "malefactors of great wealth" and his various attempts at legislation to break up combinations and reduce untoward gains were all going on during the years of Hammerstein's opera. Roosevelt was a "trust-buster" on the national scale, and Hammerstein might have been called a "trust-buster" in his own way. Many of those against whom Roosevelt raged were, in fact, directors of the

Metropolitan Opera. Hammerstein's tone toward New York society expressed the popular sentiment.

And yet with Hammerstein there was something more, something personal. His opposition to the social arbiters was too violent, too unreasonable, to be altogether a part of the climate. Perhaps Hammerstein had felt himself in some way slighted, condemned, by those to whom he referred as "society." Certainly he associated them all, lock, stock, and barrel, with the Metropolitan. For that reason alone he would not have trusted them an inch. But we gape in wonder when we encounter the evidence that he actually could not endure their support, disdained their approval, and went out of his way to be insulting to them if they offered him substantial proof of it.

For an opera manager, this constitutes not only prejudice, but something akin to mania. Wealthy society patrons can make a life-or-death difference to an opera house, and Hammerstein's rejection of them may alone have caused the eventual shipwreck of the Manhattan Opera.

To call his attitude a "rejection" is understatement. What he said as a rule was: "Tell him to go to hell!" And, as we shall see later, when he really got angry he was capable of barring his opera house to persons of the greatest wealth and power. That press agent who had called him a "cantankerous crackpot" many years before at Koster and Bial's had seen only one side of the phenomenon, but he had seen it plain. On other sides one might discern quixotism, a storm of ambition, arrogance of a charismatic or Napoleonic nature, and along with that a firm if humble conviction that the rich and great had been and always would be the ruin of independent artistic endeavor. Such was Hammerstein's weird mixture. It is quite comprehensible that his son Arthur, living so near to the phenomenon, dwelt partly in fear of it and partly in bewilderment.

2. The Hammerstein Brand of Happiness

For Arthur, who was to play so important a part in the life of the Manhattan henceforth, the first season had been a hard apprenticeship. Busy with almost every detail of the management but actually responsible for none, he toiled against a consuming inner doubt over the merit of the endeavor, its sense, and its future. He had not been shaken in his fundamental skepticism about opera itself, and he did not cease to wonder why it should so command the entire being of his father.

Oscar's satisfaction was plain to see. He had not been mistaken in his lifelong dream: the joys he had foreseen, or perhaps only half hoped for, were in fact his. He took pleasure in every moment of his activity as director of the Manhattan Opera, no matter what the difficulties. He was, in a sense peculiar to him, happy, as perhaps he had not been since the death of his first wife, Rose. Arthur has suggested that his father might never have been so obsessed with opera if Rose had been alive.

"I wonder if opera would have been O.H.'s all-consuming interest if my mother had lived?" Arthur muses in a letter. "According to my aunts and my grandmother, O.H. loved my mother very much and she had great influence over him. . . ."

This, indeed, points toward the mystery of the obsession: for this lonely man it took the place of wife, family, friends, and more or less everything else. In politics the period was fascinating, for President Roosevelt was introducing all sorts of new ideas into American life, yet, except for his unconscious echoing of Roosevelt's attack on the wealthy, there is not a trace of evidence that Hammerstein took an interest in what was going on. He lived in blinkers, he lived alone, and he lived, above all, with a singleness of purpose that must have been a nightmare at times to those nearest to him. (Nobody was close to him, but his children were nearest.) His interest in women was fitful and temporary; he was generous and forgetful; there were exceptions to the rule, but this was, in general, the way it was. The opera house and all its pullulating small internal life as well as its external existence took the place of everything else in the world.

But he enjoyed that life of the opera house, and it seems to have given him everything he expected of it. He was supremely lucky in this, that the fulfillment of his dream was not a disappointment. The dust and ashes came afterward, not with it.

3. Fun among the Stars

Aside from his own swelling exultation in his creation, his sense of power in accomplishing it all along, Hammerstein derived a great deal of common-or-garden fun out of his opera company. He joked with the singers as he had always joked with workmen, musicians, or vaudeville performers, and most of them loved it. Emma Trentini, the sprightly soprano who played *Naughty Marietta* some years later in Arthur's production, was a great favorite of Oscar's. When she came offstage after doing particularly well he would drop a freshly washed, shining quarter-dollar down her neck. She saved them all, and always sang the rest of the performance clutching her quarter in her hand. Hammerstein gave these shining coins to many or most of his singers if he happened to like their performance on a particular evening, and the singers cherished the token of his appreciation. We know, of course, that he did the same with the newsboys in Times Square. We do not know whether he gave quarters to Mmes Melba and Calvé.

His seat in the wings, the wooden kitchen chair, became a sort of galvanic focus, the nervous center of the opera house. James Huneker was convinced that the high quality of performance at the Manhattan, its freshness, excitement, point, and zest, came from Hammerstein. This would be difficult to prove from the musical point of view, for he could actually do nothing once the curtain had gone up. Yet it is possible that his presence there in the wings, once they had grown used to it, gave the singers a personal incentive they might not otherwise have had, for his personality was powerful and they were all susceptible to that as well as to his scale of wages.

Trentini's love of money amused Oscar so much that on one occasion he nailed a half-dollar to the floor near her dressing room and then watched in glee as she tried to dislodge it. He also contributed to Trentini's perpetual English lessons, which, apparently, went on all the time in the opera house; she was determined to learn the language and spent every moment studying it, pressing into service anybody in the neighborhood, at rehearsal or any other time, who could help.

It is also related of Trentini that she collected free hotel soap while she was on tour and once, some years later, returned to Europe with five grocery boxes full of it. Such a character must have seemed sheer fantasy to Hammerstein, whose prodigality, in everything except his own personal needs, was so unrestrained.

He enjoyed the unexpected quirks of singers as much as the predictable manifestations of their nature. On one occasion—Good Friday, the day of his performance of the Verdi *Requiem*—an Italian prophet or soothsayer of some kind predicted that an earthquake would hit Manhattan Island at three o'clock. At that hour all the singers who were expected for a final rehearsal had gone to Central Park to await the disaster. Oscar cheerfully gathered them all up again, laughing, and brought them back.

And if, after all, the worries, dangers, and absurdities of the opera grew a little oppressive or a little too much on any one day, he could always go home, when his work was done, to those shabby rooms in the Victoria and work at the drawing board, the lathe, or a model of one of his incessant inventions. He never stopped inventing gadgets and he never stopped composing music, although the time for both these occupations had to be taken from his sleep. If nothing else, he found it good for his health and spirits; but, as a matter of fact, almost everything he invented—if it went far enough to be patented—brought in money in large or small amounts.

Part of his amusement with singers consisted in tabulating their superstitions, which were a revelation to him because they were of such diverse origins and character. Maurice Renaud went to Mass on any day when he had a performance to give; so far as could be observed, he did not do so at other times. Pauline Donalda used to tear off a button from her costume before making her first entrance in any opera; it always had to be sewed back on afterward so that she could tear it off again. Strangest of all was Tetrazzini's habit of throwing a dagger into the floor three times before the rise of the curtain. If the dagger stuck straight up all three times, the omens were extremely favorable. As she was a pretty good dagger-thrower, she managed to encourage herself more often than not.

Hammerstein found his seashore and his mountains in the opera house. There is little doubt of his happiness there, of his well-being in both body and spirit. His good health called for comment, both publicly and privately, during these years; he bloomed on a regimen of little sleep or food, much work, and no leisure at all. His one indulgence was those cigars which he made himself ("twenty-five a day"), and to these he clung ferociously. He even smoked in the wings of the opera house, breaking the fire laws and overriding the constant protest of his own firemen on duty. He was at home here; this was his house; he had built it and filled it; who was to say him nay in anything?

4. "I Am Hammerstein"

Within a week of the ending of the season, Hammerstein was in court once more, this time for the Victoria Theatre. The Federation of Church Clubs had brought an action asking the Victoria to show cause why its license should not be revoked because of the Sunday performances—a periodical effort on the part of those who wanted to enforce the old "Blue Laws," never successful but always annoying.

Few incidents show more clearly the popular position of Oscar Hammerstein at the time. He appeared in the judge's chambers in the courthouse before a crowd anticipating his appearance. He made hardly a serious answer in the whole hearing; his sallies were greeted with laughter by the auditors, by the lawyers for both sides, and even by the referee judge, and the whole performance was reported at great length in the papers. He had been interviewed after the end of his opera season and had spoken very seriously, taking up a column and a half of the New York *Times* and more in other papers, on the subject of the Manhattan Opera's precarious beginnings and ultimate triumph in one season. Now he was giving evidence on the subject of whether or not the Victoria's Sunday performances were "sacred concerts" in any exact sense, and Hammerstein, basing himself on that fact, made mock-serious replies that the public found very funny.

When he was asked his profession, he said, with utmost gravity: "I am a director of opera."

During the hearing, when he was asked to describe this, that, or the other act, he went into great detail on the difference between clog-dancing and tap-dancing, made a good many gestures, and even tried to imitate at one point. Asked about a performance of trained elephants, whose trainer was a Negro, he said: "I saw the impresario of the elephants come in—" and at that moment was drowned out in the laughter. Everything he said produced this effect. One gets the impression not only of a completely public character known to all, but of a character for whom the general feeling was kindly, almost affectionate, with strong overtones of amusement. And the most surprising thing is the fact that this nonsense, for it was nothing more, apparently deserved inordinate attention from newspapers simply because the actor was Hammerstein.

His departure for Europe some ten days later won the same attention. On the day before the sailing he gave a serious interview in his office at the Manhattan, speaking of his hopes for the following season and of his interest in producing works new to New York. "In Paris he expects to meet Charpentier, composer of *Louise*, and Massenet and Mary Garden, who has made such a success there." (New York *Times*, May 7.) On the next day the *Times* gives an account of his actual departure, as follows:

"The great and only Oscar Hammerstein, operatic impresario, sailed for Europe yesterday morning on the *Kaiser Wilhelm der Grosse* minus his ticket. The ticket is still peacefully reposing in his private room upstairs in the Victoria Theatre—and no man may reach it because the door is locked and Mr. Hammerstein has the key.

"Mr Hammerstein went to the pier in a cab. He was exultant and had already composed in his mind a laconic cablegram to Melba: 'I sailed today.' Everything went finely until he suddenly discovered he had lost his ticket. He didn't make the discovery until he had said a fond good-bye to reporters and the boat was on the point of sailing.

" 'I am Hammerstein,' said he. Others vouched that he was The Hammerstein, yet there was perplexity on the face of the purser.

"Suddenly the impresario had an idea. He grabbed off his famous stovepipe hat and waved it in his hand.

" 'This hat!' he cried. 'It is mine and nobody else wears one like it.'

"The hat settled it. They let him aboard to stay."

XIX

New Vistas Rising

THE WEEK on shipboard gave Hammerstein at last a little time for reflection. The nature of his obsessive drive, combined with the impatience underlying every effort he made, gave him little chance to pause for thought. He never took a holiday. The enforced rest in hospital some years before, after he had fainted in the street, was the only rest we know of before his sixtieth year or for some time afterward. His days were filled to the bulging limit, and had been for many years. He could not retire to the seashore or the mountains and think things over. It was not in his nature—he would have said it was not in the circumstances: he would have said there was too much to do—and his nature was imperious. As we have seen and shall see again, his nature defied reason when reason got in the way.

1. What Next?

He was, of course, thinking much of the time, in a manner usual with busy men, like a parallel and secret existence unrelated to the work in hand. But, as far as I have ever found out, the only time he had for solitary and unified thought—thought undisturbed by immediate, necessary, practical action—seems to have been in his rooms at the Victoria as he was going to bed and getting up

—and on a trolley car. Arthur, incidentally, had furnished a suitable apartment for him in the opera house, comfortable and of some dignity as well, without being sumptuous. Hammerstein slept there one or two nights and thereafter returned to his shabby and disordered rooms at the Victoria, where the grand piano and the sheet music took up what space was not occupied by cigar-making machines and inventor's lathes.

The time he had for thinking must have been little indeed. He was in the opera house until well after midnight every night and was back there again in the morning by ten o'clock. He was the arbiter of every smallest dispute in that theater and company; his was the final word on everything and the initial word on most things besides. He never interfered at a rehearsal, but if difficulties of any sort arose, he was there as the court of appeal. At every performance without exception he sat in the wings on a kitchen chair, watching and listening. His place at stage right, house left, was in full view of the performers most of the time, although at other times he pushed the chair a little out of the way. He was accessible in his office at the opera house to singers, musicians, stagehands, choristers, and the ubiquitous press, as well as to the administrative staff. He had no time alone—and as he was essentially a solitary and, as I believe, a lonely man, this may have conformed to his needs. As a result, his processes of thinking were not those of a staff strategist poring over maps and figures, but those of a field general in the midst of battle.

On the practical side, having come dangerously near shipwreck through lack of great sopranos, he was rapidly applying the remedy. He had also given thought to his repertoire, and a good half of his public statements were on the subject of enlarging it. He had been able to give certain operas many more performances —when casting difficulties forced him to do so—than an established opera house with a big subscription list could do. In this respect, the small number of subscribers to his first season had been an advantage: there had been only $30,000 in subscription tickets when the season began. Now subscriptions were coming in at a great rate—various figures were being announced, all large— and he would no longer be able to ignore the demand of these regular ticket-holders for a different opera on each subscription night.

His repertoire, as he was well aware, was heavily weighted on the antique side. He had produced twenty-two operas in twenty weeks, if we count *Cavalleria Rusticana, Pagliacci,* and *La Navarraise* as separate operas, but only these three half-length works, plus *La Bohème,* were by living composers.

Even in a very old repertoire he had already done new things: the ensemble of his *Carmen,* for example, quite aside from its remarkable chief performer, had not been seen in living memory in New York. He had grasped the principle of forming a cast and holding it together under a single conductor for a series of unified and responsible renditions of music and drama. This would have seemed the merest common sense in the Broadway theater, where one cast usually performs a play from the beginning to the end of its run. Not so in opera repertoire, where it is the custom for the various principals available to take their turns at the task, usually without rehearsal. As all rehearsal time in opera is limited and painfully expensive, Hammerstein's way, which he came to by himself with no firsthand knowledge of the system in the great continental houses, seems the only intelligent solution. It is the method used by Rudolf Bing in all his own new productions at the Metropolitan today, but it was not Conried's method.

Hammerstein, from the first, had grasped the importance of the ensemble and tried to preserve it even in his first season. He had also fully realized the vitalizing importance of the conductor, had supported Campanini at all times, and had given him as much rehearsal time with full orchestra, chorus, and principals as was physically possible. He was spending $3,000 a week on this, it is said—at a wage scale very different from that of today. To prepare and produce twenty-two operas in twenty weeks is quite a task, even if done in the most haphazard manner, but to do it as painstakingly as Campanini required was herculean.

2. Something Really New

But, aside from these details, great and small, every one of which had engaged his attention, he must already have thought deeply on a larger question, the question of what he wanted to do with his opera house. He had not brought it into being merely to oppose, shake up, or even destroy the Metropolitan, however dear this wish was to him. His animosity toward the Metropolitan, stimulating though it was, had not originated his ambition to become an opera impresario.

In his plans for the next season he had already determined to try something new, something that had not been done before in New York—something, indeed, that was to mark the Manhattan Opera House as far more than simply another tilt at the Metropolitan, and was to form the firmest basis for his own place in operatic history.

To mount fresh, new works that had not been dinned into the ears of New York for decades—this, I think, had come to be Hammerstein's aspiration for his wonderful self-made operatic instrument. The date when the aspiration became clear in his own mind can scarcely be fixed, but traces of it appear in his public statements all through March and April, 1907: that is, while his first season was ending and just after it had ended. He had probably had something of the kind afloat in his consciousness all along. Why else would he have engaged Dalmorès and Renaud? Both were best known in contemporary works, although they sang the older repertoire.

To attribute all of what came later to Mary Garden's influence would be an error. He had never yet seen Garden, unless he had gone to one of her performances somewhere during the preceding summer. She is not aware that he did, and has told me so. She met him for the first time, in the company of M. Carré, director of the Opéra-Comique, during this spring of 1907 soon after Hammerstein's arrival in Paris. If it comes to that, why did he want to engage Mary Garden? She was famous, it is true, but all the "best judges"—which in opera means those who know all about yesterday and nothing about tomorrow—warned him that she would fail in the United States. The critic H. T. Finck wrote a long, solemn article to inform Hammerstein that Garden's "Parisian style" was unsuited to New York and that her repertoire would never be accepted there.

Hammerstein could easily have kept on forever with Bellini, Verdi, and Donizetti, throwing in Gounod and Bizet for good measure. There were more singers for such a repertoire than for the experimental innovations he had in mind. He had made most of his money in the first season out of Melba, mostly in old operas. Yet even for Melba he was busy announcing new operas for next year—*Tosca*, for instance, which she could never have done. (True, she studied it, but did she not also study—and once disastrously perform—the Brünnhilde role in *Siegfried?*)

3. *Why Mary Garden?*

"New York will be delighted with French opera," Hammerstein had predicted years before when he was casting about desperately for something to put into his first Manhattan Opera House on Thirty-fourth Street, the stillborn predecessor of his present child of brilliant promise. He had been talking then of French opera imported from New Orleans. This time he was taking steps to import French opera from its pure source in Paris.

From the first moment of thinking about French opera, he was obliged to consider what he could or would do about Mary Garden. She had sung only in France and England, but with almost stupefying results, in that preceding notions of operatic performance had to be abandoned by her audiences. Not quite, of course, but near enough to give that effect. She did not "produce beautiful tones"; she produced whatever tones were required by the music and the drama, and sometimes they were far from beautiful. Oscar knew all this by report. He had read discussions of Garden in the press of Paris and London; so had everybody else interested in opera. A great deal had already been published in the United States about her. If he engaged Garden, he would be taking a great and risky step, because she would sing a repertoire unknown to America, all contemporary, and she would do it in a style with which New York was totally unfamiliar.

And as he had already half committed himself to such a repertoire in his own mind (as I believe), how was he to do it without her? The artist and the repertoire were by now, after six years of unremitting success in Paris, more or less inseparable.

He actually had begun private negotiations a good many weeks before going to Europe. Gustave Schirmer, the music publisher, was the friendly agent to whom he appealed. Schirmer had no particular reason to love the Metropolitan Opera, which had made difficulties for him with scores, librettos, and related matters. He had also experienced the full rigors of the Ricordi treatment, which in those days, with Puccini blooming mightily and much of Verdi still in copyright, was of great note. He agreed to act for Hammerstein in the matter and wrote to the Maison Durand in Paris, which published the music of Claude Debussy and with which Schirmer had friendly business and personal connections. The date when this negotiation began is not established, but it must have been in January or February of 1907.

Durand's incentives for dealing with Hammerstein were obvious. If the modern French repertoire were to be established in the United States at all, it would have to be by way of a new opera house and accompanied by Garden's extraordinary gifts. At the Metropolitan, Verdi and Puccini had a stranglehold that was mitigated only by Wagner. Durand's firm owned a good many copyrights, but for Debussy alone—who by this time was an idol to his publisher as to the whole musical public of Paris—it would have been worth doing. The French publisher undertook conversations with Garden.

Garden herself, now scarcely thirty years old, was well aware of the nature of the undertaking. It was not in the least like the problem presented to Melba one year before. Melba had only to decide whether she wished to go to America and sing for a new manager in a new opera house, under strongly guaranteed financial conditions. What she would sing was obvious. It was opera in the grand manner as she had sung it everywhere else, works almost as familiar to her audiences as to herself.

Garden's problem was whether she could entrust herself to a company in which the prevailing style, with so many Italians present, might be totally at variance with her own. What Hammerstein had feared, to begin with, was that her fees might be prohibitive. She had been sensationally successful in Paris and was in great demand in Europe: she might "hold him up." That was the original reasoning. But as the discussion continued it was clear that the fee, substantial though it might be, was by no means the only consideration. Garden wanted to choose her own operas, their casts, scenery, costumes, even—if she could—their conductors. That began to be fairly clear early in the game. And her reasons for so wishing were quite valid. She knew that her own most successful repertoire, although centered upon herself, depended upon the ensemble of thoroughly trained artists, homogeneous in style, with whom she had performed for six years. She would have been altogether out of key and rhythm with any other kind of production.

It took a certain amount of correspondence for her to realize that Hammerstein was not at all hostile to her view in the matter. Even in the first tentative discussions, both must have been aware that they were progressing toward a contract of far more than ordinary significance because of all it involved.

Hammerstein did not scruple to make his prospects known in New York. During March and April he was so happy and expansive that no news of importance, if it was good news, could have been kept a secret. He did not have a contract with Garden, and yet he allowed the press to suppose quite freely that he did. Thus we find in the New York *Times* of March 18, 1907, in connection with the announcement of Mme Nordica's engagement, the statement that "Hammerstein's star trio" for the next season would be "Melba, Nordica and Mary Garden." The same statement appeared in other papers at various dates and was repeated in the *Times* later. At the Metropolitan, Conried may have believed the newspapers or—as he had his own good sources of information—he may have wormed out the truth of the situation, for only a few weeks later he asked Lina Cavalieri to rehearse *Thaïs* with Chaliapin as Athanaël in Paris. Obviously Conried was accepting Hammerstein's challenge to enter the lists with French opera.

Gatti-Casazza's suggestion in his memoirs, mentioned before, is that Conried might have bought up all the rights at one fell swoop and put the works away in a drawer, just to prevent Hammerstein and Mary Garden from doing what they did. How this might have advanced the cause of music and drama he does not explain. But certainly, if Conried wished to cut the ground from under Hammerstein, it would have been more effective to buy up the whole Garden repertoire, cynical as that might be with regard to the public's interest. To counter Hammerstein's move with *Thaïs* alone was futile; there were so many other French operas. As it turned out, he failed even to get *Thaïs*. Hammerstein got to Paris just in time.

New Vistas Rising

4. Long Thoughts on Shipboard

By the time he climbed the gangplank of the *Kaiser Wilhelm der Grosse* in the first week of May, Hammerstein had done all his thinking about the immediate future of his opera house. He knew what he was going to Paris for. His second season was, in his own mind, no longer in doubt.

But there were other, longer thoughts that he had time now to think. Questions he may have asked—must have asked—included at least these: Could New York support two opera houses? Was that point proved or not? If not, if one opera or the other must succumb, what was Hammerstein's chance of survival? And if he survived—which, at this stage of the reasoning, implied an inglorious collapse of the Metropolitan—what would he do?

The first of these questions he must have asked long ago and answered in the affirmative. Now the success of his first season had offered a kind of proof that New York could and would support two opera companies, at least for a while. If one of the two had to collapse afterward, there was a good chance that it would not be Hammerstein's.

The unmeasured extravagance of his dream begins with the final question: what would he do then? The later stages of his success must already have been taking shape in his mind. He had been prospecting in Philadelphia this very spring; he certainly had an opera house there well forward in his projects. An opera in Boston would come immediately afterward, and one in Chicago: these were all Metropolitan Opera cities, and if he were to kill the Metropolitan in one place, he would kill it in all. But then more, and then more, and then more—this was the way his mind worked—so that in some glowing nebula of the future he saw Hammerstein opera houses more or less everywhere in the United States, in cities of moderate size scattered about the country, ever more of them and, with incessant increase of success, right on to infinity. Where his dream becomes mania, in short, is not in what he had done up to now or would do in the next few months, but in the further goal (and the one beyond that and the one beyond that) which success at the Manhattan would make possible.

He kept his own counsel. Even his son Arthur learned with the general public, and not privately, each further step of this extraordinary obsession. Yet if I have not misunderstood him utterly, it was Hammerstein's nature to incubate these dreams for a long time before he attempted to release them into the common light of day. It must have been in this interval after having done the impossible at the Manhattan that he began to muse upon all those glittering mirages which were to be, in the end, his downfall.

He was about to have the one really great year of his life in opera, the one in which everything worked out to the advantage of his most deeply held purposes. He was now not only going to entertain New York, he was also going to *teach* it; and of the many who have tried, he is one of the very few who succeeded in that enterprise. He was about to inflict such a stinging lesson on the Metropolitan Opera, in particular, that the whole institution would be shaken to its foundations and, in the result, be renovated and reborn. He was Napoleon on the eve of Austerlitz.

Had he no misgivings? I think none. There had been warning voices, quite a few, but he ignored them. He had his own inner voices, and apparently they were the only ones he could really hear. There had been an extremely apposite editorial in the New York *Times* of Sunday, March 17, on the opera war, posing this question: "Are the two rival opera impresarios staking too much on the operatic appetite of this town and its public?" The *Times*, in cautious but serious terms, seemed to believe that they were; conceding that the public was at this moment "opera mad," it suggested fairly strongly that such an aberration could not last long and that it would be well for the impresarios to think.

Hammerstein may have read this article and probably did, but he was too well launched upon his fate to pay any attention to it. On the eve of an Austerlitz there are few indeed who can perceive through the mists of time and distance how the land lies at St. Helena.

XX

Mary Garden

O<small>N</small> H<small>AMMERSTEIN'S</small> <small>ARRIVAL</small> in Paris—he had paused in London for a thorough discussion with Campanini—he dined with Albert Carré, director of the Opéra-Comique. Carré took him to a concert, where he heard Jeanne Gerville-Réache, a contralto of singular gifts, whom he engaged for his next season. As far as it can be determined now, he met Mary Garden on the next day.

1. A Leap into the Unknown

Just how daring a step he was taking in pursuing this unusual artist, it is hard to realize fully today. Both she and her repertoire were unique in opera. In May, 1907, the works in which she had risen to her extraordinary position in Paris were like Chinese drama to most operagoers, even the most knowledgeable. The ordinary opera public in New York or London expected singing, and then more singing, and afterward more singing. Singing was understood to be the emission of beautiful sounds under beautiful control; the ideal was Melba. It is easy to see that Mme Melba had never remotely resembled any of the operatic heroines she impersonated during her triumphant season with Hammerstein: the press even says so, but attaches no importance to the fact. An

imposing and very grandiose lady of forty-six, she played successively a tubercular French cocotte in her early twenties, an Italian girl of sixteen or seventeen, a Scotch lassie, a German village
maiden of sixteen, and a tubercular grisette in her early twenties.
In all of these parts, regardless of their setting, Mme Melba was
accustomed to wear elaborate garments of the most costly materials,
velvet if possible, with a train and some well-chosen jewels. If
not restrained by force, she always wore a heavy gold chain about
her neck and over her majestic bosom, and as a rule there was
another such chain at her waist. We have all seen a large number
of Melba photographs showing this generic presentation. Sometimes
it is called Gilda and sometimes Lucia, sometimes Marguerite and
sometimes Mimi.

If one studies, even today, the photographs of Mary Garden in
various roles, one sees what a new idea of opera Hammerstein now
had to face. The photographs really might be of different persons
(my young daughter, looking over a file of them with me, said:
"But she's never the same! Are you sure that it's Garden?"). In
one picture we see the innocent or possibly even half-witted boy
Jean, the juggler to Our Lady, and in the very next the insolent
and sensuous outline of the princess of Judaea. Or the wide-eyed
and shrinking Mélisande comes next to the sensitive, bold whore
of Alexandria. The characterizations are so complete that they
actually seem to alter the features of the artist's face. It is not a
matter of costume at all, as one can quite easily prove by examining photographs of other artists in the costumes that (since Garden) have become standard for those parts.

Hammerstein seems to have been prepared to succumb to Garden's demands for a variety of reasons, the main one being that
his instinct or intellect, or a combination of the two, had already
decided he needed this artist. He may not have been altogether
prepared for her conditions, which were indeed unusual in opera.

She would not sing repertoire opera, as it is called—the bread-
and-butter works—at all, although she relaxed this rule occasionally and did sing, very successfully, a repertoire Marguerite
for him once. (By repertoire opera is meant works that are in the
repertoire all the time, in which one singer can take the place of
another without more than the sketchiest rehearsal or with no
rehearsal at all.) She would not sing with Italians if it could possibly be avoided, because their style was so totally different from

hers. She would not sing in any décor or costume that seemed to her unsuited to the meaning of the drama and music. She would not sing with any other principal artist whose style was out of key with the ensemble. She wanted, in fact, her own experienced and trained companions in so far as it could be arranged.

It took Hammerstein a little time to see the necessity for these requirements. He never had encountered a singer who cared so much about the ensemble of the production. His experience had been with those who wanted to know the fee, the number of performances, and the repertoire. That is, in fact, all that most singers want to know even today: ten Aïdas, five Giocondas, seven Normas. Garden wanted to stipulate in advance every detail of the productions in which she was to appear. An extremely intelligent woman, she realized full well how strange her repertoire was going to seem to New York, and she did not want to load it with the disadvantages it would have had, and would have today, in most opera houses.

In the end, he yielded all along the line, with one exception. He was bound to Campanini by every possible tie of gratitude and friendship as well as by contract. Campanini was his musical director, as well as chief conductor. Campanini would have to conduct the Garden repertoire.

There is no doubt that Miss Garden would have preferred one of the conductors with whom she had been working for seven years—André Messager, most likely (she has not told me this, but the whole context indicates it). She did not know Campanini, and she was, as she remained all her life, mistrustful of Italians in French opera. In the case of Campanini, everything was different: they became devoted friends and worked together for many years, long after Oscar's downfall, but in Paris in the spring of 1907 she could not foresee such a development. However, in view of her unprecedented victory in all other respects, she yielded in the case of Campanini.

What she obtained from Hammerstein was nothing less than a reproduction of the Paris production of *Pelléas et Mélisande* with the cast as it had held together for five years. He already had Dalmorès and Renaud, and with this she was extremely well pleased; now he must have Gerville-Réache, Jean Périer, Hector Dufranne, and others with whom she knew that she could do her best. And, as far as I can make out from Miss Garden's own account, both in conversation and in her book, she brought about these desirable results without actually browbeating Hammerstein at all, or even cajoling him. The main result—that which she wanted most of all, and which he may have guessed she wanted most of all—came of itself, of his own free will, after a performance of *Pelléas* which she invited him to attend with her sister.

2. The Legend of Garden

The romantic history of Mary Garden's career is too well known to require lengthy retelling here. She was born in Aberdeen, Scotland, and grew up in the United States, the daughter of a Chicago businessman. When she was eighteen some Chicago ladies undertook to pay for her study in Paris. When, after a year and a half, the money was no longer forthcoming, she was rescued from her plight by a beautiful lady, met in a chance encounter in the Bois de Boulogne, who turned out to be the California soprano then adored in Paris, Sybil Sanderson. Albert Carré, meeting her at Miss Sanderson's house, heard her sing and gave her a score of *Louise*, which was in preparation at the Opéra-Comique, to study. Then came the night of Friday, April 13, 1900, when the prima donna sang two acts with a sore throat and collapsed. Young Mlle Garden went on in the third act to sing the aria *"Depuis le jour."* Thereafter, the role—and Paris—were hers.

She sang *Louise* at the Opéra-Comique two hundred times after that, in the course of her extraordinary career. Her roles besides this one were various, and included some new operas in which she began to display her peculiar talent for characterization. In the words of a French critic of the time: *"Mlle Garden a une aimable figure, une voix aimable, et un petit reste d'accent exotique, aimable aussi."*

This *"petit reste d'accent exotique"* remained with her to the end, and, although she spoke French in those days far more than English, she always spoke it as a stranger from afar. It was this, too, which added great qualities to her incomparable Mélisande, the *"petit être mystérieux"* of Debussy's dream. One cannot hear the sharp and fluent French of real Frenchwomen in this part without longing to hear again the pale mystery of Garden's language.

Mary Garden

Claude Debussy visited Carré's office at the Comique sometime during 1901 and noticed on the director's desk a framed photograph of a girl in floating draperies (it was Garden in *Hélène*, an opera by Saint-Saens). "*Voilà ma Mélisande*," he said.

Carré, a seasoned practitioner of his craft, may have been less than anxious to bring Debussy and Garden together. Maeterlinck was famous for his bad temper and had assumed, on what authority nobody knows, that his wife, Georgette Leblanc, was to sing the Mélisande of Debussy's opera, even though she was not a professional singer. Debussy now insisted on trying Garden, and did so.

She relates the scene herself: a small studio in the Comique, with Debussy at the piano. They went through the role of Mélisande (that is, most of the work) and Debussy never said a word. When it was over, he was still silent. Garden went away to her dressing room to put on her hat and go home. A messenger came to ask her to come into Carré's office.

There she found Debussy, who was able to speak at last. He told her that she was his Mélisande (he never called her anything else after that). He asked her where she came from. She said: "Scotland." He was struck by this fact: from the mists of the north, from the far-off hills, she had come to Paris to be his Mélisande. It was singularly appropriate to the subtle and mysterious music of his masterpiece. He never had a doubt after that, and, although Paris flamed with stories of the Maeterlinck-Debussy feud, the composer himself was quite immovable. He would have Garden and nobody else; without Garden there would be no Mélisande. It has always been said, I do not know how accurately, that Maeterlinck actually climbed the stairs of Debussy's lodging in Montmartre and belabored him with a stick; it made no difference.

There followed the famous three months of rehearsals, for even at the Comique, where intelligence was more common than in other opera houses, nobody was sure of how this new musical utterance should be made. Singers and orchestra had much to learn. The hours of full rehearsal were so many that even then it would not have been possible except in a theater supported by the government; nowadays it would be impossible anywhere in the world except, perhaps, in Soviet Russia.

Garden had a wig that she loved. It took a long time to make, and she wore it throughout her stage career. It came from all over France—women with golden hair would sell one tress or several tresses to the diligent wigmaker who was engaged in the enterprise. The hair was of different lengths, but so artfully combined that on her head it was one single "head of hair," very long, covering her entire body in the scene at the fountain. Garden's wigs were famous; she told Van Vechten: "It would be difficult for me to go on the stage in my own hair." She had a particular feeling, which one finds more or less in all the French climate of the period, for hair; it was like Baudelaire's or Debussy's own: she felt that once she got into the right hair for a character, she had then become that character. All the months and years of study (and she was one of the most deliberate and studied artists who ever lived) could not make her into the character she had determined to be, but once the wig was on, she assumed the personality she had modeled and suffused with life in her own mind. The wig thus took the place of the masque in classic Greece, and was more important than costume or any other external detail.

Her gowns were like her creation itself: fragile and simple, subtle and remote. Her childlike terror, her strange longings and deep sadness, all conveyed by body and voice as one, seemed too true to be a stage performance. She never used a conventional gesture, and as Mélisande hardly any gesture; there was a defeated and helpless drooping of her entire body which conveyed more than any movements of the limbs. Many of these things she could not possibly have learned from Debussy or anybody else. Her uncanny suitability to the part of Mélisande must have frightened Debussy, I think—his strangeness when she first ran through the part with him is one sign, a clear one. He had been working on this lyrical drama, his life's masterpiece, for ten whole years, from 1892 to 1902. What must have been his wonder to find, at the very end of this period, that there actually existed an artist who could enact his dream in some respects more vividly than he had dreamed it? He wrote in her score of the work: "In the future, others may sing Mélisande, but you alone will remain the woman and the artist I had hardly dared hope for."

All this had happened five years before Hammerstein came to Paris to meet Garden. No doubt he had been aware at the time of the violent antagonism Debussy's anti-operatic opera aroused among conventional critics and music-lovers, and the equally violent partisanship of the avant-garde. At first it had seemed impossible that the work would ever make its way into the fair consideration of the public, even in Paris. And yet it did, bit by bit, week after week, until it was accepted in an almost religious spirit of reverence and the audiences that gathered for it were the most attentive to be found in the capital of the western world. This achievement was in very large part the achievement of Garden herself, with one of the most remarkable casts the Comique had ever presented: Jean Périer, Hector Dufranne, and the others, conducted by André Messager.

Meanwhile, of course, she had sung in other works as well, including *Manon* and *La Traviata*, but it was in the new operas that she made the deepest impression. And there were other operas to be associated with her name just as indissolubly as *Louise* and *Pelléas*. One was *Thaïs*, belonging to the Opéra; she had sung it only at Aix-les-Bains, where her annual visit had the particular patronage of King George I of Greece. Another was Henri Février's *Monna Vanna*, written long afterward (also for the Opéra), and still another the *Salome* of Richard Strauss. *Le Jongleur de Notre Dame*, although it belonged to the Comique, had never been sung by a woman in Paris: the part was written for a tenor, and it was Oscar Hammerstein who thought of giving it to Garden.

3. A Little Accident in Versailles

This was the Mary Garden he faced on his arrival in May, 1907—a woman whose extraordinary successes were already legendary, but who had a greater number of them yet to come. She was in a totally different category from the famous singers upon whom he had hitherto counted to fill his opera house. They were all at the end of their careers, although Melba's end lasted a long time. None of them could have learned a new role, probably; it is quite sure that none would have consented to try. Garden was ready to try anything if she felt it to be within her reach. She always disliked opera in English, for example, and yet she was willing to create the title part in Victor Herbert's *Natoma* a few years later and came very near to saving that feeble work by the vitality of her impersonation of the Indian maid. She was young, full of ideas, lithe of mind and body, resilient and determined.

Hammerstein was exactly twice her age. He admired her very much, as we know from abundant evidence, and yet there is no suggestion that he ever cherished any romantic erotic notions about her. (His taste ran, rather, to massive ladies, especially if they were not interested in him.) He saw a good deal of her in Paris that spring as she poured out her ideas to him—how opera should be produced; what a cast is; how a character is formed on the stage; what is the true meaning of *ensemble*. She took him up to Montmartre to show him where Louise and Julien lived. And she took him out to Versailles in an automobile.

Hammerstein had never been in an automobile. Indeed, automobiles were not common in 1907, as anybody can see from the street photographs of the period; they were greatly outnumbered by carriages, cabs, and other horse-drawn vehicles. Mary Garden, however, had an automobile as soon as she could, and, in fact, does not remember having been in a carriage after she left Paris for New York: characteristic of her contemporaneity, which ran through her entire being. She took Hammerstein to Versailles in her car, and one of the front wheels came off in the streets of Versailles, throwing the singer and the impresario violently to one side, with negligible injuries. The incident was cabled to America and had the unforeseen result of arousing the Metropolitan Opera to the dangers represented by Mary Garden.

It is not clear why the Metropolitan waited so long to get agitated. Hammerstein had used Garden's name quite freely in talking of his plans for the next season. It had been printed a considerable number of times that she would sing for him. Perhaps the Metropolitan thought this was all bluff; a whole new reper-toire, they may have thought, would be beyond Hammerstein's means. At all events, they knew now, from the cabled dispatch, that Hammerstein and Garden were in agreement. Late though it was, Conried's agents tried to get Garden for the Metropolitan; her contract with Hammerstein was by then signed.

Similarly, an attempt was made to obtain the rights to *Thaïs* for Cavalieri and Chaliapin to perform at the Metropolitan; and here, too, Hammerstein had been ahead of his rival—by a hair's breadth. He had come to amicable arrangements, with Carré and with the agent or entrepreneur Gabriel Astruc, which gave Hammerstein exclusive rights in New York for a long list of modern French operas, more than he had time to produce.

It was a fortunate thing for French opera that Hammerstein did obtain the rights, for the Metropolitan's stage and theater were never suited to them and the artists available in the Metropolitan company were even less suited. One cannot quite see what Chaliapin might have done with Athanaël; it would have been extremely good or extremely bad, as he had scarcely any middle ground; but Cavalieri was certainly not on the same planet with Garden. *Louise* or *Pelléas* with the Metropolitan singers of that day would have been worse.

Thus, the die was cast and Hammerstein embarked upon the course that was, more than any other single element, to characterize his contribution to American culture and social history.

4. A Sparking of Ideas

The two of them, Hammerstein and Garden, had a number of other ideas during that spring meeting. There is no doubt that both were thinking of *Salome*, Garden no doubt first. She liked and had studied the part, although she did not actually sing it until the following year at the Manhattan Opera House. Hammerstein went to Berlin to meet Richard Strauss, and their conversation turned upon not only *Salome* but *Elektra*. (As is well known, Strauss liked to rent out his operas in pairs.) At this time Hammerstein did not have an Elektra, but he was, as always, quite sure he would find the right one when the time came. (He did.) There were no engagements made on either side, but Strauss was still somewhat bruised from the experience he had had with the Metropolitan the year before—a *Salome* production with only one performance—and Hammerstein found him receptive. Garden applied herself still more to the study of the part.

It is not quite clear whether Hammerstein's idea for the *Jongleur* came at this time or later. If I may be allowed a guess, it is that he saw a performance of the *Jongleur* at the Comique in May or June, between his trips to Germany and Italy perhaps, and that the idea germinated from that. Certainly we find it well developed some months later when he proposed it to Garden. He was a showman. Now that he had acquired this astonishing piece of theater property, he was bound to have ideas on how it was to be exploited, how to get the most out of it. In any such endeavor he had a willing collaborator in Garden, whose appetite for new parts was always great. Travesty—if the word may be used of the *Jongleur*, the most delicate and natural of travesties—was probably commoner at that period than it has been since, owing partly to Mme Sarah Bernhardt. She played a man's part whenever she possibly could—Shylock, Hamlet, and others—and one of her great successes, written for her, was *L'Aiglon*. Whatever brought it into Hammerstein's head, it was a creative idea and gave Massenet's little opera a much wider vogue and longer life on the stage than anything else could have done.

Garden, of course, had won most of her points. Thus, she was empowered by her contract to pass on every piece of furniture on the stage, every detail of décor and even stage directions, all the casting of principals. Many and many a bitter quarrel was to arise over these powers, which she exercised in every opera in which she appeared. If she did not like the shape or color of a chair, it would, under the contract, have to be changed. Her quarrels with Hammerstein were ephemeral, but they seem to have been extremely numerous. And yet he passed more and more under her influence in all such matters as their acquaintance matured, until in the end her views carried more weight than any others at the Manhattan—more than Campanini's: it has been said that this alone would have been enough to cause Campanini's resignation.

One of Hammerstein's ideas for Garden which came to nothing was an opera on Barrie's play *Peter Pan* with music by Victor Herbert. He made a trip to London to see Barrie and obtained a qualified consent. It is to be assumed that he had Garden's consent beforehand and was sure of Herbert's; but, in the end, no libretto appeared and the opera could not be written. It may be just as well. Garden's English diction in the only opera she sang in that language was so remorselessly good that every word was distinct in every part of the house: the critics of the time thought this a misfortune. Like most operagoers, they could tolerate English only as long as it was unintelligible, as it usually is in singing.

5. *Two Who Belonged to the Theater*

Garden and Hammerstein had, in spite of enormous differences in intellectual structure, a great deal in common. "The show" was paramount for both of them. This enabled them to surmount any number of acrimonious disputes over details in the next three years. Garden could submerge herself into the ensemble as scarcely any prima donna known to history has done. The two of them had the tense, abstracted dimension, the extra dimension, into which the truest of theater people go on the rising of the curtain and a little before. They had in addition some less rarefied qualities that they shared, such as a natural talent for story-making and story-telling, the quality that causes its possessors to be quoted, chronicled, and described in the daily press. Earlier I have called this quality "mythogenic," which it is, but the myth-creator or natural myth-subject can never explain, nor can anybody else, how it comes to pass. Mary Garden had it abundantly, as did Hammerstein, and they understood each other quite well in these respects. Given the quality, the events tend to cluster around it in some strange way: the mythogenic personality is always going through experiences that actually do deserve the notice of the press and public.

As an example, I may mention the episode in which Mary Garden ran the elevator in the Bellevue-Stratford Hotel in Philadelphia about two weeks before her American debut. She had gone there to visit her sister. On her way down to the ground floor she was in a lift with the male operator and one other woman as a fellow passenger. The man operating the elevator had a seizure of some kind and fainted. The machine stuck between two floors, with a sensation of such tremulous insecurity that the other passenger, the woman, also fainted. Mary Garden took the controls and piloted the elevator down to the ground floor, where she called for first aid for her fellow passenger and the operator.

This episode really happened in the presence of many witnesses and some reporters. It was printed throughout the country. No press agent could have invented it. It displayed in the same instant Garden's intrepidity, her resourcefulness, her lack of "nerves" in the ordinary sense: *bref*, her strength. And, most of all, in what she said to the reporters afterward she showed the self-contained and autonomous singularity of her own character, the Scottish-American-Parisian.

"Well, what of it?" she said. "After all, we have *ascenseurs* in Paris."

From the moment she agreed to come to Hammerstein's opera she was constantly in the press. She had been mentioned often enough before; now, even before her first appearance, she became one of the dramatis personae of the newspapers, as she remained for years thereafter. It was the kind of gift Hammerstein was well qualified to appreciate; everything that happened to her was a "story." Her clothing was described in considerable detail at the opening of the Manhattan that year, for example, although she was in the house only as a member of the audience. If she had an opinion on any subject and expressed it, this in itself required headlines. No singer of the time sprang so naturally into newsprint or remained there so constantly. It was a different Mary Garden from the girl who, solitary and bereft, had walked in the Bois de Boulogne only a few years before, waiting for her salvation. It dazzled the beholder, but she may not have thought it at all remarkable—after all, we have *ascenseurs* in Paris.

XXI

The Golden Second
Season Begins

Preparations for the season that was to make operatic history began quietly enough. On his return to the United States, Hammerstein was busy putting in the much needed new entrance to the Manhattan Opera House and attending to the many details of getting his productions in readiness. He nevertheless had time to compose some music for Miss Gertrude Hoffman, the dancer, who was about to open a long engagement at the Victoria. He also had time to engage in amorous dalliance with a lady who, as we shall see, kept all his letters—a lady who, like so many of his temporary friends, wished to sing in his opera house.

The new entrance was in Thirty-fifth Street, admitting patrons through the back of the house, behind the stage and past the singers' dressing rooms. This was to relieve the congestion at the single entrance on Thirty-fourth Street, and was used chiefly by persons with tickets in the boxes and orchestra. He also made the innovation (this second season, and not the first as had been said) of "lady ushers," picked for their good looks as well as for their politeness and their knowledge of the house. Many were the jokes and cartoons that reached print about these "lady ushers" during the next season or two, but the evidence is that they were efficient and resourceful as well as pretty.

1. New Productions and Old Prima Donnas

Aside from Mary Garden and the new ideas that came with her, Hammerstein had made a real discovery of another kind on his trip to Europe. It was in London, in a theater where a comic-opera company from Berlin was playing, that he heard Offenbach's fantasy-opera *The Tales of Hoffmann.* It struck him at once that this sentimental work, with all its prettiness of décor and self-conscious charm in the characters, would be likely to succeed in New York.

It was virtually unknown there, having been once performed in 1882 at the Fifth Avenue Theatre and then forgotten. Offenbach's last work, completed by a friend, it reached the Opéra-Comique in February of 1881. It was immediately successful at the Comique, and still is, but its success in central Europe was delayed by the fact that at its first night in Vienna in December, 1881, a terrible fire broke out in the Ringtheater and some in the audience were burned to death. A superstition clung about the work for at least two decades. Later the opera became very popular in German —indeed, it has come to be considered, as *Hoffmanns Erzählungen,* practically a German work—and it has never ceased to command audiences in France. America was unaware of it.

This, Hammerstein saw, might be the kind of successful production which his *Carmen* had been the year before, good for almost incessant repetition. He asked Renaud to undertake the three principal baritone parts and thus ensured a focus of rare quality for what is otherwise an episodic concoction. His acumen as an opera manager was seldom so brilliantly demonstrated, for the work was an immediate success. To the present generation it seems odd that it was ever anything else, as it has been often performed in the years since and at least one of its set pieces, the duet called the "Barcarolle," is familiar by now to the most unheeding ear. In 1907 it was, surprisingly enough, a novelty.

In the spring he had intended, or at least announced, that Melba should open his season—one report said it would be in *Aïda.* What correspondence passed between him and Melba has not been revealed. She did not return to the Manhattan. No doubt Hammerstein was content that this should be so, for, although she did pack the house at every performance, her fees were huge and he was now well supplied with prima-donna sopranos. He chose for his opening night *La Gioconda*, with Lillian Nordica in the title role, Giovanni Zenatello making his American debut as Enzo, and the great Polish basso Adamo Didur making his American debut as Alvise. Campanini conducted, but no longer was he marked on the advertisements as simple conductor: he was "Musical Director" from now on.

This, of course, was a production new in every detail; he had two such in his first week, the other being *La Damnation de Faust*, and both were ambitious as far as décor and spectacle were concerned. His production of operas new to the Manhattan, some of them also new to America, was high in this season, but those he promised and did not produce were even more numerous.

Some allowance must be made for the fact that it was actually a good tactical maneuver, now that the opera war was open and declared, to annoy the Metropolitan by making announcements that challenged their superiority in some vital regions, such as Wagner, or threatened them with dangerous novelties. Hammerstein had gone the limit in this kind of activity. The Wagner announcements were perhaps the worst, because they involved so many announcements of so many different kinds. At one time Hammerstein said he was endeavoring to get Siegfried Wagner to America to conduct *Tristan* and other works; later it was Hans Richter who was coming; all sorts of prominent names were mentioned in this connection, and, as far as one can tell now, it was never anything but a press campaign, a "war of nerves" against Conried. Color was given to these Wagner reports and statements by the engagement of Mme Nordica, who was a famous Isolde and Brünnhilde, and by a contract for the contralto Ernestine Schumann-Heink.

As far as is known, no other Wagner artists of renown were even approached, but the report alone was enough to stir up the Metropolitan to new efforts. It was in this season that Conried, after months of effort, succeeded in persuading Gustav Mahler to come to America as conductor for works of his own choosing, with special privileges in the way of orchestral rehearsal. (He did *Tristan*, *Fidelio*, and *Don Giovanni*.) In this season also, Olive Fremstad, the Swedish dramatic soprano, who was just coming into her years of greatness, sang her first Isolde. The net result of Hammerstein's lavish announcements was certainly an improvement at the Metropolitan, so perhaps they were objectively justified.

The same can hardly be said of Hammerstein's treatment of singers whom he had, in the flush of success as his first season ended, engaged for numerous performances at high fees. It makes one feel hot and embarrassed to read of how he treated Mme Nordica—how he "got rid of her," as his friends said. And it was certainly a new and strange experience for Mme Schumann-Heink to sing one single performance in a whole opera season for which she had a contract. Nor can it have been altogether pleasant for Mme Calvé to come in at the very end, sing a few (very few) Carmens, and end with a popular-priced Saturday-night performance. These were cases in which Hammerstein was really quite ruthless—not only inhumane, but inhuman. If famous singers are too old to compete with younger ones, then famous impresarios should not give them large contracts. The fault was clearly Hammerstein's, to start with; in his mania for fame, he engaged singers who no longer commanded the public he wanted inside his opera house. One can understand how he happened to do it. He was filled with exuberant self-confidence and he had Mr. Woolworth's $400,000 in the bank; he had risked a shipwreck in the early part of his first season for lack of prima-donna sopranos; he was, like most opera-lovers, bedazzled by the great names. He seems to have taken no account whatever of the fact that underneath the great name there was in every case a human being, sometimes a very sensitive and cruelly injured human being. This chapter of his activity at the Manhattan is one that does not redound in any way to his credit. If he had "got rid of" his contracts in some frank and simple way, such as telling the singers that they did not justify the expenditure on their fees, he could have been sued for breach of contract. By offending them instead, he escaped his obligations, at least legally, by forcing the offended artist to retire. Such devices were certainly unworthy of a man who in that same season was to give America its first opportunity of seeing and hearing *Pelléas et Mélisande*.

2. Gala Opening, with "Society"

The opening night of the second season at the Manhattan was November 4, 1907, two full weeks before the Metropolitan's opening. It was a brilliant occasion; a good many subscriptions for the boxes and the orchestra seats had come in during the summer; "society" refused to be discouraged by Hammerstein's attitudes and turned out in force; an immense amount of favorable publicity had attended every move the impresario made during that summer and autumn. All the auguries were good. Compared with the first season's subscriptions of only $30,000, we are told that for this second season subscriptions passed $175,000. The figure varies, like most of those Hammerstein allowed to become public, but it is not in doubt that he began the second season with a great deal more money in the till than he could rationally have expected.

Some of this was due to the personal activity of Mrs. Clarence Mackay, a woman of great wealth and position, who had begun coming to the Manhattan during the Melba engagement and never stopped. Her enthusiasm for the new company was such that she undertook to sell subscriptions among her friends, and did so on a really considerable scale. Arthur Hammerstein knew all about it, of course, but did not care to tell his father for fear of an outburst against "society." Mrs. Mackay's interest continued throughout this season and she did a great deal for the Manhattan, but Arthur kept silent. It should be explained, perhaps, that Mr. Woolworth's benefactions were all right because he was a self-made man—he was not in "society" and had nothing to do with the Metropolitan—whereas Mrs. Mackay was from the pinnacle of the New York oligarchy and thus taboo to Hammerstein.

For the opening night the newspapers sent reporters of all sorts —one to describe the dresses and jewels, one to list names, one to give a general story of the evening, and one to write about the music. All this made columns of print and was fully equal to the attention given two weeks later to the opening at the Metropolitan, although the list of names for the Manhattan was shorter. Miss Mary Garden, who sat in a stage box with her father and sister, shared the major attention of the curious with the young Duchess of Marlborough, born Consuelo Vanderbilt, who was in Mrs.

Mackay's box just opposite. Miss Garden, we learn from the *Times*, was "very beautiful in a gown of black spangles," and the Duchess of Marlborough wore diamonds. Some special interest attached to her presence because it had actually been her father, at the insistence of her mother, who had created the Metropolitan Opera House, and up to this night no member of the Vanderbilt clan had visited the Manhattan, so far as is known.

The new entrance to the house received approval, and the incoming audience passed by the dressing room where Zenatello was "trying out B's and C's." There was a great deal less confusion than on the opening night a year before, although the crowd was almost as huge. Standing room had been exhausted at seven o'clock; indeed, so many tickets had been sold for this space that it was almost impossible to walk about during the intermissions. The "lady ushers" were highly appreciated.

As for the opera itself, Campanini drew more praise than ever for his powerful and incisive beat; Nordica "displayed her voice and vocal art in all their plenitude and potency"; Zenatello, coming to America with a high reputation, justified it fully with his "rich, sympathetic, warm" tenor voice; Mmes de Cisneros and Gerville-Réache were highly appreciated; Ancona was well received, as always; and the new basso, Didur, was welcomed, although not in terms that might even have suggested his long and distinguished subsequent career. It was, in short, an auspicious beginning.

3. Good-by to Mme Nordica

Hammerstein was not satisfied, just the same. Every element of success was present, but he was no longer in the frame of mind in which he had engaged Mme Nordica to sing. She had a contract for thirty performances and her fee was one of the highest paid to any singer of the time, probably close to $2,000 for each performance. It appears that he resolved even in the first week to rid himself of this heavy obligation. He had in production very few operas of Nordica's repertoire, and all the fine projects for the production of Wagner had evaporated during the summer; his new efforts were to be in another direction.

The Golden Second Season Begins

This idea grew on him when he perceived, by the second *Gioconda* (Friday, November 8), that Mme Nordica was not a magnet for the public any more. The first night had been crowded because it was a first night; the second *Gioconda* was only moderately attended. When he gave her an *Aïda* for the beginning of his second week (Monday, November 11), the conviction grew upon him that she was a heavy liability and that thirty performances from her would throw his whole season out of balance and cause him severe financial loss.

He then began a systematic campaign to induce her to break her contract. She had an abhorrence of cigar smoke. From his place of vantage in the wings, sitting on the kitchen chair, he was never without the cigar, fire laws or no. She had to pass by him. He saw to it that she was compelled to walk through a cloud of the obnoxious smoke, which he did not scruple to blow into the air directly in front of her face. When he did this at a morning rehearsal, she left the stage and refused to see him or speak to him again.

Mme Nordica at this time was about forty-eight years old and had been a very celebrated singer, first at Covent Garden and then at the Metropolitan, for at least two decades. She had the imperious manner of a prima donna of the old school, and she was not at all acclimated to Hammerstein's behavior. The probability is that they never liked each other to begin with. At all events, after she had decided not to speak to him again, they communicated through secretaries. He had a new plan: he was going to put on a series of extra performances on non-subscription nights at cheap prices, with Mme Nordica as the principal soprano in each of them.

When the full meaning of this proposal sank in, Nordica retired to her country house at Ardsley-on-Hudson and sang no more at the Manhattan. The press was extremely curious about the affair and printed a number of versions of it. Hammerstein said: "She has a contract for thirty performances, but they don't all have to be in December, do they?" Nordica herself gave no statement until the end of the year, when she announced that her connection with Hammerstein's company was at an end but that her relations with the impresario were "amicable." It is quite possible that some compensation was paid her for the remainder of her contract. She sang only five of her thirty contracted performances—*Gioconda* twice in the first week and twice in the second, and *Aïda* once in the second week. Each subscriber (that is, Monday, Wednesday, and Friday nights and Saturday matinees) heard her once, and the Monday-night subscribers heard her twice.

4. Garden Makes Her Entrance

Hammerstein's first week consisted of the new production of *La Gioconda* on Monday and Friday, with *La Damnation de Faust* on Wednesday and Bressler-Gianoli's Carmen for the Saturday matinee. At the Saturday-night "pop" he offered *Il Trovatore* with Jeanne Jomelli, Mme de Cisneros, a new tenor called Carlo Albani, and Ancona and Mugnoz, Parelli conducting. Bressler-Gianoli's Carmen was also offered at a special matinee on Tuesday, November 5, the day after the opening.

La Damnation de Faust was a strange choice for an impresario who aimed at either novelty or financial success, for it was neither. It had been produced the year before at the Metropolitan with Geraldine Farrar, amid public indifference and critical disfavor. Hammerstein no doubt wanted merely to show how much better he could do it, and this point at least was proved. Maurice Renaud as Méphistophélès was a somber and sinister apparition and made a great impression on the critics. However, *La Damnation de Faust* has never been a popular opera anywhere, probably because it is not in reality an opera. Renaud and the ballet made Hammerstein's production less of a bore than the Metropolitan's, and Campanini's conducting gave the music every advantage it could receive in a theater. Incidentally, the Metropolitan's unfortunate conductor Arturo Vigna had now departed from that company as a result of the constant comparison with Campanini.

The second week was distinguished by the *première* of *Les Contes d'Hoffmann*. Nobody in New York remembered the one performance it had had twenty-five years before. It came to the public as a new work and leaped into popularity at once. The singers were Alice Zeppilli, Jeanne Jomelli, and Eleanora de Cisneros, with Dalmorès as Hoffmann and Renaud in three parts: Dr. Miracle, Coppélius, and Dapertutto. This, of course, was a field day for Renaud, who had ample opportunity to display his talent for make-up and diversity of characterization. There were parts for Gilibert and for Armand Crabbé, a dependable baritone who had made his debut in *La Damnation de Faust* and was to remain in the company to the end. In this case, Hammerstein enjoyed a triumph of judgment, for the work had been lying ready to anybody's hand for decades and had not really been noticed. It became a mainstay of his company then and afterward.

The third week of the season had been planned to culminate in the American *première* of *Thaïs* and the eagerly awaited debut of Mary Garden on Friday, November 22. When Friday came, Garden sent for Hammerstein and told him she could not sing. He was stunned—the house was sold out—and made some attempt to protest. She went to the piano, played a chord, and sang a phrase for him. Convinced, he went back to the opera house and sent out notices for the cast of *Les Contes d'Hoffmann* (he had already repeated it on the Monday of this third week). There was no time to make the change known to the public, so the crowd arrived expecting *Thaïs*. Once they got there, most of them stayed, although the management offered to refund their money.

Garden rested and submitted to doctoring at her apartment in the Loreley, at Forty-fifth Street and Madison Avenue, where she lived that year (she was afterward a confirmed dweller in the Ritz-Carlton, which was not then completed). The chances are that she brought herself up to singing pitch by sheer will power as much as anything else, for she did actually make her debut only three days later, and three days are not much for a case of the grippe.

Thaïs, on Monday, November 25, 1907, was the opening of a new era of opera in the United States. It was so recognized, whether with delight or with misgivings, even at the time. The crowded house seemed eminently pleased, and Mary Garden was almost buried in flowers at the end. The *"Méditation"* for violin solo, between the two scenes of Act II, was played by Leandro Campanari, the regular first violinist of the orchestra, but a rumor got about and may be heard even to this day that Hammerstein had engaged Mischa Elman (anonymously—a likely story!) to play it. It was wildly applauded, perhaps on the basis of this same rumor, and had to be repeated. I have it on Mr. Elman's authority that he did play the *"Méditation"* for Hammerstein at a Sunday-night concert in the Manhattan some weeks later, but by no means anonymously.

The work itself was judged with severe justice, without indulgence, by a corps of critics who seem to have been curiously obtuse to any merit in it. It took some years for the repertoire of which it was an example to be received for what it was—skillful music of a sentimental and sensuous kind, wonderfully adapted to the theater. True, it is operatic music of the third or fourth category, but so are many of the Italian works that the same critics accepted quite solemnly for years. What distinguishes *Thaïs* and a number of other operas by Massenet is the theatrical effectiveness of which they are capable in the hands of really good performers.

The cast consisted of Garden, Dalmorès, and Renaud, the best that could have been assembled anywhere. Campanini conducted, beginning a long career of activity in a new repertoire that became as much his own as the Italian in time.

Richard Aldrich, critic of the New York *Times*, observed that this was "the first American appearance of Miss Mary Garden." He goes on:

"Her coming has long been awaited as one of the important contributions to New York operatic enjoyment that Mr. Hammerstein expects to make this season and there was much interest aroused in her first appearance. This had been delayed from last Friday because of her vocal indisposition, and although it was announced that she had entirely recovered, it is likely that a wholly fair judgment of her voice was not to be made last evening. . . .

"Miss Garden disappointed those who expected beauty and richness of voice and purity of vocal style. Her voice has something of an acid quality and has no longer the freshness and sensuous charm that doubtless once belonged to it. . . .

"It is as a dramatic artist that she creates the deepest impression. She has beauty of face and figure, and a swift litheness and graceful activity upon the stage, an incessant play of plastic pose, a rich suggestiveness of facial expression. She is an actress of the true vein and her denotement of the changing phases of emotion through which she passes are clear, incisive and subtle. There is an unceasing intensity and dramatic poignancy in her dramatic style. She made all that there was to be made of her experiences under the spell of Athanaël's influence and represented, in the last condition of her soul as a member of the White Ladies, a true tragic note."

Reginald de Koven (New York *World*) said: "Something new has come into opera." The *Sun* said that Garden was "in almost every way worthy of her reputation." W. J. Henderson amplified that "almost." He said: "Whatever Miss Garden may have been in the sweet summertime long ago, she cannot now be called a singer. . . . There may have been a voice once, but it and that method could not long dwell together."

5. *"But Is She a Singer?"*

Thus began the incessant dispute, lasting many years, over whether Mary Garden was a "singer" or not. A compromise to which many critics had recourse was to call her a "singing actress," thus begging the question. The obvious truth is that she was a singer of a kind new to New York who never at any moment separated the vocal and the dramatic parts of her performance. Her characterizations were impregnated with music; she could never have acted any part without singing. Her vocal method was French, to begin with, which gave it some "open" or "white" tones less common among Italians; but, whatever it might have been, she could never have given it any sort of pre-eminence over the dramatic significance of a scene. Thus she had, as she has herself said, not one but many voices—a different voice, in effect, for each character. Almost twenty years after this American debut I heard all her performances of Mélisande at the Opéra-Comique —those organized for the tenth anniversary of Claude Debussy's death—and some of the sounds that came from her had an un-earthly and mysterious beauty, whether they were "singing" or not.

The public, at all events, made no mistake. From the beginning onward, with the single exception of the second *Thaïs*, she sang to crowded houses. Some of this may have been due to curiosity at first, because she had received so much attention from the press, but a public of confirmed Garden addicts came into being with considerable rapidity and formed the heart of all her audiences in many cities. This special public of hers included a large number of fashionable personages and a great many of the young; she had, among other things, what is called "snob appeal," an attraction for those who wish above all things to be *à la page*. She had also in some works of her repertoire a great appeal to persons interested in music but not normally addicted to opera as it is usually performed. And, finally, in her first season as in her last, she had an irresistible attraction for other singers: half the Metropolitan Opera company could be seen at the Manhattan on some of the nights when Garden sang.

This last point gave Hammerstein a chance to perpetrate one of his jokes. On one of the Garden nights there were three very famous prima donnas in a stage box before the curtain rose, three ladies well past their prime but still reigning at the Metropolitan. Hammerstein, speaking to the artists on the stage before the curtain rose, told them about this and then, burlesquing Napoleon's speech to his troops before the Battle of the Pyramids, he added: "Illustrious artists, uphold my honor and yours! Three thousand years gaze down upon you!"

Garden's debut was a success from the moment of her extraordinary entrance, lithe and vivid, scattering flowers. On that night Clarence Mackay, in a box with his wife, sent for Arthur Hammerstein and told him to tell his father not to worry about money: if the opera company got into financial difficulties, he, Mackay, would come to the rescue. Arthur was delighted by this message, which sounded like a guarantee for the company. He hastened backstage to tell his father. "Tell Mackay to go to hell," said Oscar, and refused to discuss it further.

The second *Thaïs*, on the Saturday matinee of that same week, faced an inexplicable slump in the sale of tickets. It is said that only $200 worth of tickets were sold in the balcony and gallery, usually crowded at the Manhattan. This was the occasion on which Hammerstein said to Miss Garden (as she has told me): "Mary, there isn't enough money in the house to pay the light bill." Without a doubt she gave a better performance on that second occasion than on the first, for she, like Hammerstein, was combative and determined. A new singer, however famous in Europe, in a new opera of unfamiliar style—this combination might easily have failed in New York, as quite competent observers had predicted that it would.

However, in that strange way which is endemic to theaters, everything changed in a few days. The third *Thaïs* (Wednesday, December 5) and the fourth (on Friday the thirteenth) drew very large houses, and the sequence might have continued indefinitely if Garden had not, at this moment, just when *Louise* was ready for production, relapsed into the grippe again.

This time it was a terrible problem for Hammerstein because he had nothing else new to produce. For the week of Garden's debut (the fourth) he had filled in with *Carmen, Faust,* and *Aïda,* all of which had been done often before, adding a production of *Ernani* (Friday, November 29) for no reason that can be discerned. It had an inferior cast (Russ, Albani, Ancona, Arimondi) and the opera had failed dismally at the Metropolitan only a few years before with Sembrich, Scotti, and Édouard de Reszke. In the fifth and sixth weeks, aside from the Garden performances, he had stopped up the holes with *Hoffmann,* which was proving a gold mine, and *La Gioconda* with Russ in Nordica's part. Zenatello's *Faust,* sung with a cast not otherwise remarkable, was also of considerable use, but the attendance at these routine performances was not what he liked to see. *Hoffmann* and *Carmen* could not go on forever, although each of them did duty, sometimes twice in a week.

Sammarco's arrival provided some relief, for he could fill the house whenever he sang *Pagliacci.* Hammerstein put this on twice in Sammarco's first week (the sixth) and once in each of the next two, coupling it with Gerville-Réache in *La Navarraise.* But the situation was extremely uncomfortable because even now, in his second season, he did not have enough operas in repertoire, rehearsed and ready, to take care of all the emergencies that arose.

What the press referred to as "the disastrous illness of Miss Mary Garden" kept her out of the opera house for three weeks, from December 13 to January 3, while operas that had been produced the year before were hastily brought out and rehearsed. This brought about a first-rate crisis two days after Christmas when the orchestra, which had rehearsed *Don Giovanni* for five solid hours, refused to work any more. Campanini, who was in a fever to do justice to that masterpiece on the following day, had been worked outrageously himself, and no doubt his nerves were frayed. He had to conduct *Un Ballo in Maschera* that night as well—and the orchestra had to play it—because *Louise* was again postponed. He flew into a violent rage when the orchestra struck; he walked out of the opera house, swearing that he was going back to Italy, never to return. It was up to Hammerstein to recapture his indispensable conductor and calm down the irate or-chestra, both of which tasks he accomplished with his usual magic, although not without effort.

The American *première* of *Louise* was to have been on Decem-ber 20. *Rigoletto* was substituted, with Sammarco; although it was never one of his great roles, the beauty of his voice carried the performance. *Louise* was next announced for December 27. *Un Ballo in Maschera* was substituted for it, with Zenatello and Sam-marco giving superlative performances to a disappointed audience (the women were Russ, Zeppilli, and De Cisneros).

The first *Louise* was actually performed on Friday, January 3, and with immense success. Garden returned to the stage in much better voice than she had enjoyed before her illness, and her triumph was decisive. Along with her, Mme Bressler-Gianoli as the Mother, Dalmorès as Julien, and Gilibert as the Father were re-ceived with downright acclaim. The point of ensemble was begin-ning to penetrate. Critics who had seen only *Thaïs* could not really, in spite of Garden's creation and that of Maurice Renaud, begin to take in what the new acting-singing style at the Opéra-Comique meant. With the *Louise* production, so utterly different in dramatic content, the sharpness of differentiation struck the most dull-witted and prejudiced of observers. There was genuine enthusiasm from the public, and the opera received eleven perform-ances that season. It could have gone on much longer (as it did in subsequent years) if there had been time, and if the demands of *Pelléas* had not supervened.

Thaïs, of course, depended not only upon Mary Garden but upon Maurice Renaud, whose Athanaël was a superb creation of character in singing and acting. He was obliged to leave the United States in early February to fill engagements in Europe, so that the seventh and last *Thaïs* was given on Monday, February 3. (Garden and Renaud resumed their long series of *Thaïs* perform-ances in April of that year, when she made her debut at the Opéra in Paris.)

By this time it was abundantly proved that the public of New York did have an appetite, hitherto unsuspected, for French operas aside from the perennial *Faust* and *Carmen*. How much of this was due to the excellent casts Hammerstein provided, how much to the personality of Mary Garden, and how much to sheer novelty, it would be difficult to say. The proof was made, however, and *Pelléas et Mélisande,* the most problematical of the new works, was put into rehearsal. It presented few difficulties to the cast, once they knew the stage of the Manhattan, for they had been imported from Paris almost intact; but it was a terrific challenge to Campanini, who had never seen or heard the score and was totally unfamiliar with Debussy's ideas of musical utterance. Miss Garden's intelligence came into play in this matter, and her long collaboration with Campanini probably had its deepest roots in the weeks during which *Pelléas* was prepared. It was to be, for Campanini as for herself, a victory memorable in the history of opera.

XXII

The Fabulous Tetrazzini

MEANWHILE, another feature of Hammerstein's golden season was ready for the plaudits of New York. Luisa Tetrazzini was a coloratura soprano, then thirty-seven years of age, who had sung throughout Italy, Spain, Portugal, Russia, Mexico, and South America for about twelve years without causing riots in the streets. She had a high coloratura of the utmost brilliance, as her surviving records (or reprints of them) prove without question, but the lower part of her voice was not strong and she did not have the even, pure cantilena of Melba. What she did with the upper part of her voice was so phenomenal that nothing else mattered, and when her moment came she took the world by storm, as only a coloratura (or, in rare cases, a tenor) can do.

1. Hysteria in London

She made her debut at Covent Garden on November 2, 1907, in *La Traviata*, and the London public, not much given to hysteria, was struck with one of its occasional seasons of madness. The crowds at every performance she gave were very nearly beyond control; the enthusiasm in the opera house was unbounded, the demonstrations were without parallel in living memory (Melba had been, in comparison to this conflagration, a very slow growth indeed). All of this was duly cabled to America and to other parts of the world and made Tetrazzini an object of the keenest interest everywhere.

It happened that she was the younger sister of Eva Tetrazzini, Campanini's wife, and had received a good deal of vocal instruction from her. The story of their estrangement had never been told, but at this period and during the subsequent era of Luisa's reign in the opera house they were not at all friendly. Campanini conducted when his sister-in-law sang, but did not talk to her otherwise. It was not through his good offices that Hammerstein brought Luisa to America. His son Arthur did it.

The first dispatches from London about Tetrazzini aroused Arthur Hammerstein's interest. He was by this time deep in all the affairs of the opera house, and, although he never shared his father's intense preoccupation with opera in general, he had the interests of the Manhattan at heart and longed to bring off a coup of his own that might compel his father's approval or admiration. He sent the opera company's chief linguist and interpreter, Brignoli, to London to hear this sensational new singer and, if she was all the newspapers said, to offer her a contract. Brignoli was unable to get into Covent Garden on the night he arrived, as Tetrazzini was singing and the crowd was immense; he bribed his way in at the next performance and heard her. (She was singing *La Traviata*, *Rigoletto*, and *Lucia* in rapid succession, over and over, just as she did later in New York and throughout the world.) Brignoli talked to her; she knew all about the Manhattan and Hammerstein—who in opera did not, by this time?— and she was willing, but she could not come until February. Arthur cabled Brignoli to get a contract immediately, specifying a fee of $1,000 a night to begin with and a progression to $1,500 per performance.

Meanwhile, the Tetrazzini enthusiasm in London passed all bounds and was the subject of repeated cablegrams to the New York newspapers (seasoned London operagoers say there never was such a sudden outburst as took place over this singer). Oscar Hammerstein, although his season was fully planned, could not ignore such an unusual occurrence and sent for his son Arthur to say so. Undoubtedly what impressed him most was that Londoners should behave in this untrammeled fashion, cheering themselves hoarse like Italians and packing the public streets to look at a soprano. By rearranging the later part of his season, he could bring her into the Manhattan.

While this conversation between father and son was going on, Arthur received the telegram from Brignoli saying that Tetrazzini had signed the contract. It was, or should have been, a tremendous moment for Arthur, a vindication of his position in the management of the company.

Underneath everything else, Hammerstein the elder was no doubt pleased that his son had shown such initiative, particularly with respect to a singer who promised to be of immense value. But at the moment his anger took the upper hand and he gave Arthur a stinging reprimand for sending Brignoli away from New York in the midst of the season (this although he had not even noticed Brignoli's absence). Hammerstein at the time was so deep in his plans for Mary Garden that he had no need of an Italian interpreter, and the whole maneuver, lasting about three weeks, had taken place without his knowledge.

Tetrazzini was able to rearrange her engagements in such a way as to get to New York in January and make her debut on Wednesday, January 15, 1908, in *La Traviata*.

2. The Unsolved Mystery of a Coloratura

It was one of the most surprising first appearances in the long record of such events: it surprised the police as much as the Manhattan Opera staff and the newspapers. The only thing in this century at all like it was the first appearance of Galli-Curci about ten years later. Caruso, Melba, and the other reigning singers of the century did not have sensationally successful debuts and did not arouse hysteria among masses of people until they had been singing for some years. Tetrazzini brought out such a mob that it was difficult to handle it, and from the time she began to sing, that mob was in delirium. Such wild scenes have been witnessed on few occasions in New York. The soprano herself was in floods of tears, the audience was, as the *Times* said, "frenetic," and it was altogether beyond the usual limits of a musical event, however important.

The Fabulous Tetrazzini

Searching for some explanation of the Tetrazzini phenomenon, we find in all the newspaper writing, both in London and in New York, an element that we who have not heard her could not possibly expect. She is said to have had an "extremely emotional voice" in the passages that permitted or called for its use. This we could never have learned from the phonograph records now accessible. From those we are able to perceive a very long breath and a remarkable high coloratura, but no emotion at all. At the actual performances in the opera house there was apparently some almost electrically emotional quality, because it is stressed again and again by quite competent reviewers. *Grove's Dictonary*, for example, makes a point of her success *as an actress* in addition to her triumph as a singer. Such a combination would be, of course, irresistible. It had not occurred for a very long time, possibly not since Jenny Lind, for Melba was devoid of feeling and Sembrich much too correct to do more than suggest it. At all events, whatever it was, it had the property of driving audiences into hysteria from about 1907 to 1914, more at the beginning of the period than at the end.

When we see photographs of Mme Tetrazzini now, we find them a trifle ridiculous. Her weight was excessive by our standards, and seems worse because it was so obviously encased in rigid armor. That a woman with such an appearance could have been an actress, and could with her acting and her voice reduce an audience to tears, is hard for us to believe. And yet the evidence is all there, many columns of it in the New York press of the time, providing at least a psychological basis for the unreasoning mania with which her appearances were attended.

What she did as a coloratura we know—that is all fully shown by the public prints—and it was remarkable enough, although we can understand it technically. She had absolute control of runs, trills, staccati, and every other ornament of the coloratura soprano voice in all its upper range. This alone might dazzle an audience, but it could never shake them emotionally in the way described by those who heard Tetrazzini. There was another quality, probably apparent only in an actual stage performance, which no recording device could capture.

3. An Impresario's Dream

At her debut she sang "*Ah, fors' è lui*" with this aforementioned and incomprehensible emotional power, ending it on a high note of extraordinary quality which swelled to a forte and then diminished in a perfectly even tone to nothingness. The "*Sempre libera*," which follows, was performed with the most dazzling agility and ended on the E-flat above high C as a straight, strong, and clear note. Her crescendo-diminuendo, as at the end of "*Ah, fors' è lui*," was done with such ease and beauty that it seemed a natural phenomenon owing nothing to art, and sometimes she obliged the delirious audiences of that season and the next by doing it double (that is, two swells on the same note). Obviously her breathing apparatus was physically developed to an astonishing degree at this stage of her career and had not been in the least impaired by twelve years of incessant traveling and singing. Quite the contrary: it had grown by experience, for it is said that Tetrazzini had been much less remarkable in all these respects only a year or two earlier. This was, in fact (lucky Hammerstein!), the exact time when she arrived at the maximum of which she was capable.

She had actually appeared in the United States once before, in San Francisco, on a journey up from Mexico City, where she was singing in opera. Her success in San Francisco had won her the contract at Covent Garden. At the same time Conried had taken an option on her services for the Metropolitan, but, doubting the wisdom of such speculation (as he had never heard her), he had allowed it to lapse.

As far as the general public of New York was concerned, Tetrazzini was unknown before January 15, 1908. The operagoers had read the dispatches describing her unprecedented successes in London, and this was what brought out the great crowd at the Manhattan. The general public woke up the next morning to find Tetrazzini plastered over the front pages of the newspapers, the newest and most sensational of singers. Her supremacy in her own field was not challenged from that time until she retired: Mme Sembrich made her farewell in the following season, and Melba was far too wise to sing the same repertoire in the same city at the same time as Tetrazzini. Melba outlasted Tetrazzini, as she did everybody else, and there can be little doubt from the critical accounts given of the two that Melba had the lovelier voice and the more exquisite control, but I have a fairly good idea that if I had been able to hear opera in those days I should have admired Melba but spent my money on Tetrazzini.

The joy at the Manhattan Opera was as great on January 16 as the consternation at the Metropolitan. Conried had missed the boat as far as Mary Garden was concerned, and that was bad enough; but missing on Tetrazzini, when he had actually held an option on her, was unforgivable. Great changes were about to take place at the Metropolitan. These changes, which for some years rejuvenated the Metropolitan and gave New York some of the best performances it ever heard, were to a very considerable degree Hammerstein's doing. The Metropolitan might have been content to go on forever in the same old way, counting on Caruso to fill the house, if Hammerstein had not thrown out his defiant challenge.

Meanwhile, Tetrazzini was the impresario's dream. All he had to do was to announce her appearances and they were sold out within an hour. She sang *La Traviata, Rigoletto,* and *Lucia di Lammermoor* over and over, twice a week. In those days repetitions were closer, anyhow, than they would be in a repertoire house today; for Tetrazzini it did not matter how close together they came. She sang two performances of *La Traviata* in her first week, two of *Lucia* in her second, and two of *Rigoletto* in her third. After that, Hammerstein mixed them up for a while and also brought *Dinorah* out of the warehouse of last season. His only new production for her was *Crispino e la Comare* by the brothers Ricci, which she sang three times.

But neither production nor casting meant very much to the public in a Tetrazzini performance. They came for the fireworks and the peculiar thrill that she added in her "emotional" cantilena. The cast with her at her debut was the same Melba had had the year before: Bassi and Ancona. She occasionally drew Zenatello for *La Traviata* later on, and she had him for *Lucia* throughout, but the "querulous and mouselike" Bassi was her usual tenor. She sang once in *Rigoletto* with Maurice Renaud (Wednesday, January 29), and this was, like the Melba-Bonci-Renaud performance of the year before, a very spirited and keyed-up performance in which the audience went quite wild. The demonstrations at the end of *"Caro nome"* were such that Campanini was forced, as he had been only once before with a singer, to give in and allow it to be repeated. Sammarco was her Rigoletto on January 31 and shared honors with her in *Crispino e la Comare* when it was exhumed on March 4.

"It is useless to discuss the phenomenon," wrote Krehbiel of the New York *Tribune*. "The whims of the populace are as unquestioning . . . as the fury of the elements."

W. J. Henderson in the *Sun*, describing Tetrazzini's cadenza in *Lucia*, said: "There were leaps, runs, staccati, double swells from piano to forte, twice repeated, and a finish on the high E-flat." The whims of the populace may have been reprehensible in many ways, but they could not bestow vocal technique where it did not exist, and this Tetrazzini clearly possessed. Her final appearance in opera in New York occurred February 2, 1912, at the Metropolitan, with Caruso and Renaud in *Rigoletto;* two thousand persons were turned away from the doors, the police were obliged to intervene, and there was some use of clubs, some injury to the populace, but she retained her strange dominion. Her New York career, both at the Manhattan and at the Metropolitan, thus lasted almost precisely four years, but its brevity was recompensed by a brilliance without parallel. It seems to have been, quite literally, a riot from beginning to end.

So now Hammerstein had two artists (so fantastically different —lucky Hammerstein!) who between them could provide enough variety for the subscription audiences and take care of the box office very nicely indeed. Garden sang her *Thaïs* and *Louise*, and Tetrazzini her three staples. Miss Garden could not create mobs in the street as Mme Tetrazzini did, nor were her audiences so maddened with enthusiasm, but she seldom saw an empty seat in the house. And Mr. Hammerstein was bursting with pride and renewed ambition; he thought of nothing but the new opera houses he was now going to build in various other cities.

But before many weeks he was to unveil something newer even than a new opera house: an opera such as New York had never seen.

XXIII

A Historic *Première*

$\mathbf{A}$T EIGHT O'CLOCK on the night of Wednesday, February 19, 1908, the curtain rose on the first performance of *Pelléas et Mélisande* in the United States. Musicians and persons interested in music had come from all parts of the country to hear it. Perhaps it was felt that the work was too much for New York and would not be heard again. Indeed, we know that Mary Garden feared some such result, as Hammerstein may have also, although his ebullience would not permit him to say so.

1. When Paris Heard Pelléas

Hammerstein may have feared—or, showman that he was, he may have hoped for—a reception such as Paris had given the work a little less than six years before. On that occasion there were disturbances in the theater itself and in the streets outside; apparently no one had heard the opera calmly. Chaliapin, who went with Rimski-Korsakov, has recorded in his memoirs how violently angry the Russian composer became. His feeling that Debussy had somehow thumbed his nose at all his predecessors and had thus, somehow, brought the whole majestic procession of music to an abrupt end; his resentment of a genius so much more

233

original than his own; his dislike of the shimmering, changing color, the subtle and constant modulations of harmony, the musical utterance of the characters, and the terrifying understatement in moments that most composers would have made into sharp climax (*"Voyez-vous le gouffre, Pelléas?"* is an example)—all this reduced the polite and courtly Russian composer to gibbering rage in a public café. There were many quarrels that night, but I have found Rimski's quarrel with himself one of the most interesting. He may or may not have known that the only discernible influence upon Debussy—the only one that has deserved much attention from the musicologists—was that to which he was subjected during his one year in Russia, and in particular the influence of Musorgski, Rimski's old friend and roommate whose scores he had undertaken to "civilize." There almost certainly was, in the uses to which Debussy put that influence, a criticism of Rimski's conformism—implied, of course, as Debussy seems to have been unconscious of Rimski's existence, but enough to let loose a torrent of rage. It was four years before Puccini saw and heard *Pelléas*, yet when he did, he wrote home to Milan about it in terms of sincere (if unwilling) admiration. It was the difference between the Italian sure of himself and the Russian who had never been sure: Puccini could afford to recognize a genius so alien and Rimski could not.

Garden herself voiced her expectations of the New York *première* to Carl Van Vechten. He was then writing interviews for the New York *Times* and had several with her, which were reprinted about a decade later in his book called *Interpreters and Interpretations*. Speaking of *Pelléas* to him a week before the *première*, she said:

"It took us four years to establish *Pelléas et Mélisande* in the repertoire of the Opéra-Comique. At first the public listened with disfavour or indecision, and performances could only be given once in two weeks. As a contrast I might mention the immediate success of *Aphrodite*, which I sang three or four times a week until fifty representations had been achieved, without appearing in another role. *Pelléas* was a different matter. The mystic beauty of the poet's mood and the revolutionary procedures of the musician were not calculated to touch the great public at once. Indeed, we have to teach our audiences to enjoy it. Americans who, I am told, are fond of Maeterlinck, may appreciate its very manifest beauty at first hearing, but they didn't in Paris. At the early representations, individuals whistled and made cat-calls. One night three young men in the first row of the orchestra whistled through an entire scene. I don't believe those young men will ever forget the way I looked at them. . . . But after each performance it was the same: the applause drowned out the hisses. The balconies and galleries were the first to catch the spirit of the piece, and gradually it grew in public favor and became a success, that is, comparatively speaking. *Pelléas et Mélisande*, like many another work of true beauty, appeals to a limited public and consequently the number of performances has always been limited, and perhaps always will be. I do not anticipate that it will crowd from popular favor such operas as *Werther*, *La Vie de Bohème* and *Carmen*, each of which is included in practically every week's repertoire at the Opéra-Comique.

"We interpreters of Debussy's lyric drama were naturally very proud, because we felt that we were assisting in the making of musical history."

2. *Preparation*

During the week preceding the *première* Tetrazzini had to sing three times. Miss Garden did not appear in public at all; aside from rest and rehearsal, she must have given much thought to the great effort now demanded of her.

Garden's relationship with Claude Debussy was one of the high peaks of her existence. It was brief, intense, and imbued with the spirit of artistic creation. It was not in any direct or ordinary sense sexual. ("Claude Debussy?" she said to me. "I'd as soon have a love affair with the Pope!") Whatever it was, it was a relationship of great power and beauty and it suffused her entire life. This, and the sense of immersion in his music which she had from her earliest experience of it, must have made the American production of *Pelléas* a supreme test for her.

The artists who were to appear with her were the same with whom she had played the opera for five years, and who had shared the experience of rehearsing the opera line by line, scene by scene, with the composer. Debussy did not want mellifluous vocalization—"There is too much singing in opera," he said—but he did not want a declamatory *Sprechgesang* either. He abhorred Wagner, and wanted to avoid anything that might suggest a Wagnerian style of declamation. The luminous quietude of his music for the voice, its peculiar dying fall, its effect of avoiding effect, all had to be explained in one way or another. He wanted his notes sung as written, of course—all composers want that—and in the values of a phrase delivered on one note, that was sometimes difficult. One speech of Mélisande shows this peculiar difficulty more clearly, perhaps, than most others; it is the line at the fountain: "*Non, nous ne la retrouverons plus, et nous n'en trouverons pas d'autre non plus.*" To sing this musically but with every word distinct, each note having its precise value but none exceeding the other in explosive delivery (no consonant percussive, no vowel exaggerated), is a small miracle, and Debussy slaved to bring it about.

This was the opera on which Oscar Hammerstein, with no visible evidence of trepidation or doubt, raised the curtain of his Manhattan Opera House on that memorable February evening in 1908.

3. *The Great Opera Controversy*

There was no disturbance at the American *première*. The audience behaved extremely well, with a certain reverence for the work and an outburst of enthusiasm at the end. How much of musical or intellectual snobbery there was in this welcome would be difficult to say. *Pelléas* is not easy to understand at first hearing; I have heard it many times for many years and still hear, at each repetition, something I have never heard before (it happened just recently at the Metropolitan in New York). The superlative performance given by Garden, Gerville-Réache, Périer, and Dufranne and the memorable conducting of Campanini combined with the witchery of the music itself to make an impression unlike that of any other work since the first years of Wagner. The public was so impressed that it crowded the opera house seven times in all to hear this work, and there could have been another performance or two in the last week but for the enforced departure of Jean Périer for European engagements.

The New York critics, nevertheless, were not of the same mind as the public. There came a sort of Great Divide among them. Those beyond a certain age found *Pelléas* repellent and shocking, musically speaking. Old Mr. Krehbiel of the *Tribune*, for whom music had ceased with the Nibelungen Ring, objected to "combinations of tones that sting and blister and . . . outrage the ear." W. J. Henderson of the *Sun* thought the first two acts were "deadly dull, monotonous, wearisome." Younger men did not share these opinions, nor did the men who wrote in musical reviews and the periodical literature of the time.

In the New York *Times* Richard Aldrich gave the music very respectful but cautious appreciation and offered unreserved praise for the performance. He viewed Garden's Mélisande with wonder for its extraordinary irreality and poetic evocation, so totally different from anything she had shown to New York before. Toward the end of the work and in the death scene, said Aldrich, she "rises to a height of tragic power that ought to put her among the greatest of lyric actresses." All the principal workers in the vineyard were praised. Dufranne, perhaps, made the deepest impression; his Golaud remained before the public for many years thereafter and was always a wonderful creation. Jean Périer was ideal both vocally and in person for Pelléas. Mme Gerville-Réache was the Geneviève who made that part, so easily misunderstood and reduced to insignificance, into a memorable element of the whole.

But Campanini, whose mastery had never been so fully accepted before in New York, was now worthy of all the grand words and the full diapason. Aldrich, after telling how he had to absorb so new and startling a work in a short time, had nothing but admiration for his results. "Never has the commanding genius of this great artist so completely established itself as in this achievement," he said.

4. *Hammerstein Takes Another Bow*

At the end of the evening, after many bows, Miss Garden scattered some of her innumerable flowers among the orchestral players. She went into the wings and brought out Oscar Hammerstein, who acknowledged the cheers of the thoroughly excited audience and said:

"If a work of such sublime poetry and musical grandeur meets with your approbation and receives your support, it places New York at the head of cities of musical culture throughout the world. As for myself, I have had but one object in presenting the opera—to endear myself to you and to perpetuate myself in your memory."

This may have been the frankest confession Hammerstein ever made about his life in opera. *Pelléas*, his highest achievement, was done for one reason only: to endear himself, to perpetuate himself. He said nothing of what he was doing for music, for Debussy, or for American culture. What arises from any contemplation of his character is that he was probably telling the truth. He was fiercely self-centered, ferociously ambitious, avid for fame and power. The desire to aggrandize Oscar Hammerstein was in all probability the principle of energy at the heart of all his effort, with music and a possible service to music in second place, if not quite blatantly regarded as a simple means to an end.

It makes no difference. Thomas Jefferson tried to buy a small island off the mouth of the Mississippi and ended up by buying half a continent. Whether Hammerstein wished above all to enhance his own ego or whether he wished to serve music, he did in fact serve music. The production of *Pelléas et Mélisande* was a milestone in American musical culture, as it had been in the French. It caused innumerable fixed ideas to be shaken and revised; it set young minds on new paths and opened up vistas of the possible. It has brought no school of imitators—it had little of the kind even in France—but in the mind of the auditor it dethroned the past and enlarged the frontiers of the beautiful.

Nor did the impresario lose money on it. We have no details of his expense—he had caused an exact copy of the Paris production to be built—but it was a work that he could repeat as long as he had artists in his company capable of performing it. This, after all, in such an extravagant enterprise as the staging of opera, is the chief practical desideratum. Another of Hammerstein's importations in the latter part of this season, Giordano's *Siberia*, was also expensively mounted and cast (Zenatello, Sammarco), but he could get out of it only two performances at regular prices and one "pop" night, all received with indifference. *Siberia* had to go into the warehouse. *Pelléas* remained, an exotic opus, in the repertoire.

XXIV

Lucky Hammerstein,
Unlucky Conried

THE SEASON ended with Hammerstein in the empyrean. It is said that he had piled up profits of about $250,000. This hardly seems possible, even with Garden and Tetrazzini, but it is on the record that his opera house was almost always crowded. He had every reason to be in high spirits.

1. The Forgotten Prima Donnas

For some of his prima donnas the end of the season was less happy. Calvé now claimed her contract performances. Hammerstein by this time was in no mood for famous singers past their prime; he had discovered that new talent cost less and paid more. He gave Calvé three performances of *Carmen*, two at regular prices and one on a Saturday "pop" night, in the eighteenth and nineteenth weeks. Whatever adjustment had to be made between them was not made public. This was by no means a fulfillment of her contract, but since the previous year her appeal to the public had declined and every time she sang he lost money.

His attitude toward contracts was capable of great flexibility in both directions. His contract with Mary Garden was for twenty performances, and in spite of her two illnesses she sang twenty-one times. His contract with Tetrazzini was the same and she sang twenty-two times. For Nordica he had contracted thirty performances and gave five; for Calvé he had contracted at least ten and gave three. His contract with Melba was canceled by mutual consent.

Among his broken contracts, if one may be allowed to call them that, was one with Ernestine Schumann-Heink, who sang for him exactly once, as Azucena in *Il Trovatore* on January 27. Only a year before, he had thought that his opera company would be secure with famous names (Melba, Calvé, Nordica, and Schumann-Heink), but now he no longer wanted them. He had tasted the intoxication of creating his own famous names, as he had done— as far as New York was concerned—with Garden, Tetrazzini, Renaud, Dalmorès, and Dufranne. From this time onward he never again hankered after the established celebrities of the Metropolitan, with the single exception of Caruso, and it was his greatest joy to be able to do with others what he had done with Garden and Tetrazzini: burst them in the face of New York like bombshells. He succeeded once or twice more—certainly with Mariette Mazarin and John McCormack—but what he did not know or refused to recognize was that this was a very exceptional season from every point of view and could not be expected to occur again. He was immersed, by the end of the season, in plans and dreams that would have required the resources of the United States Treasury to carry out in full. It was the old story: he was the same in opera as in vaudeville, and the one thing fatal to him was success.

2. A Gala Season's End

In the twentieth and final week the jubilant Hammerstein allowed himself some antics not usual in opera houses. Perhaps in this most prosperous of all seasons he felt that to end conventionally would be unworthy of his originality.

During this week he staged a single performance of *Andrea Chénier* as a benefit for Campanini, with Eva Tetrazzini, Campanini's wife, singing Maddalena. This singer, a dramatic soprano successful in Italy, had not appeared in public for some years, and perhaps her sister's phenomenal record that year in New York had induced her to emerge again. It was a gesture to Campanini, who received the profits, but to produce an opera for one single performance and that a benefit for somebody else—well, it is not the royal road to riches.

And for his last night Hammerstein contrived a "gala" performance with choice bits from the repertoire. This hodge-podge elicited wild applause from a crowd that filled the house to its limits. It began with Luisa Tetrazzini in Act I of *La Traviata* (with Bassi) and then hopped to Zenatello and Sammarco (with a soprano named Agostinelli) in Act I of *Pagliacci;* then unfolded the Garden Scene from *Faust* as sung by Mary Garden with Zeppilli, Dalmorès, and Arimondi. At this point Tetrazzini trotted out the Mad Scene from *Lucia,* and the proceedings terminated with the Triumphal Scene from *Aïda.* There was nothing in the least new in any of this except that Garden, who had not sung anything of the old school in New York before, startled the aging critics with her extremely polished and sensitive performance as Marguerite. It was the first time that these gentlemen had heard or seen her in something they really knew, and their pleasure seems to have been equaled only by their surprise. *Upon my word, she really* can *sing, after all!*—that was the tone of their remarks: it did not, however, cause them to reflect that her style of singing was changed to suit the character, or even that such differentiation was possible.

3. Trouble at the Metropolitan

During this second Hammerstein season the Metropolitan Opera had suffered some stunning blows from the competition and from its own inner weaknesses, as well as a certain amount of bad luck. The Tetrazzini conflagration was sheer luck; nobody could have foreseen it. The luck was good for Hammerstein and bad for Conried. But there was more than luck involved in the failure of Feodor Chaliapin to attain either critical acclaim or popularity in this, his first New York season. He went back to Russia swearing that he would never return, and he did not do so until his conquering invasion in 1921, when he more or less took over opera in the United States for several years. In 1908 he was too much for the New York critics and even the public. They objected to his "mugging," to his "vulgarity," and to other qualities or defects that those who saw and heard him in his second coming regarded as elements of genius. His singing was severely criticized, more severely than Garden's. As his method of characterization, in spite of the wide difference in the music they sang and the characters they created, was not unlike Garden's, one wonders how she escaped the same fate. She escaped it, judging by the newspapers, on beauty and what was called a "captivating personality." The nature of her art was no more appreciated by the orthodox critics than Chaliapin's.

Meanwhile, no other artist of the company, save only Caruso, aroused the public. Sembrich was approaching retirement, as was Eames, and both sang very carefully. Farrar had not yet conquered the audience that was later so loyal to her. Poor Conried's blight was such that even artists who subsequently came into high repute were not at their best this season.

He counted on Gustav Mahler, composer and conductor, enticed with some difficulty from the Vienna Opera, to retrieve everything. On New Year's Day, Mahler conducted a memorable *Tristan*. His *Don Giovanni*, *Fidelio*, and two of the Ring operas in the annual cycle were admirably presented, and it seems certain that he did not condone any of the Metropolitan's ordinary laxities, such as excusing principal singers, if they were important enough, from attending rehearsals (Sembrich and Eames were notorious offenders in that respect). His work was on such a high plane that it commanded unflagging respect and was followed by large and attentive audiences. Even so, the Metropolitan had nothing to oppose to the furor that was going on at the Manhattan about Garden (in one kind of public) and still more Tetrazzini. Mahler's greatness was acknowledged without a question, but the time had not yet come when any conductor, however great, could arouse the frenzy of the widest public.

Conried, ill and depressed, did not know until the season was half over that he was to be replaced as general director of the Metropolitan. The negotiations with Gatti-Casazza and Toscanini in Milan had been going on for some time before he was informed of them. The engagement of Gatti-Casazza was announced on February 20, 1908, the day after the first American performance of *Pelléas,* and roughly six weeks after the debut of Tetrazzini.

Great changes were in preparation for the Metropolitan, for Gatti would bring with him, with linked contracts, Arturo Toscanini and also Frances Alda, whom he afterward married. Alda in her memoirs (*Men, Women and Tenors*) has given a lively account of the high diplomacy that accompanied and preceded these events. All of them were at present at La Scala in Milan and the Metropolitan's need was so great that emissaries had to be sent and, in effect, humble prayer made before the two possible saviors, Gatti and Toscanini, would consider their offers. The prime mover in all this was Otto Kahn, the most active member of the Metropolitan's board of directors, who was soon to be elected chairman. Between them they were to bring about, within about two years, a wondrous transformation of the old opera house and the elimination of the new. It was not without some point that Otto Kahn had been a regular attendant at the Manhattan for both of its first two seasons.

4. And Joy at the Manhattan

It is more doubtful if Oscar Hammerstein suspected what new strength was to come to the Metropolitan with the retirement of his old enemy Conried. Probably he felt some regret at the disappearance of an antagonist, for he had cherished an animosity against Conried for many years and in such matters one misses an opponent even more than a friend. But the chances are that he saw in the event a certain number of advantages, one of which was that the works of Puccini would now be available to him. Conried had held these operas for the Metropolitan under a personal contract with the publisher Ricordi, which lapsed at his departure. (A good many contracts were made personally in those days, even with singers, and constituted part of an impresario's stock in trade.)

At the end of this season, in which Hammerstein's profits were quoted by his son Arthur as being in the immediate neighborhood of $250,000, the Metropolitan lost almost $100,000. The exact figure is $95,806.

What did Hammerstein learn from his second season? A certain smoothness of administration, perhaps, a greater ease of manipulation in singers, repertoire, and press relations. But the success of this season unquestionably led to all those wild expansions which were his downfall. Like every empire-builder from the beginning of time, he did not know where to stop and was by temperament incapable of learning any such prosaic wisdom. He had had the pleasure of telling Mr. Clarence Mackay to "go to hell," and probably never knew that his son Arthur did not deliver the message. He was aware that the Manhattan had become eminently "fashionable" and was crowded, especially on Garden nights, with the elegant younger members of the plutocracy. He knew that the directors of the Metropolitan and a large number of its singers frequented his house on Garden and Tetrazzini nights. He noted with pleasure that even Caruso came to his *Hoffmann*, which was, next to the two prima donnas, his prize discovery of the year. With it all, he really knew the box-office figures. Even more level-headed buccaneers might have been a little puffed up by all this, and Hammerstein had always been one to shoot for the moon when a star fell his way. By temperament his assertion to the universe was like Calonne's response to Marie Antoinette: "If it is possible, it is done. If it is not possible, it shall be done." He was now progressing rapidly toward the second term of that proposition.

XXV

Love, Opera, and Real Estate

THE GOLDEN GLORIES of Hammerstein's second season were accompanied by some of the inconveniences contingent on success. These included persecution by vocal aspirants of all sorts, bent upon appearances at the Manhattan, and from time to time some awkward lawsuits. Hammerstein by now was no longer a man who could keep out of the press if he wanted to do so, and there is no indication that such was his wish. Consequently, every time he fell among thieves the whole world knew it.

One story of the time concerns a young lady who, unable to obtain an audition at the Manhattan, threatened to commit suicide. Hammerstein was possibly worried that she might do so, or, in any case, curious about her fierce determination. He sent for the lady and she sang for him; after she had done so, he said not a word, but reached into a drawer of his desk and handed her a revolver.

1. The "Texas Patti"

The case that caused the most stir was that of a soprano named Frances Lee, whose admirers in her native state had taken to calling her the "Texas Patti." This lady brought suit against Hammerstein

245

for $100,000 damages to her reputation, on the ground that he had repeatedly promised to put her on the opera stage and had not done so. The suit was settled out of court, on undisclosed terms, but while her threat was in being it afforded considerable amusement to the newspapers. The lady said she had about five hundred love letters from the impresario, and, upon being urged to give some samples, she did so. These specimens of Hammerstein's amatory prose style were printed far and wide.

Miss Lee was not reticent.

"I was always so unsuspecting," she said. "I never dreamed but what he would fulfill all his fine promises made to me. Time and time again he has promised to make me a great singer, to place me above everyone, where my beautiful voice entitled me to be, and poor soft little Frances took it all in and acted accordingly."

One of the letters published ran thus:

"My dearest darling Boosie: Your letter of yesterday I just got. I know I missed writing to you the day before yesterday, but I felt sick all day and swallowed eighteen headache powders.

"You had a bad dream, did you? Well, I had one last night about you. You're a nice thing, you are.

"I dreamed I saw you walking in Central Park with Brooklyn Bridge on your arm. Then a dog came along and hired a cab, into which you stepped with your left foot first and the right one in the bath at the Waldorf Hotel. In a little while the train began to move and I saw a diamond ring swim in a can of condensed milk, while you kissed me on the cheek for fifty dollars.

"It was raining awfully hard boiled eggs, and I saw great clouds of satin foulard drag a little dog into your cab. Then the driver played Tannhäuser Overture with his whip and a great crowd got on board of the boat. The driver rested his arm on his face, from which a piano was suspended.

"Well, all of a sudden, your brother-in-law, President Roosevelt, began to owe me some money and then paid me in potato salad. Then I finally said, said I, is this King Edward—?

"Bruce you are a damned fool. Don't dream so much. Love me as I love you. Your Oscar."

The elephantine humor of the dream has some revelatory notes in it. After all, "you kissed me on the cheek for fifty dollars" does not sound either like love's young dream or satisfied eroticism. Oscar was sixty, a round-bellied little man, and there is not much likelihood that he deceived himself over the degree or kind of response he was likely to evoke from a soprano in need of money.

"Yes, I wrote 'em," he said of the letters. "I don't try to squirm out of anything. What's more, I meant every word I wrote. Can't a man write love letters? I wanted to and I did. I am not sorry. I meant every word in them. I'm a man of temperament and impulse and my letters probably make it evident. It gives me pleasure to write sweetly to those I do love and I am not ashamed of it either.

"Miss Lee, who is really Mrs. Salter of Denver, was the most charming, the most attractive, the sweetest woman imaginable. Perhaps the thing that appealed to me most was a certain little air of sadness in her. She was a comrade, a firm friend, a most sympathetic and beautiful woman, and when I first knew her and heard her voice, it was my firm conviction that in her were all the essentials that go to make up a great dramatic singer. At last one day I heard her sing again, and to my surprise she had scarcely any remains of her really beautiful voice. I was dumfounded. It didn't seem possible. I took her up to Walter Damrosch. He looked at me in a pitying way after he heard her sing.

" 'You must either be terribly stuck on her, or mad,' he told me. Then I took her to Herr Conried and others, and they all thought the same. About two years ago I decided to give Miss Lee a chance on my own hook and I had her sing at a performance of the *Stabat Mater* one Sunday night.

"Oh, it was awful! I couldn't try her again. Let her publish my letters. My family knows I have been interested in Miss Lee's career. It is all understood. Besides, a man in the theatrical business is allowed more liberties than his business brothers. His business demands it."

Some days later another statement betrays a note of anger.

"On my calendar of contracts on hand and in stock brought by talented people who in reality or by hope have received promises of a chance in grand opera, either in the capacity of scrubbing floors or singing behind a net, this case is marked 43.

"By a majority of the fraternity called shyster lawyers I am considered a professional defendant. I have established a schedule of prices in settlement of such suits. All up to one thousand dollars I settle for ten dollars. Suits for one hundred thousand dollars I cannot afford to settle for more than thirty-five dollars.

"The plaintiff is, in this present case, a Mrs. Salter. The lady had a voice when I first met her, but when I met her next, the voice I met no more. If the plaintiff, Mrs. Salter, had been injured by any letters of encouragement in what I considered a bright professional future, her claims for damages are much too low and her lawyers are not fit to represent her. It is a shame to employ lawyers who do not know how to appraise true virtue. I would make further statements but I am interrupted by the service of a summons for $65,000, for criticizing a pimple on a tenor's nose. I am hourly expecting suits for the alienation of the affections of a Maltese cat belonging to a prima donna of this city. *Next!*"

The case of Miss Frances Lee, which never came to trial but attracted a great deal of newspaper attention, prompted one New York paper to remark: "P. T. Barnum has come to life again and his name is Oscar Hammerstein."

It is certain that Hammerstein's infatuations with singers, of which a number are recorded, were temporary and not at all "serious" in that they did not alter his life or involve him in any course of action he would not otherwise have taken. Yet if Miss Lee was correctly stating her case, he had continued some kind of relationship with her for ten years, which is far and away the greatest period of time ascribed to any of his fancies. It is practically certain that during these ten years a number of other charmers shared his absent-minded attention. The most extreme of his devotions some time later (that for Mme d'Alvarez, the contralto) was a sort of moth-and-star relationship in which he never received much encouragement. It is not easy to avoid the conclusion that Hammerstein's amorous inclinations were of secondary importance in his life—secondary, at all events, to the ruling obsession that took up most of his time and energy.

2. Philadelphia Beckons

Hammerstein had been dreaming of Philadelphia for some time now. He had first started to roam the streets of that city, looking for sites for a theater, in the spring of 1907, and it was at that time that he allowed rumors to escape and get themselves printed without denial. One might not think of Philadelphia as precisely the best place for an opera house. It is so near New York that those who really want opera can always get it. Chicago, Boston, and San Francisco have been most hospitable to opera, and all are far enough from New York to justify the building of huge theaters for that purpose.

Hammerstein had his own reasons for thinking of Philadelphia first. He never missed an opportunity to challenge the Metropolitan in every possible field, sometimes when it was contrary to his own interests, giving his performances on the same evenings as the Metropolitan, even producing operas merely to show that he could do them better than the Metropolitan. But beyond sheer animosity, he had come to realize that it was a question of survival, that the "opera war" was a war to the death. After this triumphant second season, with its big profits and the discomfiture it inflicted on the Metropolitan, Hammerstein must have had a genuine hope, amounting almost to confidence, that he would be able to smash the Metropolitan and emerge as the one and only impresario in New York or, in fact, the United States.

The Metropolitan had been going to Philadelphia on Tuesday nights for a good many years, giving performances in the beautiful Academy of Music. If he could defeat the Metropolitan in Philadelphia, the injury to its prestige and to its income would be serious. That, it seems to me, was the original motive in his plan for a house in Philadelphia.

In addition to this purely emotional and rather neurotic impulse, there were, of course, some practical considerations. Philadelphia's nearness could be an advantage, in that whole productions could be moved there and back without great difficulty, and less expensively than with any other city. To a born expansionist, a natural empire-builder, there could never be any question of standing still, and we already know that Hammerstein dreamed of many opera houses in many cities. The city nearest at hand, the richest and one of the largest, was Philadelphia.

How much thought Hammerstein gave to the physical and financial strain of running two seasons at once—how carefully he estimated the expenses of two orchestras, two choruses, two ballets, and two sets of stagehands—we cannot determine. My guess is that he did not study it with any real attention to detail: we know how often in the past he had built theaters without having any clear idea of what he was going to put into them. Even at the Manhattan he did not have his seasons planned in every detail, and surprises were frequent. Thus, he nourished his notions about Philadelphia in his usual grandiose way, but in secret.

3. How to Build an Opera House

He began to give performances of the Manhattan Opera Company in Philadelphia on one night a week in the spring of 1908, his second season, as a challenge to the Metropolitan. It was not insuperably difficult to take a whole production down from New York once a week, and it not only fed his ego, but pleased the principal singers and aroused great interest in Philadelphia. His company performed at the Academy of Music, just as the Metropolitan did, and the response was very pleasing, financially and otherwise. Arthur Hammerstein knew no more about his father's cogitations than did anybody else, until one night, late that March, when Oscar said to him:

"Don't go out at the end of the act. I'm going to say something to the audience when the curtain falls and I want you to hear me."

It was a performance of *Louise*. When the second-act curtain fell, Hammerstein appeared to speak.

"He did not tell me," Arthur says, "that he had bought ground through a holding company to build an opera house. Imagine my surprise when I heard him tell that great audience that he would open the opera house on the following November 15 and that it would be located on the corner of Poplar and Broad streets, opposite the Majestic Hotel. This news was greeted with thunderous applause, and when he came back behind the curtain, I said: 'Do you mean it?' He replied: 'Did you ever hear me say anything to the public that I did not mean?' He then said: 'I want you to be at the Victoria Theatre early tomorrow morning and we'll talk over the plans with McElfatrick.' [That was the architect.]

"Then I knew it was settled. The first thing I did was to call up the steamship company and cancel passage to Europe for my family and me, as we had planned to spend the summer there. Then I met Father and we walked over to the architect's office. The 'Governor' told the architect what he wanted and wanted mighty quick. The next day I came over to Philadelphia and before night I had a gang of men hired. We began to take down the old O'Hara mansion on April 1. As I stood on the back porch of the O'Hara mansion and watched these men loading the first wagon with earth, I realized I was up against the biggest job of its kind ever undertaken. I was to do the job in at least one year less than anything like it had ever been done before. It was not only to be so much larger than other opera houses, but was to include a great many new ideas in theater construction.

"I had talked many times with my father about what he would do in the next house we built. I say 'we' for the reason that I had built all of his ten theaters in New York and I knew he would never want to stop building while he lived. He just couldn't help it, although I hoped he had reached the end of building with the Philadelphia Opera House. This place ought to have been enough of a monument for any man.

"I knew it would be impossible to get any structural steel before June 1, so I had plenty of time to get ready for that. We dug a massive hole, 240 by 160 feet and 18 feet deep, and at the same time took down the old house, which contained two million bricks. These we afterwards used in the new building. We began to put in a concrete footing for the foundation on June 1. Meanwhile, I had bought locally all the materials except the steel. I had to buy nearly seven million hard-pressed bricks. We used twenty thousand tons of structural steel, metal lathing, and iron work. On June 1, when the building began in earnest, we found the finest quality of sand on the premises and that was a great help and saving.

"I built the house as nearly absolutely fireproof in every detail as possible. I don't believe there is another building of its kind in size, anywhere in the world, in which there was so little lumber or other inflammable material used.

"In the second week in June I began to get deliveries of steel and on June 24 the first steel column was put in place. In order to expedite work on the building we reversed the usual order of things by putting in the front first and then going back and erecting the stage last. On June 25 we laid the cornerstone; my father officiated. On August 10 we were up to the roof, and within a week the roof was on.

"The plans were so complete that we went right straight ahead. I made some changes as we progressed, the most notable being the creation of the great promenade over the lobby. It was a daring thing to do, under the circumstances, because it required some changes in the steel structural work and the addition of some columns, but it worked out with success.

"To gain time, we had the stage made in sections over in New York by our Manhattan stage carpenters. That was the only work besides the steel and iron work which was not done on the grounds. Being an ornamental plasterer by trade, and a practical caster and modeler, I rented the adjoining building and made my own plaster casts for the decoration of the house. I engaged two noted sculptors from New York and one from Philadelphia for the figures, and five modelers and twenty-five casters. They did all the work promptly and well."

The heavy strain on Hammerstein's finances for the building of his Philadelphia house was accompanied, of course, by the outlay for his next opera season, so he was obliged to look for money aside from his own profits and those of the Victoria. He still owned the Lew M. Fields Theater in Forty-second Street and succeeded in selling it, at the right moment, for $225,000. This sum brought him through the summer of 1908 and enabled him to open the doors on time both at the Manhattan Opera in New York and at the new Philadelphia Opera House. His star seemed very much in the ascendant, and he was now casting a favorable eye upon both Boston and Chicago for the next steps in his mission.

4. Impresario's Creed

For it had become a mission by now, nothing less. He was so fond of joking about his own most serious affairs that his deeper convictions seldom had a chance to be quoted in print. During the building of the Philadelphia Opera House he did give an interview in which his attitude toward opera (that of the worshiper, the adorer) is explicit, although sometimes expressed with an emphasis that makes the reader blink. He said these words, or allowed them to appear in print with his approval:

"Grand opera is, I truly believe, the most elevating influence upon modern society, after religion. From the earliest days it has ever been the most elegant of all forms of entertainment. This was true when grand opera was extremely crude, as compared with today, when it employs and unifies all the arts.

"It is the embodiment of all that is gentlest and tenderest; it embraces all that is bravest and most heroic; it runs the entire gamut of every human emotion; and whether its theme be love or war or both, it is true. Perhaps it is sometimes truth idealized but it is always truth. But to me, grand opera so uplifts the soul that I forget its material side and leave the house with the same feeling I might have after hearing a great sermon or a great church ceremonial.

"I sincerely believe that nothing will make better citizenship than familiarity with grand opera. It lifts one so out of the sordid affairs of life and makes material things seem so petty, so inconsequential, that it places one for the time being, at least, in a higher and better world. There cannot be the slightest question about its refining effect upon a community. European governments, more paternal than ours, appreciate its importance in this respect and grant subventions to sustain it. They know it makes their people better and happier, educates them in the refinements of life and elevates the tone of the home life.

"In support of this contention I might cite the fact that the German government subsidizes the grand opera house in Berlin to the amount of $115,000 annually, and to that the Emperor Wilhelm adds from his private purse $200,000. Nothing could be a better practical illustration of the ideas of this progressive government.

"Grand opera is not regarded by me as a money-making enterprise. It must not be considered so. It is a physical impossibility to make it such a thing. But my experience has taught me that it can be made self-sustaining, by the people, not only to their pleasure but to their profit—a profit that cannot be computed in dollars and cents—and makes of the people lovers of art. That will create a nobility of thought to be reflected in the ordinary pursuits of life. That will endow them with an appreciation of the good, the beautiful, the true, which will be shown in their homes and even in the faces of the people. That will establish a brotherhood of art which knows not race or creed and makes all the civilized world akin; that will erect a shrine of beauty in form, color, and tone, before which all may bend the knee.

"Grand opera is more than music. It is more than drama; it is more than spectacle; it is more than social function; it is more than a display of passion, whether subdued or fierce; it is more than a song or tale of love; it is more than a series of pictures; it is all these things and more. It is the awakening of the soul to the sublime and the divine; and this is, I believe, the true mission of grand opera."

Whew!

There is no reason for doubting that these constituted Hammerstein's sincere sentiments on the subject. His predilection for opera had shown itself early and its power over him had grown steadily. Now he had been immersed in opera for two years—really immersed, for he never missed either a rehearsal or a performance and played scores to himself at the piano between times. The result was not only to confirm and magnify his obsession, but to give it all these civic, social, and psychological virtues, this air of world-salvation, to which he alludes in the last and the penultimate paragraphs of the quotation. It will be perceived at once that the regenerative and ennobling influences of opera (or music drama), its unique position as a combination of all the arts, its function in the establishment of a brotherhood of art, a shrine of beauty, are notions we have run across before. Words like these are to be found in the prose writings of Richard Wagner, who went even further in world-salvation and the attempt to put it into effect. To heal the *schreckliche Wunde* and achieve a better world was the purpose of Wagner's "Music of the Future."

We accept such high generalization from Wagner (if we do) because he was a creator, one of the most fecund of modern times. We look down our noses at similar utterances from a theater-builder, an impresario, by definition a businessman or a speculator, whose talent does not include the direct creative gift. However, it is impossible to leave the subject without observing that Hammerstein, the impresario and speculator, the showman and the builder, died penniless, whereas Wagner amassed a very respectable fortune and hung on to it, leaving to others the privilege of paying for his operas.

Whether Hammerstein ever read Wagner's prose seems doubtful; however, the ideas there expressed had been much repeated, and may have colored or enhanced or simply encouraged Hammerstein's own. I think, however, that in the main these were his own ideas, a natural growth, and if Wagner came to his aid on two or three points it was in the nature of confirmation rather than revelation. Certainly Hammerstein showed no sign of being or of becoming a Wagnerian in this, the most active period of his life, and his chief contribution to the opera theater in the United States was of an anti-Wagnerian nature, aesthetically speaking, for even his productions of *Salome* and *Elektra* were by way of Paris.

5. *Good Real Estate Helps*

But it is gratifying for an impresario, holding such exalted views of the world-mission of opera, to be at the same time a shrewd and skillful operator in real estate. We have seen that Hammerstein did have an extraordinary sense of the future about property values, in some instances: Times Square is a monument to his perspicacity. He was wrong about the Pennsylvania Station, which, according to his guess, was going to bring a whole new theater and shopping district to its neighborhood when it was completed. It was upon this guess that he built the Manhattan Opera, which never ceased to be "inaccessible" in the eyes of most operagoers from beginning to end. I have heard Philadelphians complain that Hammerstein's Philadelphia Opera House, for all its splendor and its 4,100 seats, was also "inaccessible." In these cases the impresario triumphed over the real-estate operator, because Hammerstein did succeed in filling both of those opera houses most of the time in spite of the difficulty of getting to them. Without his own opera company and its magnetic appeal to the public, neither theater did much after his departure.

He was a builder, as his son Arthur said, more or less by compulsion, by inner necessity. His real-estate operations in all the latter half of his life were neither self-indulgence nor financial speculation: they were the acquisition of land for building. But we see in him the intricate and sometimes bewildering interaction of quixotism and egotism in all these matters, the desire to shower benefits on the public and acquire merit or fame, but yet to lose as little money as possible or even to gain if possible. These motives and desires were not in alternation, but simultaneous, so that only the most acute observer would have been able to tell which was uppermost at any given moment.

The value set on Hammerstein's Philadelphia Opera House at its opening in the coming season (his third as an impresario) was $1,250,000. He asked for, and obtained, a mortgage of $400,000 on it from Philadelphia financiers before the season was over. He said publicly that Mr. and Mrs. Joseph Widener, who raised the money for him or guaranteed it, were willing to advance him $750,000 if he wished, with that theater as security. And yet in the final contract between the opposing opera magnates the Philadelphia house was transferred to E. T. Stotesbury for $400,000 —that is to say, for the mortgage, which by this time Mr. Stotesbury owned. How the $1,250,000 had shrunk to $400,000 is not explained, and must be added to the many other cloudy questions in the story of Hammerstein's finances (or perhaps, in this case, of Stotesbury's).

During the summer and autumn of 1908 Hammerstein was not worried about the future—his confidence was seldom so exuberant. He went to London, Paris, Berlin, made a new contract with Melba, saw Richard Strauss and arranged for the rights to *Salome;* he was full of new ideas, new plans, including a production of *Le Jongleur de Notre Dame* with Mary Garden in the boy's part. This, I suspect, may have been somewhere in his mind since the year before—*Salome* certainly was, and Garden was studying it all that year—but at the suggestion of Maurice Renaud it now came very much to the front. With such projects, and with the unfailing and infallible Tetrazzini to count upon, he could certainly have had a triumphant season at the Manhattan in New York. It was now his intention to double it by a triumphant season in Philadelphia of equal length—that is, of twenty weeks: four subscription performances a week and an extra on Saturday nights. How the real-estate operator became entangled with the impresario, and the difficulties that ensued for all concerned, might have been foreseen by a bystander, but not by Hammerstein. He disdained the difficulties in advance, welcomed them when they came, and conquered them with an air of bravado. This, at any rate, was what could be seen: in his heart he may have trembled at times, but he was not one to show it if he did. For the ultimate purpose was too great for fear. What he intended to do—his "bridge of opera"—was for the whole United States, and there would then be only one impresario in the whole country, Oscar Hammerstein, unique and invulnerable. The fulfillment of his ambition demanded and presupposed the extinction of the Metropolitan Opera, no longer as a main objective, but as a stage on the road to glory.

XXVI

The New Order in Opera

O<small>N</small> S<small>ATURDAY</small>, October 31, 1908, the *Lorraine* of the French Line came into New York harbor with forty opera singers on it, and the rival opera managers of New York went down to the pier to meet it. One was, of course, Oscar Hammerstein, more effulgent than ever in his top hat and morning coat. Among the singers he welcomed were some newcomers: Félix Vieuille, the basso of the Opéra-Comique and the original King Arkel of *Pelléas;* an American contralto named Augusta Doria, who was to sing important parts in the coming season; and a new dramatic soprano from La Scala, Maria Labia, who was of the great Venetian family and was accompanied by her mother, the Contessa Labia.

1. The Old Order Ending

The other manager on the pier was Giulio Gatti-Casazza, who was about to begin his first season as general director of the Metropolitan. He also greeted old singers and new. There was Maria Gay, the "Spanish beauty" who was soon to make her debut at the Metropolitan as Carmen. And there was Mme Emma Eames, now entering her last season on the stage, who gave a long interview attacking singers who depended upon "personality" rather than singing; her language left little doubt as to the particular singer she meant. The old order was passing, and with it Mme Eames, but not without a parting shot.

A bulwark of that old order, in opera as in a good many other aspects of life in New York, had been removed only the evening before, with the death of Mrs. Astor. She had been queen of the Metropolitan Opera House and of New York society for as long as most people could remember. She had never set foot in Hammerstein's house, and, although her power had waned with age, her example still shed a baleful glare on those members of the old Metropolitan boxholding oligarchy who dared to visit the Manhattan.

What comfort such signs of the old order's ending might have been to Hammerstein was alloyed by another portent, the presence of Gatti-Casazza on the pier. Thanks largely to Oscar's own activities, the new order had already gained entrance at the rival opera house also. For its opening night the Metropolitan had announced *Aïda* in a new production, with "scenery and costumes designed and executed by artists of the Teatro alla Scala in Milan." The cast included Emmy Destinn and Amato in debut, Didur in his Metropolitan debut, Louise Homer, and Caruso—and the conductor was to be Toscanini, making his first American appearance. Other new singers, new settings, and another new Italian conductor were in prospect, besides new stage directors and even new operas.

However Hammerstein read the signs, he had reason to look forward to a brilliant season of his own. Tetrazzini and Garden were returning, and for Garden he had another fine supporting artist in the basso Vieuille, although the departed tenor Périer would be missed. He was preparing two new operas for Garden, each with a promise of some excitement: *Le Jongleur de Notre Dame*, in which her role had never before been sung by a woman, and *Salome*, which had already won notoriety in this country with its one performance at the Metropolitan two years before. Melba was returning and was to sing in a new production, *Otello*. And Hammerstein had other surprises in store. Besides all this, he was to open his stunning new opera house in Philadelphia on the night following the Metropolitan's opening in New York and just eight days after his own season began at the Manhattan. On its glittering surface the season held every promise of joy for the ebullient Oscar.

The New Order in Opera

2. *Gowns and Jewels as Usual*

Hammerstein always preferred, if possible, to make a direct challenge to the Metropolitan, but as far as opening nights were concerned, he had sense enough to see that the attention of the press ought to be undivided. An opening night at either opera house received several columns of newsprint, and if the two houses opened on the same evening, the space for each would probably have been greatly reduced.

The Manhattan therefore opened first, on Monday, November 9, with Maria Labia, Zenatello, and Renaud in *Tosca*, Campanini, of course, conducting. The tenor and baritone were praised, as they always were, but Mme Labia's voice in its upper reaches was found a little wanting, even though she had an expressive dramatic style and considerable mastery of the stage. The newspapers gave plenty of space to the audience, gowns, and jewels, as usual, and reported that the loyal Mrs. Clarence Mackay filled her box with Lord and Lady Northcliffe and other distinguished guests. The house was "thronged from pit to gallery with a crowd that showed much of the brilliancy traditionally supposed to belong to opera."

The second performance brought Garden in *Thaïs*. She had allowed her contract with the Opéra-Comique to lapse in order to come to America for Hammerstein. Now she had become a member of the Paris Opéra, and her debut there in *Thaïs* with Renaud had been one of the great events of Paris the preceding April. Her voice, style, and confidence had all benefited by this and by her American success. She was, by all accounts, at the zenith just during these Hammerstein years, and although her contract was always fixed at a minimum of twenty performances, she sang many more than that each year. She had also learned how to deal with the severity of the New York winter, which had given her two such disastrous illnesses the year before, and she was to get through this season without a hitch.

With this performance of *Thaïs*, however, the critics came up with a discovery: the music was too high for her voice. The truth is that it always had been. In later years she omitted some of the high notes when she felt so inclined, but at this period she sang them all, and it was the complaint of Richard Aldrich in the *Times*

259

that the high part of her voice sounded "shrill and acid," which contrasted with the much finer quality of her middle tones. He spoke of the "dramatically colored phrase" and the "innate musical beauty" of her singing in the middle voice.

Thaïs had been written for Garden's friend Sybil Sanderson, whose voice was phenomenally high ("a voice like the Tour Eiffel," said Carl Van Vechten). Mary Garden did not consider a dramatic impersonation, or a music drama as a whole, to be dependent on a few notes at the top of the scale. I once asked her if she had ever studied or considered studying *Esclarmonde*, which has a G above high C and was also written for Sanderson. She said no: it was not the high note that discouraged her. "You can deal with that quite easily—just leave it out," she said. She had not studied it because it did not interest her. *Thaïs* did interest her and she adopted it as a favorite, and so it remained, for the performer as for the public, another twenty years or so.

For his third offering, on Friday, Hammerstein chose *Samson et Dalila*, which was known in America only as an oratorio, rarely performed, and by some familiar excerpts for contralto solo. It had actually been sung once at the Metropolitan by Mantelli and Tamagno in 1895, but had been forgotten immediately, and came to the audiences of 1908 as a novelty. Mme Gerville-Réache was very highly praised as Dalila, as were Dalmorès, Dufranne, and Vieuille.

Tetrazzini made her re-entry on Saturday night—no longer "at popular prices"—in *Il Barbiere di Siviglia*. This was a success of the usual Tetrazzini variety, with an audience on the brink of hysteria and a crowd outside unable to get into the theater. It leaves us amused and somewhat incredulous to think of Tetrazzini bouncing about the stage as Rosina, but apparently she was an accomplished comic actress and really did enliven the second act as few singers could. She did not embellish *"Una voce poco fa"* quite so extravagantly as Patti used to do, the critics remarked, but there were plenty of fireworks and the audience was vociferously pleased. With her was a tenorino by the name of Colombini who left the company soon afterward (Hammerstein dismissed him out of hand because he refused to sing the secondary part of Cassio in *Otello*), along with Sammarco as the Barber and Gilibert and De Segurola as Bartolo and Basilio. It would appear to have been the liveliest *Barbiere* New York had seen for a long time. (At the Metropolitan it was something like a song recital.)

Criticism was friendly to Hammerstein during this first week, as it generally was, and the press gave a great deal of space to all aspects of his enterprise. The *Times*, in a sentence of warm content but curious structure, remarked after the first night: "The ingenious, resourceful and indomitable Oscar Hammerstein saw the opera established that he has built up without anybody's help except that of the public he has interested."

3. Dazzlement in Philadelphia

Hammerstein's Philadelphia Opera House opened the next Tuesday, the 17th, with Labia, Dalmorès, and Renaud in *Carmen*. It was a tremendous affair. The traffic police said they cleared 1,600 carriages "and machines" through Broad, Poplar, and Carlisle streets before the first act began. Every one of the 4,100 seats in the house was occupied, and there were between 1,500 and 2,000 persons standing behind the seats and in the aisles. Philadelphia had two operas that night, for the Metropolitan opened its season of Tuesdays at the Academy of Music with *La Bohème* (Sembrich, Caruso, Scotti). In spite of the competition, Philadelphia's richest and grandest, enumerated in the *Times* as "the Van Rensselaers, the Griscoms, the Cassatts, the Clothiers, the Drexels, the Lippincotts, the Leidys and the Cooks," were out in force for Hammerstein, and there was a dazzling display of precious gems.

Campanini on that night told the reporters that the new house was "the most beautiful opera house in the world." An opinion not altogether dissimilar was expressed by a good many of those who reported the occasion in the press. Mindful of the first troubles at the Manhattan, Hammerstein had given this new house "many entrances and exits on Broad Street," so that the crowd of about six thousand persons (besides those who could not get in) might be handled expeditiously.

When the impresario was called before the curtain, amid scenes of great enthusiasm, he made a brief speech that contained one note of premonition: "It all depends on you," was the gist of it— an appeal to the Philadelphia public to support the opera now created for it.

Hammerstein could not help knowing how costly a hazard he

261

had invited. His expenses in running two concurrent seasons were frightful. For his first night he had to have three special trains: 421 persons went in nine cars on the principal train; there was another for stage carpenters and scene shifters, with gear; there was still another for wardrobe workers and their paraphernalia. Everything was transported from New York except Hammerstein's old kitchen chair, on which he was accustomed to watch performances from the wings; another had to be found hastily in Philadelphia.

Still, the brilliance of its opening, to Oscar's sanguine temperament, could be nothing less than a promise of success for the Philadelphia venture. The Manhattan, meanwhile, continued to give him cause for gratification, with Tetrazzini's *Lucia* entering the season's repertoire in this second week, and *Les Huguenots*. This opera must have been a personal favorite of Hammerstein's; otherwise, one must wonder why he persisted in giving it, for he never had enough singers of both sexes for the superlative singing it requires, and only Campanini's iron hand made it acceptable with the casts Hammerstein gave it.

Some of the new names appearing in casts with Tetrazzini also indicate a certain respect for economy on the part of the otherwise lavish impresario; at least, one hopes that the singers came cheap, because they added nothing to the renown of Hammerstein or his house. It did not matter who sang with Tetrazzini; the public could be depended upon to swoon with delight in any case. Later in the season Hammerstein made some amends by bringing to her support the very fine Spanish lyric tenor Florencio Constantino, whose Bonci-like style can be detected on a very few old records even now.

4. The Juggler of Our Lady

The first new role for Garden, and the season's first distinct success, came with the American *première* of *Le Jongleur de Notre Dame* in the Manhattan's third week.

I have hazarded a guess that Hammerstein thought of Mary Garden for the role of the boy Jean even before her debut, when he first thought of *Salome* for her. It would have been like him to incubate such an idea for a year and then spring it full-blown as a surprise. Miss Garden herself, however, attributes the inspiration to Maurice Renaud, and that, too, is more than likely —besides which, she must know. Renaud had created the part of Boniface in the Monte Carlo *première* of the opera (1902) and was fond of it as an opportunity for his fine singing and acting. Jean was written for tenor and had never been sung by anybody but a tenor. Renaud is supposed to have told Hammerstein during the preceding season that Garden would be right for the boy. At all events, Hammerstein accepted the notion with enthusiasm, and Garden had been studying it since the preceding spring (along with *Salome*, most of which she already knew).

There is some dispute about whether Massenet made any modification of the score for the change from tenor to soprano. Miss Garden has assured me that not one note was changed, that she sang it exactly as originally written. Anybody's memory might slip on detail after forty-six years, and yet this is the kind of detail in which a singer is seldom wrong. For the record, it should be stated that Brockway and Weinstock, in their valuable book called *The Opera*, and Irving Kolodin, in his *Story of the Metropolitan Opera*, disagree; the former say that Massenet "remodeled" his opera for Garden, and Mr. Kolodin refers to the "modified role of Jean." The only score available shows no variations: the part of Jean is marked *tenor*, but obviously any soprano could sing it, as far as tessitura is concerned. It has no very high or very low notes.

Hammerstein had heard this opera the past spring, certainly, if not before: Miss Garden (in *Mary Garden's Story*) informs us that he went to the Opéra-Comique and heard Thomas Salignac sing it. This tenor, well received at the Metropolitan in 1896–1900 in such operas as *Faust*, *La Traviata*, and *Pagliacci*, could hardly have had the face, figure, or voice of a young boy in 1908. After hearing (or seeing) this performance, Hammerstein was more than ever convinced that Garden could re-create the whole opera by a piece of her inspired characterization.

And that is precisely what she did. In the first performance on Friday, November 27, 1908, and at regular intervals for twenty-odd years afterward, she held audiences in New York, in many cities throughout the United States, and in Paris and Brussels by her strange transformation into an innocent, gentle, and quite possibly dim-witted young boy. As a performance it may have been the most remarkable tour de force in a repertoire that consisted of nothing else. It was surpassed in beauty, of course, by her Mélisande, but nothing could have been more astonishing than the reality (from the inside out) of the poor little juggler who loved Our Lady and had nothing to offer her but his juggling.

For the benefit of those—an increasing number with every passing year—who never saw Garden on the stage, it should be mentioned that she weighed ninety-eight pounds at her debut in Paris in 1900 and was at that time without noticeable breasts, hips, or thighs. She acquired a bosom by dint of much singing, but she never at any time had perceptible hips or thighs, and she controlled her weight rigorously, by a truly Spartan regime, throughout her life. At the time of her first *Jongleur* she probably weighed 106–110 pounds, no more. She was also a short woman (five feet four inches), although she had ways of making herself seem tall on the stage when she wished to do so, notably in *Thaïs* (holding her arms above her head, holding her head back, etc., etc.). As for the bosom, providing it is truly a bosom and not a stomach, anybody acquainted with the stage knows how easily it can become a chest.

Thus, Garden was physically perfect for the part of the boy juggler, as in fact no adult male singer possibly could be. (It is surprising that Massenet did not write it for soprano in the first place.) Moreover, her other-worldly voice, the one she used with a different coloration in Mélisande, was ideally suited to the music of the juggler's part. She conveyed, even by the time I saw and heard *Le Jongleur*, such utter absorption into the child's dream that it was quite impossible to doubt the creation. It was far and away superior to the music provided for it by Massenet, although that, too, is not without some special charm. It has passages of folksong, passages of old ecclesiastical music or what sounds like it, and moments of considerable tenderness and pathos, not too heavily sugared. It actually merits revival more than a good many works—such as *Thaïs*—that are rather often revived. The trouble is, however, that while there is anybody left alive who can remember Mary Garden, no singer would dare to undertake it. When she retired from the opera stage it disappeared from the repertoire everywhere, even at the Opéra-Comique.

Hammerstein's judgment and courage—what I have earlier called his "creative management"—were brilliantly justified in this enterprise. With Garden appeared Maurice Renaud (at his best), Dufranne, De Segurola, Vallès, Vieuille, and Crabbé. Campanini conducted the first of the very long series of performances he was to give of this work throughout the country. Henderson of the *Sun*, who remained for years an anti-Garden writer, thought Miss Garden had a certain "feminine archness" that did not quite suit the young boy; this, by the context, must have referred to facial expression more than anything else. It was not the opinion of most who saw the performance then or later.

5. Melba Again, and Cavalieri

The rest of the repertoire—Tetrazzini's warhorses, Sammarco's *Pagliacci*, and Gerville-Réache in *Samson et Dalila*—continued as before until the return of Nellie Melba on December 14 in *La Bohème*. She was, as she had been two years before, in perfect voice, and all testimony concurs in admiration of her exquisite vocalization. There was now appearing a tendency, however, to observe that she did not characterize her roles at all, but merely sang them to perfection. This may have been due to the intensive course of instruction New York had been getting from Garden and Renaud in the art of characterization on the stage; at any rate, it appears in the Melba criticisms for the first time. As long as she could sing so angelically, nobody much cared that she looked and acted the same in all parts.

Her season with Hammerstein was short. We do not know all the tensions and awkwardnesses that arose in the company. We can guess a few. Tetrazzini had an iron-bound contract for forty performances and she could jam the house to suffocation whenever she appeared. Her fee was probably $1,250 to $1,400 for each performance in this season, for we know that it rose to $1,500 in the next. But even this, princely though it may sound, was far below the fees paid Mme Melba. Hammerstein's diplomacy and tact were undoubtedly tried to the utmost during the brief weeks when the two great coloraturas were together in his company. Tetrazzini retained all the coloratura parts and Melba sang only one of them, once—a *Rigoletto*, with Constantino and Renaud, for her farewell on January 11. Otherwise, her appearances were confined to *La Bohème* and *Otello*.

The *Otello*, produced for the first time on Christmas night, 1908, was one of Hammerstein's real triumphs. He had such a good cast, staging, and musical performance, thanks to Campanini and Jacques Coini, that even after Melba left, the opera continued to play to crowded houses. Zenatello, in the title role, is still remembered as one of the great performers of that difficult part. According to Henderson, he had "precisely the right kind of voice for this role, a hard, brilliant, pealing tenor, with far-reaching high notes." Sammarco sang Iago, and his great voice, blended with Zenatello's at the end of the second act, produced "such a storm of applause as is rarely known in an American opera house." Melba in the last act must have approached celestial beauty of voice: it was ideal music for her. She sang it more or less everywhere in the world during the second half of her career, but this was the first time she had been heard in it in the United States.

Mary Garden continued with *Le Jongleur* during December and January, sometimes singing it twice a week and interspersing it with an occasional *Thaïs* or *Pelléas*. The *Pelléas* this year had only four performances, however, compared to seven the year before. It was the same production, and had in addition the perfect Arkel in Félix Vieuille, who had sung it for Debussy in the Paris cast; he was still wonderful in the part when I heard him at the Comique almost twenty years later. But unfortunately there was no Pelléas. The part was sung by Dalmorès, a tall and robust man, one who made wonderful effects as Don José and Manrico. He was, by every account I have seen, a really fine artist, but no big tenor voice belongs in the part of Pelléas. It is light baritone, high baritone, and unless the young man can give a suggestion of adolescence, the meaning of the drama is destroyed. He should sing it almost as if his voice had changed only about a year before.

Tetrazzini went on and on with *Lucia, Rigoletto, Traviata*, and *Crispino*, and on December 5 a tenor who was worthy of her, the Spaniard Florencio Constantino, made his debut as the Duke to one of her numerous Gildas. Later on in the season, because he could manage all the high notes, she had a fling at *I Puritani* with him.

Another debut of interest, although not perhaps of strictly musical interest, was that of Lina Cavalieri, whose story belongs in the catalogue of Hammerstein's various feuds with the Metropolitan and will be told in that connection. It is curious and rather diverting to observe that those who mention Cavalieri's debut with Hammerstein in books of memoirs and the like never get it right. Garden says the debut was in *Carmen*, and an unpublished work of research made for the present-day Hammersteins says it was in *Les Contes d'Hoffmann*. Apparently the debut did not matter much, or make much impression, whichever opera this lovely lady graced by her presence. At all events, she actually made her first appearance on Monday, January 25, in *Tosca*, with Zenatello and Sammarco, and, although the house was filled with curious persons, the performance was not admired by the critics and was not repeated. She sang *La Bohème* three times in the next two weeks, and that was her season (four performances). Obviously Hammerstein had engaged her only to annoy the Metropolitan's board of directors, in a tangle of feuds and rancors which was to distinguish this season above all others.

6. Richard Strauss's Aphrodisiac

The high point of the year for Hammerstein was his production of *Salome*, which was revealed on January 28, 1909—a Thursday, and therefore a special performance outside the subscription. For this short opera, beginning at nine o'clock, sung by a cast that had appeared often in other works at ordinary prices, the canny impresario charged extra. He could well do so, for the uproar in press, pulpit, and public had been going on at fever heat for weeks past, and curiosity had been excited beyond reason or measure.

New York remembered very well what a tempest had been created by the Metropolitan's attempt to produce this work in January, 1907. It had had a dress rehearsal on Sunday, attended by many persons who had just come from church, and a public performance on the following Tuesday. It was sung by Olive Fremstad, who, to judge by the photographs, bore not the slightest resemblance to a vicious little Oriental princess of sixteen. She retired from the stage when the dance began (as most singers did before and after her), leaving that dramatic center of the action to a ballerina. The boxholders at the Metropolitan were shocked by the general tone and meaning of the work, and one in particular, a daughter of J. P. Morgan, viewed it with horror. It was accordingly, after a brief struggle on Conried's part, dropped from the schedule after that one public performance.

To most of us nowadays the tremendous moral indignation aroused by *Salome* is difficult to understand. True, it is aphrodisiac music and the orchestra revels throughout in the perversity of the Judaean princess, but no law compels those who object to such representations to attend them. Even on the phonograph, without any of the action visible except to the mind's eye, the finale of the opera conveys, in the symphonic intensification and in the vocal line itself, so consummately fitted to the words, an impression of sensuality degraded to its utmost abasement. In this respect it would be difficult to imagine representational music carried any further. One is, in fact, shocked, but shocked exactly as the composer intended one to be. This shock is the purpose of the composition. Dante could achieve the same aesthetic purpose in a line or two; for Richard Strauss nothing less than the largest orchestra and the most extreme explicitness would suffice. We do not outlaw Dante because he describes the circles of hell, nor do we (nowadays, that is) endeavor to suppress *Salome* for its woeful sensuosity. There is, even, to our ears, some element of sympathy for the fatally impassioned creature. Her evil is intensely evil, but in such lines there comes out a sense of its fatality, of her helplessness in the tempest of her own passion.

Oscar Wilde's play is a much milder rendition of these reprehensible occurrences than Strauss's music. The opera's libretto is as close to Wilde's French text as the German language permits, but to my ear the German words sound worse ("worse" in the sense of thicker and more lush). But Strauss's music! This takes the words and blows them up a thousand times. Every violet shade, every crimson suggestion, is spread out in an orchestral plenitude that becomes at times orgiastic. What Wilde wrote was a distinctly depraved little water color. What Strauss wrote was, in his own terms and with his own means, something like the Last Judgment.

The characterization of *Salome* had interested Mary Garden for some time. The original play was written for Sarah Bernhardt, who rejected it because she could not bring herself to the action involved. It was the Wilde play that first caught Garden's imagination—that and, no doubt, the Bernhardt story. The Strauss opera reached production in 1905, first in Dresden, and afterward made a triumphal tour of Germany, but Garden did not see any of these performances. Her creation was absolute, straight from the words and music. She dined with Strauss in Paris in the summer of 1907, around the time when she signed with Hammerstein for America, and discussed it with him. It was Strauss himself who told her that he had provided ten minutes' rest for the singer before the Dance of the Seven Veils and that he could not understand, therefore, why the singers always refused to do the dance themselves. He did not expect that they would cavort like ballet dancers, but he thought they could at least indicate the dance without hardship.

7. *Wild, Wicked Salome*

Garden, therefore, resolved to do the dance herself, and spent a good part of the summer of 1908 composing it in the studio of the *première danseuse* of the Paris Opéra. She was equally thoughtful and industrious in the composition of her costume. Her study of the dance movements and of the music led her to use five veils, not seven, because the main dramatic incidents are more naturally in that form—and also, of course, because there are only a few ways in which a veil can be discarded with grace, sinuosity, and a suggestion of lecherous promise.

The astonishing thing, musically, about her performance was that she was at her best in the difficult finale, to which she gave some extraordinary singing—wild and wicked and rather frightening, on the whole, but just what Strauss had written. The voice was not Wagnerian, but it was penetratingly expressive and it had the faculty of carrying well over that huge and tempestuous orchestra. The voice of the most successful Salome of recent years, Mme Ljuba Welitsch of the Vienna Opera, has or had something of the same color—that of a degenerate adolescent.

Hammerstein had every reason to be delighted by this production, which filled his house to capacity ten times in what remained of the season and did the same in Philadelphia and Chicago when the season was over. Boston would not have it because of the tremendous pother about its moral content. The chances are that the moral indignation of the clergy was a great help to Hammerstein. On one occasion he invited a whole covey of clergymen to come and see it; most of them refused, although they continued to inveigh against it. One pastor in New York preached a sermon against "the Salome spirit," which he said had invaded the land, and brought off the interesting feat of not mentioning either Hammerstein's production or Mary Garden. The chances are that his congregation knew what he was talking about.

The New York critics gave great space to the production and to Garden's performance, although this was analyzed for its characterization rather than for the voice. Some of the gentlemen of the press were horrified by the Dance of the Seven Veils. Henderson in the *Sun* said: "Miss Garden cannot sing a phrase of Strauss's music." In this he disagreed with the composer, whom, of course, he never understood at all. (He understood Verdi and Wagner and nothing else of consequence: Henderson's limitations are shown more pitilessly in his novel called *The Soul of a Tenor* than in all of his criticism put together.)

Garden was now singing at least twice a week and often three times. On one Saturday (March 5) she sang *Louise* in the afternoon and *Le Jongleur de Notre Dame* at night. She could sing *Salome* on Wednesday and Friday of the same week and crowd the house each time, as she did on February 3 and 5. (With her in the *Salome* cast were Mme Doria and MM. Dalmorès, Dufranne, and Vallès, of whom Dufranne alone made any impression separate from that of the central character.) This left very little room for aught else but Tetrazzini in her infallible, if monotonous, rotation of display pieces. Hammerstein did achieve one other new production, entitled *Princesse d'Auberge*, a work (by Jan Blockx) that he seems to have bought chiefly because it had a showy carnival scene that he liked. It was sung by Labia, Gerville-Réache, Dufranne, and others, made no impression, and is not even mentioned in the standard reference books of today.

The season was, as far as New York was concerned, brilliantly successful, although it reposed upon two sopranos, Garden and Tetrazzini. One wonders what would have happened to Hammerstein if either of them had fallen ill. Garden, except in her first American season, was practically never ill, and Tetrazzini never. This is a brilliant vindication of both schools of thought on diet— that which says we should eat almost nothing and that which says we should eat what we want when we want it. Mme Tetrazzini was one of the most prodigious trencherwomen of all human history. By chance, years later, I once watched her eat, at the restaurant called the Castello dei Cesari overlooking Rome, for about two hours, and when I left she had scarcely embarked on the middle of her meal. Miss Garden ate only one meal a day, which was lunch.

One sang *La Sonnambula* and the other sang *Salome*, as might have been expected.

XXVII

"A Man Never Makes a Mistake"

A MAN never makes a mistake,"
Oscar once told his son Arthur. "He does the best he can, at the
time." He might have been looking back at his third season when
he said this.

A certain pathos arises from the fact that this season was, as far
as the Manhattan Opera was concerned, immensely successful. If
he had restricted his activity to New York alone, he would have
had no immediate trouble. Nothing that was performed at the
Metropolitan this season aroused the general public as did the two
additions to Mary Garden's repertoire, *Le Jongleur* and *Salome*.
No singer at the Metropolitan, not even Caruso, evoked such
storms of approval as did Tetrazzini. There was not one singer at
the Metropolitan with either the prestige or the vocal beauty of
Nellie Melba (whatever Sembrich had been a decade before, she
could no longer compete). And some extremely notable Hammerstein productions, such as *Pelléas* from last season and *Otello* in
this, were superior to anything in the Metropolitan's repertoire
outside of Wagner. All this the public knew, and responded eagerly. If the Philadelphia Opera with its huge seating capacity
had not hung like an albatross about the mariner's neck, Hammerstein could have made port quite easily for another few seasons, at
least.

"A Man Never Makes a Mistake"

1. What It Costs to Run an Opera House

As to the normal running expense of the Manhattan *without* the Philadelphia season, let us take the account given by Arthur Hammerstein. He says that Tetrazzini, Renaud, and Sammarco were guaranteed forty performances each, and Mary Garden twenty.

"Outside of the persons named above, my father paid to his principal singers $245,000. This matter of the salaries of singers seems to be the only one in which the public is particularly interested; but the expense of opera-giving is far more wide-reaching. Take, for instance, the orchestra. The cost was $6,000 a week, but for such special productions as *Salome* and *Elektra* it was the custom to hire fifty extra men at $10 to $25 a man for each performance. Our concertmaster, the first violinist, received $175 a week, the harpist $150, the oboist $120. Campanini was paid $1,000 a week. De la Fuente and Anselmi, other conductors, received $500 and $350 a week respectively. There was also the expense of extra orchestra rehearsals, in addition to the two two-hour rehearsals given without extra cost. The chorus cost $2,500 a week, the ballet $700, the stagehands $3,000. Then there were the four storage houses where the scenery was kept, the rental of which was $250 a week. The expenditure for shifting the scenery ran to $1,000 a week. And there was also the expense of what is called 'the front of the house': the treasurers, ushers, doormen, porters, cleaners, and whatnot, which was $2,500. Add to these items $30,000 for the round-trip-passage fares, from and to Europe, for the principals and chorus, and that will give you an idea of what it cost to produce opera in New York. This does not take into consideration the taxes, insurance, interest on mortgages, and loss of interest on investment."

All of this expenditure was not, of course, doubled by the addition of a concurrent season in Philadelphia, but it was very substantially increased. On Saturdays, for example, Hammerstein was giving four performances, two in New York and two in Philadelphia. The hundreds of persons involved in any opera production had to be augmented, as were chorus, ballet, and orchestra, for the strain of running two theaters at once.

It is more than probable that Hammerstein knew before the

273

season was very far advanced that his chances for winning his war had now sensibly diminished. Dating from his opening-night admonition to Philadelphia, the tone of his speeches and statements begins to contain a note of reproach to the public. Whenever a crisis was surmounted the impresario was blithe and confident again, but it must have been dawning upon him that his resources would never keep up with his vaulting ambition. Unless the Metropolitan could be bludgeoned into silence, leaving the field to him alone, Hammerstein's scheme of nationwide opera, or even of opera in a few leading cities, could never be realized.

2. *Oscar Berates Philadelphia*

Immersed in the gruesome difficulty of making both ends meet in Philadelphia, Hammerstein finally lashed out at the city that was causing him so much anguish. There, on New Year's Eve, only six weeks after his brilliant opening, he made a speech to the public, criticizing Philadelphia in general and its financiers in particular for ingratitude. He upbraided the magnates for not coming to his support. He threatened, as he was to do repeatedly from now on, to give the theater over to vaudeville. He assumed the air of an injured benefactor, although the simple fact was that his deficit was becoming unbearable.

After this speech, he said, Mr. and Mrs. Joseph Widener offered him $750,000, but he asked only for a mortgage on the house for $400,000. As soon as he was assured of the sum, which was in a few days' time, he ceased to heckle his public and became urbane again. "This has cleared my way to building a new house in New York," he said to the reporters.

He also declared, perhaps on sound reasoning, that if he wished to form a stock company to build his new house, he could get five millions "within twenty-four hours." However, this was never put to the test.

The little man in the remarkable top hat was quite probably talking through it just at this time (January, 1909). He certainly knew that the Philadelphia Opera House was too big and that there was small likelihood of filling it often enough, now or in the future, to ensure its permanence. The truth of the matter was that Philadelphia had no use for so much opera: it was getting two nights a week from the Metropolitan now, instead of one, and Hammerstein's house gave five a week. Most Philadelphians were quite content with their Tuesday nights at the Academy of Music, and if they wanted more, it was not in the least difficult to get on a train and go to New York for it. The Metropolitan's Tuesdays were a tradition, and Philadelphia was then, even more than now, devoted to tradition. All this cut down the attendance dangerously at Hammerstein's house. He had been operating at a deficit almost from the second performance.

He had invited a costly hazard, and had done so just at the moment when the old Metropolitan was undergoing rebirth.

3. A Rift at the Metropolitan

Meanwhile, as far as the Metropolitan was concerned, Hammerstein was still very much alive and very much a menace. The older house was gradually pulling itself out of the doldrums, but not without considerable internecine warfare. This company now had two full orchestras and two full choruses, with a repertoire of acknowledged masterpieces and the two most famous conductors—Mahler and Toscanini—in the world. Yet Hammerstein was still making money at the Manhattan Opera House and threatening the foundations of this one. A united authority was needed to bring the Metropolitan up to its own possibilities, and this was not achieved in the first year of the new regime.

The season had begun with a curious duplication of directorships. Out of a fear among board members that Gatti-Casazza would give only Italian works, Andreas Dippel had been retained for the German repertoire. This arrangement continued uneasily until the failure of *Tiefland,* a disastrous novelty from Germany for which Dippel was responsible. An announcement to the press on December 7 stated that Dippel was released as co-manager while Gatti and Toscanini were confirmed in their contracts. But some of the principal singers, including Farrar and Caruso, signed a petition in Dippel's behalf, and he lingered on as an assistant of some sort to Gatti. It has been thought that Gatti may have resented this, to the detriment of the petitioners later on.

Meanwhile, there was another and greater headache: what could the Metropolitan do with two such conductors as Mahler and Toscanini? Toscanini had made a great part of his reputation up to this time by his mastery in operas that belonged to the repertoire of Mahler and of Hertz, who was still on duty. He had expected to conduct *Tristan* and *Die Meistersinger*, but Mahler conducted the first and Hertz the second. Mahler had objected violently when he heard of the plan for a new production of *Tristan* under Toscanini, and this did not in fact take place until the following season, when Mahler was no longer with the company.

The details, obscure and contradictory, do not concern us except that they indicate a rift in the inner councils of the Metropolitan and a consequent slowness to take advantage of the new arrangements. Mahler and Dippel had to go, and eventually they did—the former to the regret of all music-lovers. His *Figaro*, for which he had twenty rehearsals, and his *Tristan* were long remembered.

Certainly the Metropolitan in that particular season must have been a house of unease, suspicion, and turmoil, with the Hammerstein competition at its fullest and the new regime not at all solid on its feet. And yet Toscanini, whose welcome on his first appearance had been merely warm, was making a deeper impression with every performance; within only a few months the praise for him was to become ecstatic. And with several new singers of quality and a more serious rehearsal policy, the Metropolitan, in spite of disharmony under the surface, was displaying a vitality and discipline beyond anything it had known for years, like an army of tired troops when a new and resourceful commander appears in the field with some well-calculated increases of rations.

4. A Musicale and Its Fatal Consequence

Hammerstein always pretended to make light of the Metropolitan. It was a tactical attitude: he feared and hated it almost as strongly as he loved opera. The two emotions—or even passions—were intermingled. Perhaps they were the opposite sides of the same medal. At all events, he was far too shrewd not to realize, from the early part of this season onward, that Jack now had a far mightier giant to kill than ever before.

"A Man Never Makes a Mistake"

Whatever its inner difficulties, the Metropolitan was a continuing, growing threat to his very existence as an impresario, and the Philadelphia house continued increasingly to sap what resources he could muster to maintain his position while it was still tenable. And yet it was in this winter that he quarreled with his own most valuable allies, Cleofonte Campanini and the Clarence Mackays.

There was a kind of fatality in all this. Hammerstein wanted to "go it alone," as we have repeatedly seen, and had never accepted the freely offered help of Mr. and Mrs. Mackay, who were financially and socially as powerful as anybody he could have found in New York. They had been enthusiasts for his opera from the beginning. They had become friendly with Arthur Hammerstein, who had received—and never delivered—the famous message telling them "to go to hell." The Mackays understood the vagaries of temperament well enough, and had, then and afterward, much dealing with musical artists; they made no attempt to force themselves on Hammerstein, but worked for him indefatigably just the same. Mrs. Mackay actually went out and sold subscriptions among her friends in order to gild the boxes and orchestra stalls for the Manhattan. She did this by arrangement with Arthur Hammerstein, who was careful not to tell his father. Sometimes Arthur was able to influence the repertoire judiciously to suit Mrs. Mackay's tastes when he knew she was coming to the opera. A relationship of comprehending friendship grew up betweeen the harassed young man, trying to save his father from shipwreck, and the kindly benefactors. The Manhattan owed a great deal to the Mackays during its first three seasons.

It so happened that just at this time, when Hammerstein's nerves were probably stretched to their limit by the Philadelphia troubles, Mrs. Mackay gave a large dinner party with a musicale afterward. The occasion was propitious: Miss Beatrice Mills, a New York heiress, was to marry the Earl of Granard on the following Thursday, and on Sunday night, January 10, 1909, Mrs. Mackay's party was arranged in their honor. When dinner was over, "the boy violinist, Mischa Elman," played first. It was a season of triumphs in America for him, and he had played several times for Hammerstein's concerts; he also played the *"Méditation"* in the *Thaïs* performance of Monday, March 22, by "special arrangement."

When Elman had finished, Cleofonte Campanini and the entire Manhattan Opera orchestra, which had just finished a Sunday-night concert in the Thirty-fourth Street house, arrived at Mrs. Mackay's and gave a performance of *La Mer*. Debussy's tone poem, at that time barely four years old, was unfamiliar to many in America: it is to be seen that Mrs. Mackay's guests were treated exceeding well.

All this had been discussed with Arthur, and he had put it before his father. Hammerstein was at first reluctant to give permission because the orchestra was on duty Sunday night and to play for Mrs. Mackay would necessitate terminating the concert at ten o'clock, earlier than usual. He did give his permission, just the same, and told Arthur it was "with his compliments"—that is, that no charge would be made. If it is true that some thirty to forty per cent of the subscriptions in boxes and orchestra were due to Mrs. Mackay's efforts, this was indeed handsome but not excessive.

The Mackay musicale was brilliantly successful and is fully documented in the press of the day. Arthur Hammerstein afterward remembered best of all how Campanini was bilked of his supper that night, and how the maestro complained. Arthur had said: "Don't eat dinner—there'll be a big buffet supper," and so there was, but Campanini was kept so busy being introduced to social luminaries that he had no time to eat it. Oscar, of course, was not present (he was no doubt in his old room above the Victoria, tinkering with a cigar machine).

In the week following the musicale Mrs. Mackay sent valuable presents to everybody connected with it. To Campanini she sent an emerald ring that was valued at $5,000. Word of it reached the Old Man, and he lost his temper badly.

He seems to have been a little jealous of Campanini in a number of ways and to have disliked the attention the conductor received from Mrs. Mackay in particular. There were other complications: Campanini had been insisting upon more and more rehearsal time to meet the new and dazzling competition at the Metropolitan.

All of this probably played some part in the outcome: nothing is really simple. At all events, the Old Man sent for Arthur, asked him if it was true that Mrs. Mackay had sent valuable presents to Campanini and everybody else, and then remarked: "To me, not even a letter of thanks." He then gave Arthur a sealed letter addressed to Mrs. Mackay and told him to deliver it. The letter told her that she was never to enter his opera house again.

Arthur destroyed the letter and said nothing until his father sent for him three days later. Then he confessed, and declared that he could not deliver such a letter to a woman who had done everything for the opera.

Hammerstein wrote another letter then and there, sealed it, put on his hat, and went out, saying: "I'll deliver this one myself." He did.

The disaster was tremendous: it robbed Hammerstein of the conductor who had had most to do with his success, and at the same time of the most important element in his social and financial backing. Not only did Mrs. Mackay stay away from his opera house: her friends followed her example. The subscriptions fell disastrously, and in the following season even the opening night did not attract enough "social" interest to fill a quarter of a column in the press.

5. Farewell to Campanini

Campanini's feelings, of course, were deeply involved: Mrs. Mackay was his friend and had admired him for three years. He had other reasons for dissatisfaction. He could not get enough rehearsal time to compete with Toscanini (the Metropolitan had two orchestras to the Manhattan's one). Hammerstein, possibly from jealousy, had shown himself less and less attentive to Campanini's suggestions during this year. Moreover, the maestro had been having appalling difficulties with Nellie Melba this very month of January; she would *not* follow his beat properly, even in *Otello*, a masterpiece he held very dear. To rehearse with her was an ordeal, and sometimes to perform with her was worse; on one occasion he actually put down his baton and let a substitute continue the opera. It is quite possible that he was having some of his constant quarrels with Mary Garden at the same time (*Salome* could very well have provided a few). They had so many quarrels, then and through the years of loyal and devoted collaboration which followed, that nobody could possibly pin down which was which. At all events, Campanini was ready to go back to Italy; in February this became known, and in March it was announced.

It was a sorry business, and could so easily have been avoided that one wonders at all of them. If Oscar Hammerstein had put on his best bib and tucker and gone to Mrs. Mackay's musicale himself, as she undoubtedly expected him to do, none of this would have happened. But he never went out into society, and it probably never crossed his mind that she wanted him to come. In all the accounts I have read or heard of this imbroglio nobody has mentioned what seems to me the main point: that Hammerstein himself was far from courteous in staying away from the party in the first place. The lady would have thanked him sufficiently for his orchestra, in that case; but as her invitation was disregarded, she did not trouble to write him a letter. The tempest may have been in a teapot, but in this case the teapot was the whole Manhattan Opera.

Hammerstein lashed out more or less wildly toward the end of this season. In one announcement he said he was going to "drop Italian opera" for the next year. (This was, presumably, in some reflex of rage at Campanini.) It is hard to understand how he could say such things seriously. It may be possible for an opera manager to "drop Italian opera," of course, but so far none has; a season would be almost impossible without it. Certainly Hammerstein, who had Tetrazzini, Zenatello, and Sammarco under contract at that very time, could hardly have contemplated such a thing. But he was in one of those moods in which he would say or do almost anything to retain the interest of the newspapers and the public, undoubtedly because anxiety was beginning to gnaw at his inner certainties, hitherto so solid.

6. A Bid to Caruso

The Metropolitan's revival, the mounting deficit of his own house in Philadelphia, the damaging quarrels with Mrs. Mackay and Campanini—all this made the last part of Hammerstein's third season a period of gathering clouds, a foreshadowing of the end. There were a few other disappointments and minor intrigues, of which two may be mentioned. The first was a serious effort on the part of Arthur Hammerstein, operating for his father, to detach Caruso from the Metropolitan.

"A Man Never Makes a Mistake"

Arthur knew that Caruso frequented Martin's Restaurant, near the old Knickerbocker Hotel, where he then lived. Arthur, too, frequented the restaurant, made Caruso's acquaintance, talked to him at some length, and broached the great subject after a while. The terms the Hammersteins were ready to offer were startling: $5,000 a performance for twenty weeks, three times a week if Caruso wished. Arthur explained that the whole sum could be deposited in escrow if the tenor so desired. (He mentioned four performances a week, but it is very doubtful that Caruso or any other singer would have considered such a possibility.) Caruso's fee at the Metropolitan was $2,000 for each performance in this season (1908–1909) and he sang there forty-two times, plus seven performances outside New York at $2,500 each. This was the highest fee paid to any singer, but Hammerstein would have more than doubled it in single fees and almost doubled it in number of performances. There can be little doubt that Caruso was tempted. In the end he refused, and the reason he gave Arthur was that he felt he would lose his voice if he ever abandoned the Metropolitan. He is known to have been superstitious, but it seems to me that other reasons besides a superstition about his voice must have operated in the matter.

7. *The Cavalieri Story*

Another episode involving Hammerstein with the Metropolitan was the engagement of Lina Cavalieri. This singularly beautiful creature—who retained her beauty for another thirty years or more, as many can bear witness—had given mortal offense to the interlocking directorate of the Metropolitan. A young man of the Astor clan, Robert Astor Chanler, whose fortune consisted of a million dollars as his share of a family trust, married the lady in Paris during the summer of 1908. She asked and received a paper making over to her the whole of his fortune as a marriage settlement. The honeymoon lasted one week, after which the young man escaped to America and found that his older brothers had no intention of honoring the marriage settlement, which was illegal in any case because it involved part of a family trust. The matter was settled out of court for something less than the young man's whole million, but not until an immense amount of publicity had appeared in the newspapers. After this, it was impossible for Mme Cavalieri to sing at the Metropolitan, especially as she was said to have been extravagantly admired also by a young man of the Vanderbilt clan.

This induced Arthur Hammerstein to engage her, in his father's name, for a few performances in the spring of 1909, and to give her a much bigger contract for the following season. Her fee was not large ($333 for each performance) and she undoubtedly spent more on her costumes than she earned on the stage, but her mere presence in the Manhattan Opera company—or in New York at all, for that matter—was a constant irritant to important elements in the Metropolitan's directorate. Her appearances were sometimes made to crowded houses because of the curiosity she had aroused, but her real value to Hammerstein was that of annoying the Metropolitan.

There were other episodes of the same kind, such as the engagement for the following season of a tenor called Carasa. This upset Caruso exceedingly, as he feared the similarity of names. (He need not have done so.) There was also a project afoot to bring Mme Giachetti, Caruso's former common-law wife, to the Manhattan Opera in the coming season. She had made Caruso's life unbearable in various European capitals, and he now dreaded the same situation in New York. All such maneuvers had little to do with the business of producing opera, but they revealed, above all, the nervous, anxious tactics of a doomed enterprise.

The Cavalieri engagement led to a heated exchange between Oscar Hammerstein and two reporters for the New York *Morning Press*. Hammerstein considered that the reporters insulted him and wrote to their editor to say so. They lay in wait for him and assaulted him in front of the Knickerbocker Hotel one evening, were arrested, and had to appear in the police court. After their fine had been paid, they offered to do the same to Arthur if he appeared at the Jefferson Market Police Court at nine the next morning. He accepted the challenge, met the reporters, and, thanks to his excellent physical condition and some training as a boxer, laid them low; it was then Arthur who was lodged in jail awaiting trial. This descent into straight brawling was accompanied by a libel suit, finally settled months later by a nominal payment to Hammerstein.

8. Opera Houses Everywhere

All these are indications of the tension that prevailed in the Hammerstein camp as the third season drew to an end. Even so, the Metropolitan's wounds were severe: its seasonal loss was $205,201. During this same season the Manhattan Opera is supposed to have made a profit of more than $200,000—the figure given by Arthur Hammerstein some years ago was $229,000. Such a profit was enormous for any opera house. Against it there were, of course, the huge and growing losses of Hammerstein's Philadelphia enterprise and the steady drain of cash into his really harebrained buying of real estate for future opera houses in various cities. At this time and well on into his last season he was roaming the countryside at every opportunity, promising opera houses to this city and that, buying properties in Brooklyn, Cleveland, Boston, and anywhere else where there was a suitable piece of land. His Brooklyn site cost him $160,000 and was never used. He was constantly giving interviews advocating opera houses for such cities as Atlanta, for example, chiefly on the ground that the Metropolitan visited there for a week each spring.

When the season was over in New York, Oscar took his company to Boston, Pittsburgh, and Chicago, besides completing the Philadelphia season. The Boston engagement was marked by the fact that the mayor of the city forbade any performance of *Salome*. The rest of the Garden repertoire was given there for the first time, *Pelléas*, *Thaïs*, *Louise*, and *Le Jongleur*. These works reached all the principal cities with an operagoing public during the season or at its end, and Hammerstein was immensely praised for his courage as an innovator. This may, and probably did, console him for the fact that his ventures into the other cities were not profitable. He could always reflect that the Metropolitan, too, was finding these travels a drain on the purse. The two companies between them were greatly "over-extended," as the business expression has it: that is, both were trying too hard and doing too much.

Hammerstein seems to me, from this distance in time and circumstance, to have lost his sense of reality at some period toward the end of the 1908–1909 season. He had always talked a certain

283

amount of nonsense, some of it shrewdly calculated nonsense; his natural inclination to bravado, to rhodomontade and sheer invention, had made him a delight to the newspapers, but now he was going to almost any length. Some little spring must have snapped along the way, perhaps with the mounting failure in Philadelphia, perhaps with the Mackay-Campanini disaster, perhaps simply from age and overwork. He was sixty-two and had lived on nerves for many years. There were those who doubted that he ever slept (James Huneker was one).

From now on his genius for self-destruction seems to have taken over control of a perceptible part, even a growing part, of his life. He would offend and dismiss his most invaluable aids, even his son Arthur, when this state was supreme. And his awful irony, a sense of humor slightly misplaced and twisted askew, now evidenced itself at the most inopportune times and places. It no longer mattered to him whom he alienated or antagonized. What he had said to the Mackays was now what he said to the whole world, including many persons invaluable to his opera house—it was "go to hell" not once but many times, recklessly and with a distinct sardonic pleasure. It was as if, seeing the abyss before him, he doubted his ability to avoid it, and, doubting, began already to accentuate his risks. There was always a chance of winning, even now; so the dizzying trapeze artist dares and dares again, up to the point of folly, while the band plays and the crowd roars, though there may be silence in the sawdust afterward.

XXVIII

Disaster Waits in the Wings

THERE WAS an intuition afloat, or at the very least an informed guess among those nearest to it, that the Manhattan Opera would not outlast the season of 1909–1910. Probably this did not extend to singers and other artists, whose contracts were in some cases for a longer period and were literally interpreted by that tribe of the eternally unwary. Businessmen connected with the two opera houses, including Arthur and Willie Hammerstein, were thoroughly aware of the situation. Willie's relationship to the opera was chiefly that of making as much money as possible out of vaudeville at the Victoria Theatre so as to sink it all in the Manhattan; Arthur by now had become his father's alter ego in the opera houses, carrying on negotiations in his name and, as we have seen, making repeated efforts to fend off disaster.

1. Oscar Undismayed

Although he liked opera no better as time went on, Arthur got to know it well in those years, well enough to shuffle repertoire and casting, well enough to economize where he could and keep the machine running in all emergencies. Lyle Andrews, the treasurer and box-office manager, had the herculean task of keeping some kind of order in the finances, which became almost impossible whenever a payroll had to be met. Oscar Hammerstein's idea of money was that it should be taken wherever it could be found— from the subscription accounts, from the Victoria Theatre, from the box office, or from any other repository that, according to his way of thinking, was his own and could be tapped. It proved a superhuman task to convince him that current expense should not come, for example, out of the money subscribed for the entire season, or indeed that any one account was different from any other. This is why, with the best will in the world, it is sometimes difficult to credit the figures given for Hammerstein's operations, either in profit or in loss. The nature of the situation indicates that nobody really knew how the finances stood. And, finally, Billy Guard had the congenial and eminently successful task of keeping Hammerstein and his opera company well to the forefront of public attention at all times, even out of season.

The impresario himself never betrayed in public any sign of trepidation, and it is quite possible that he felt none for some weeks. His extravagance became in some instances quite beyond reason: he paid out more than $100,000 in royalties this year, it is said, and some of this for works that were never written. He paid $18,000 in advance to Richard Strauss against a guarantee of a larger sum for his *Elektra*, for instance, and spared nothing to make that production, Hammerstein's last of historic consequence, worthy of his ambition.

Money paid down on real-estate holdings was not, of course, lost: the properties in Brooklyn, Cleveland, and elsewhere, purchased for opera houses that were never built, did represent values. But some of the money spent on the most legitimate business an impresario can have, which is the actual production of opera, seems very nearly to have been thrown away. There was a *Tannhäuser* sung in French, for example, new from head to toe, which was performed only three times and had a real audience only once. New York was no longer in a mood for operas performed in any but their original languages (or else, sometimes, in English), and Hammerstein had no very persuasive reason for this production at all. The idea of *opéra bouffe* in French, another novelty of the season, was again unsuited to the New York of 1910, although less obviously so. It might have been acceptable in the 1880's, but *Les Cloches de Corneville* and *La Fille de Madame Angot* seemed actually more old-fashioned and creaky in 1910 than they would seem today. On these and similar notions quantities of money were poured out, and, although the staples of the company—Garden and Tetrazzini, Tetrazzini and Garden—continued to provide big audiences, they could not overcome the losses now mounting for both the New York and Philadelphia houses.

Hammerstein provided an "educational series" in the early autumn as a prelude to this season. It consisted of a series of performances at reduced prices, employing singers who had not been members of the company before, most of them new to New York. Some of these remained for the regular season, and one in particular, Mme Marguerite d'Alvarez, the Peruvian contralto, engaged Hammerstein's exaggerated admiration. It seems that this lady fanned into flame some erotic sparks that had been briefly dormant, and the Old Man made himself the legend of Thirty-fourth Street by his useless pursuit of her. He also insisted on casting Mme d'Alvarez in leading contralto roles as often as other contracts would permit (or oftener). She was a very large lady, and many now living must remember her imposing, not to say gigantesque, apparition in *Samson et Dalila*, the opera in which, at Chicago in 1921, she very nearly disrupted a Norman Bel Geddes setting by falling on the first of innumerable hieratic steps.

2. *Another Salome*

The Manhattan opened a week before the Metropolitan's opening. The opera was the *Hérodiade* of Massenet, the date Monday, November 8, 1909, with the already well-publicized Lina Cavalieri in the role of Salome. Hammerstein was attracted to this work probably first of all because it dealt again with the Salome story, which had become a kind of epidemic in all forms in New York for the past two or three years. "Salome dances" were popping up everywhere, in every form: Gertrude Hoffman in vaudeville (at Hammerstein's own Victoria) and Maude Allen in more pretentious entertainments were at the peak of their success. At this very moment a play called *Herod* was running, with William Faversham in the title role. Mary Garden's phenomenal *Salome* the year before had set all this off, or perhaps was the outstanding symptom of a widespread malady; at all events, the Salome story in any form was regarded as entertainment.

In addition, Massenet had come into favor in New York as a composer in both opera houses, and there was something in the air which the newspapers called "Massenetitis." Mary Garden was responsible also for this, in the main, for it had begun with her *Thaïs* and *Jongleur;* the Metropolitan was about to succumb with its revival of *Werther* (Geraldine Farrar, Edmond Clément, and Alma Gluck), its refurbished *Manon* (Farrar), and so on through several other works for several years.

Doubtless Hammerstein felt that the combination of the Salome story and Massenet's extremely sweet but usually effective theater music would make the box-office a Golconda. This did not prove to be true with *Hérodiade*, but there was enough curiosity about Lina Cavalieri's Salome to justify five performances of the work (the fifth with Mazarin instead of Cavalieri). *Hérodiade* seems thus to have exhausted its American public, for, as it was not heard before, it has not been heard since.

3. Gone the Glitter

It seems to be—according to the best judges—a feeble work on the whole, with some spectacular scenes and a few pieces of effective sentimental writing. Lina Cavalieri, making her first appearance as a regular all-season member of the company, had Hammerstein's best French singers (no doubt the best in the world) to aid her: Gerville-Réache was Herodias, Dalmorès was Herod, and Renaud was John the Baptist. The conductor, making his American debut, was Henrique de la Fuente of the opera house at Antwerp. She herself, however, was the center of attention. The *Times* thought she "showed an intelligent effort at improvement." Nevertheless, the contortions that represented her effort to characterize Salome were judged to be "not only excessive but also awkward."

This opening night was different from each of the preceding ones at the Manhattan. The house was crowded but not exceptionally so, not as the opening-night houses had been crowded before. Significantly, New York "society" was less in evidence than ever before, and Mrs. Mackay, the mainstay of the house, was absent. For some reason the opening night this year did not obtain the front-page display in the leading newspapers which had been given in the three preceding seasons; it was reviewed inside the papers, in the usual place for opera reviews. These and other indications, from the outset, seem to suggest that some of Hammerstein's magic had worn off—the newness, perhaps, the surprise, that which he most of all had to offer and could least afford to lose. He may have felt it himself: his curtain speech, when he consented to make one, was a model of brevity—one sentence and a word of thanks.

4. Charming John McCormack

On the second night of the season John McCormack made his debut as Edgardo in *Lucia* with Mme Tetrazzini. He was then twenty-five years old and, according to the New York *Times*, looked even younger, but his *bel canto* style had already been formed by seasons in Italy and at Covent Garden.

The *Times* printed an interview with McCormack before the opening of the Manhattan season in which it said that he had "a frank, boyish expression and a manner of speaking which renews the traditions, so often forgotten in New York, of the Irish blarney." The *Times* reporter found him unlike all other opera singers in that he grew tired of answering questions about himself and began to ask some of his own: when was Mme Sembrich going to give a song recital? When could he hear the Boston Symphony Orchestra? The young tenor further threw tradition overboard by saying that he admired Caruso intensely, that he had learned more by hearing Caruso sing than he had from any teacher, and that he would be embarrassed to sing *La Bohème* (as he afterward did many times) in a city that had usually heard Caruso in it.

As for Mme Tetrazzini, he called her his "fairy godmother" and said that he would not have obtained the engagement with Hammerstein if it had not been for her. In expatiating upon Mme Tetrazzini's kindness to him he told a few anecdotes, one of which was about a *Lucia* performance in London when he had had a bad cold. She had helped him at various points, and at one moment in the duet had sung his high A for him.

All of this refreshing modesty and candor had startled the press even before he sang. Now, after the first *Lucia*, the better-than-opening-night house received him extremely well, and the newspapers took to him at once in spite of his total innocence of anything that could be described as acting. His "delightfully sympathetic voice" was praised, as well as his "discreet and refined" style. He became a favorite in this season, as he was afterward at the Metropolitan and other opera houses until, some years later, he abandoned opera altogether for the vast rewards of a concert public such as no other tenor has amassed.

Tetrazzini—who, in addition to her predilection for McCormack, was an invariably good-natured woman—led him out with her in all her bows after the first act was over. She, like Caruso, had known his quality from the time he had first appeared at Covent Garden three years before. (Caruso was the first visitor the young Irish tenor had in his dressing room after his London debut.) It was well known that Melba would not permit him to take bows with her at Covent Garden. Tetrazzini had been his almost invariable partner in the London performances after that.

Mme Tetrazzini must have been a rather startling vision that night. She had gained weight, as she did every year, and thus seemed to have lost stature. She made her first-act entrance, says the *Times*, "in an extraordinary gown of blue satin, gold meshes and diamonds," blowing kisses at the audience the while. When she settled down to her singing, there were no more complaints—that C and that E-flat, not to speak of all the hops, skips, and jumps between, were what the audience wanted to hear. She was cheered to the echo, and with John McCormack and Sammarco for good measure, it was an exciting night in the Manhattan. The conductor was Oscar Anselmi, making his debut.

For the third performance, Hammerstein introduced two new singers in his *Aïda* production: Mariette Mazarin, the dramatic soprano from Brussels who was to illuminate the season later on with her Elektra, and Mme d'Alvarez, the Peruvian contralto. Zenatello and Sammarco sang with them. In view of the commotion stirred up by Mme Mazarin a few weeks later, it is interesting to observe that she made no great impression at her debut.

In his second week Hammerstein initiated his series of *opéra-bouffe* performances (Tuesday and Saturday nights, at $3 for the most expensive seat instead of $5) and persisted for some weeks against the indifference of the public. For these he had imported a whole cast of principals from Paris. Later he restricted them to Saturday nights and then sent them to Montreal and Quebec for a few weeks in an attempt to recoup the losses they had incurred.

The gifts of Cassandra were not needed to see that deficits would ensue and that the persons best equipped to endure heavy losses would alone survive. Even the public, which is inclined to take extravagance on the part of producers in very good part, was disturbed. Letters actually began to appear in the newspapers before the new season was far advanced, suggesting that the competition was ruinous, that too much opera was being given, and that some combination ought to be made. From what shows in the newspaper comment of the winter, most people did not want Hammerstein to disappear or to combine with the older company: they wanted the competition to continue, but realized that it ought to be held within limits or kept to a reasonable scale.

Hammerstein paid no attention to the gathering whispers, but went on talking as if his plans extended for decades into the future. Nevertheless, the idea of combination persisted throughout December and January, and sometime in January the first serious talks were begun which were to end in an extraordinary solution.

5. *Garden in* Sapho

In the second week, also, he brought forward his first "Garden novelty" of the season—Massenet's *Sapho*, which pleased neither critics nor public, had only three New York performances, and was thereafter dropped. Miss Garden had put into the part of Fanny Legrand all that she thought or felt to be in it, and some very good judges, Carl Van Vechten among them, considered it one of her best creations; it was, however, "unsympathetic," just as the character in the Daudet novel was unsympathetic, and it puzzled rather than pleased. "She has not given so unsympathetic a performance in New York before," said Aldrich in the *Times*. She played it harshly, of course (what was Fanny Legrand if not a highly commercial prostitute?), and this meant both vocally and dramatically; she "lapsed into the speaking voice" from time to time. Even the frailest heroines in Garden's repertoire had hitherto either benefited by that sound operatic device, redemption through love, or had offered the spectacle of vice highly alluring but severely punished; *Sapho* did neither. Hammerstein would have done far better to spend his money on *Monna Vanna*, in which Garden had just been having one of her great successes at the Paris Opéra; he did consider it, but chose *Sapho* instead. Musically, there is nothing to choose between them, but it should have been obvious that *Monna Vanna*, with its intensely appealing heroine and its strong parts for tenor and baritone, was the proper work for Garden, Dalmorès, and Renaud.

Meanwhile, an Italian dramatic soprano named Carmen Melis arrived; her beauty was observed and noted, but the public took no great interest in *Tosca* when she sang it. She did better later on in *La Bohème* with John McCormack. Tetrazzini and McCormack added to her staples a revival of Donizetti's *La Figlia del Reggimento*, in which Mme Tetrazzini must have been a rare sight indeed wearing a uniform and beating a drum. Cavalieri sang various operas, none of them well except one of the three parts in *Les Contes D'Hoffman*.

There were few surprises in any of this. As on the opening night, the gloss of Hammerstein's achievement seemed to be wearing off, and there was a diminution of that curiosity and excitement which had attended most of his doings for three years. The Garden and Tetrazzini repertoires were now more or less fixed. They drew big houses, but nothing else did; and even their big houses, although remunerative by any standard, did not have the tension and excess in all directions which had marked the preceding two seasons.

Garden's principal surprise was, in fact, neither her new parts nor her familiar roles but her Marguerite in *Faust*, which she had not yet attempted in the United States except for the one scene in Hammerstein's gala at the end of his second season. Her "mystic, dreamy Marguerite" was praised by all the critics, who saw in it some resemblance to her Mélisande. The *Times* said: "The garden scene attained a height of poetic beauty through her imaginative presentation which it seldom achieves in the performances of *Faust* heard nowadays in opera houses." She had not the vocal flexibility for the Jewel Song, but in other passages, such as the King of Thulé and the duets, her singing was thought to be lovely. Garden's own explanation of her exceptionally good reviews in *Faust* is simple: "They liked it because at last I was in something they knew."

It was during this season that Hammerstein, who was using Cavalieri as often as possible, announced her in *Thaïs* on a Friday night. Garden served notice that if Cavalieri sang it Friday, she, Garden, would sail for Europe on Saturday. Hammerstein protested (all this was reported in the press), but was at last convinced that she meant what she said; Garden sang the part. They seem to have had more quarrels than usual in this last season, including one about money. She had been paid in dollars instead of francs, as her contract required, and he contended that she gained on the exchange. However that may be, it is significant that Hammerstein at the very end of his life could say of her, as he did to Van Vechten: "Garden knows she is great, but does she know *how* great she is?"

6. Elektra, *and a New Star*

The principal new work of the year was the *Elektra* of Strauss, upon which Hammerstein lavished everything he had to give in production and in preparation. It was under way for about two months, with many extra rehearsals of an augmented orchestra directed by Henrique de la Fuente. The cast included Mariette Mazarin as Elektra, Mme Gerville-Réache as Klytemnestra, a tenor named Duffault as Aegisthus, and Gustave Huberdeau as Orestes. It was sung in French, of course, although it seems that during the preceding summer Hammerstein had hoped to get together a German cast. The translation used was by Henri Gauthier-Villars (the novelist "Willy"), who had made the French arrangement of *Salome.*

This *Elektra* swept the critics and public from their moorings. It had longer and more favorable reviews than anything else Hammerstein produced except perhaps *Pelléas et Mélisande.* The extreme care with which it had been rehearsed was evident to all the critics, although Mme Mazarin took pride in saying afterward that she had learned her part in a month. The entire production was tremendous in its effect, but chief of all (as in any good *Elektra*) was the impression made by Mme Mazarin.

This singer had made no very unusual stir in her previous performances in *Aïda, Cavalleria, Carmen,* and *Tannhäuser.* As Elektra she had New York by the ears. Apparently she had once visited a lunatic asylum for some length of time and had even done some nursing in one; at all events, she said she modeled her terrifying characterization on some women she had observed in such an institution. The results were such that the critics, although dutifully shocked by the music, found her performance an experience without parallel. It is seldom that a singer has received acclaim of this kind without a dissenting note.

De la Fuente's conducting style is said to have made the score less violent than it has sometimes seemed under German direction. It was, nevertheless, praised as a triumph of musical integration, and he shared the honors with Mazarin. The lady herself, who had been through an ordeal on the first night such as only Elektras know, swooned into the footlights as she was taking her final bow.

Mme Mazarin did not return to America after this season, and her subsequent career was not so brilliant as this success might have suggested. But for at least two months she held a large public enthralled with horror at her performance of a single role.

7. The Metropolitan Is Sensitive

Meanwhile, the Metropolitan was doing very well indeed, although at vast expense. It opened its Brooklyn season with Farrar in *Manon* and its New Theatre season with Farrar in *Werther*, thus making its own bow toward Massenet. The Metropolitan's own theater opened with Destinn, Homer, and Caruso in *La Gioconda*, with Toscanini conducting (November 15). On the second night Leo Slezak made his American debut in *Otello*, with Toscanini—a very solid achievement that lasted out this and other seasons. There were, later on, extraordinary performances of *Tristan* under Toscanini, and on December 23 his famous revival of *Orfeo ed Euridice*. There were three Isoldes: Gadski, Nordica (once—a farewell), and Fremstad. No coloratura could yet be found to counterbalance the unfailing attraction of Tetrazzini at the Manhattan; several were tried and found wanting. There were also some excursions into *opéra bouffe*, no doubt in rivalry with Hammerstein.

Disaster Waits in the Wings

Hammerstein was having his effect at the Metropolitan. A number of French singers were engaged and new French operas were produced, including Bruneau's very interesting work called *L'Attaque du Moulin*, which keeps the stage nowadays only in France. Toscanini's repertoire remained unaffected, but the repertoire and casts otherwise were noticeably influenced. Geraldine Farrar began during this season a line of development which was to lead her more and more into the category of the "singing actress"— more into the style, and finally even into the repertoire, of Mary Garden. Many new productions were designed and brought over bodily from Europe.

Hammerstein's gibes at his rival were now often ill-tempered, even unfair. On one occasion he remarked to some reporters in Philadelphia that the older house held only "antiquated lemons." Fair or not, his remarks, and even more his activities, were met with considerable sensitiveness at the Metropolitan, and with increasingly feverish as well as expensive efforts to show New York something new of their own.

8. Too Much Opera?

It sometimes seems to us that during the Hammerstein period, and perhaps largely because of Hammerstein, the United States had in truth gone "opera mad." The Metropolitan was involved in the New Theatre in Central Park West, where a combination of opera and theater repertoire was initiated; it had added new cities to its touring list; it kept to two performances a week in Philadelphia and one in Brooklyn. Hammerstein again had his tour engagements, his New York and Philadelphia seasons, and added a week in Washington at the Belasco Theatre during January. (All of this was Garden and Tetrazzini, plus the *Tales of Hoffmann*.) In addition to the operatic fare thus offered, a new company had been formed by Henry Russell in Boston: the Boston Opera Company, with an amicable arrangement for the exchange of singers with the Metropolitan.

XXIX

The End of the Dream

THE EXTRAVAGANCE of running two opera companies in New York on a competitive basis—each trying to outbid or outdo the other, each attempting to spread out to other cities, usually the same cities—was just as apparent at the Metropolitan as it was at the Manhattan. The expenses of 1909–1910 were ruinous for both houses. The difference was that the Metropolitan could endure its losses with much greater equanimity than the Manhattan, which relied upon one man alone. If it were asked which must yield, the answer would seem obvious: the shorter purse must, in such a case, be emptied first. It did not seem so obvious, however, to contemporaries who had already seen Hammerstein pull so many rabbits out of his much-caricatured hat. There was an uneasy feeling that he might even yet be capable of some extraordinary stroke that would turn all the operagoers in his direction at once and leave even Caruso singing to empty seats.

1. Mr. Kahn of the Metropolitan

At the Metropolitan, Otto Kahn, banker and connoisseur of the arts, especially of opera and ballet, was now beginning his long career as the principal financial power of the Metropolitan. His

The End of the Dream

taste and judgment were as powerful as his purse, and it is fair
to assume that a good many of the Metropolitan's ventures out of
its shell of tradition at this time, in its effort to counter Hammerstein, were initiated by him. We know that in one instance Kahn's
wishes ruled: the importation of Pavlova and Mordkin for a ballet
season cost the Metropolitan a considerable financial loss, but it
initiated a taste for ballet in New York which has steadily increased ever since.

It was during the winter, probably early in January, that Otto
Kahn and Arthur Hammerstein first began to talk about some
possible solution for the disastrous competition between the two
opera companies. They talked very cautiously at first, and only at
intervals, but afterward with considerable frankness.

Kahn had been interested in Hammerstein's venture from the
beginning and had been a frequent visitor to the Manhattan. It is
possible that he may have considered, at one time, turning his own
highly developed passion for opera into another channel than that
provided by the Metropolitan, where for many years he was denied even the right to hold a box. If this were ever so, he learned
early that Hammerstein prided himself, above all, on solitary splendor. Kahn's interest for two or three years may be fairly characterized as primarily artistic, with no ulterior motives in particular;
after all, the Manhattan did offer a variety of works and singers
which the Metropolitan could not duplicate. But during the season
of 1909–1910 Kahn's interest seemed to grow stronger, and it occurred to a number of persons, of whom Arthur Hammerstein
may have been one of the first, that the astute and many-sided
banking genius was considering ways and means of dealing with
an intolerable situation.

This story will never be quite clear to anybody. Those who par-
ticipated in the negotiation are dead, including now Arthur Hammerstein, whose chief motive at the time consisted simply in the
effort to save his father from ruin. He tried and he succeeded. We
wonder a good deal about the motives of Kahn, of Stotesbury, and
of others concerned in the matter. The Metropolitan must have
been losing a great deal of money, possibly a good deal more than
shows on the books, and must have been very much afraid of
Hammerstein—almost superstitiously afraid, because in fact he did
not damage them much this last year.

But I cannot help guessing at two other motives that, at whatever degree of strength, must have played some part in the development. I believe that Kahn was in part actuated by a perfectly sincere admiration for Hammerstein's lone effort and a desire to see him emerge from it without irreparable damage. This gives Kahn credit for an enormous and substantially unrequited generosity: it squares with what is known of the transaction, just the same.

As for Stotesbury, the case is much more complicated. He had taken over Hammerstein's mortgages on the Philadelphia opera house and had also advanced him a sum ($67,000) to cover the deficit of operations in the preceding season. Stotesbury was at the same time a director of the Metropolitan Opera. He seems to have been on both sides of the fence. As a member of the Metropolitan oligarchy and, of course, a partner in the house of Morgan, he stood to gain by Hammerstein's disappearance; as a creditor of Hammerstein he stood to gain even more, and more concretely in cash, from the payments made. It looks from this distance as if Stotesbury was able to make his debtor and competitor pay up and give up at one and the same time.

And whose cash, after all, was involved?

We are obliged to defer consideration of this interesting (although possibly academic) question until we have seen what actually took place.

2. Arthur's Story

Arthur Hammerstein was clever, presentable in a high degree —Oscar called him "my Beau Brummel son"—and well aware of all the social and financial classifications that his father had chosen to ignore. He had been on quite friendly terms with Otto Kahn for some time. They had, in fact, been talking, off and on, for a year: the first date on which they discussed the relations between the two opera houses is set by Arthur Hammerstein as being in December, 1908. In his statement he declares that Kahn even at that time, in the preceding season, was willing to concede that Hammerstein was the only real impresario in the field, and was further willing to consider putting Hammerstein in charge of all opera in New York—that is, of the two competing houses. This was at the moment when the rivalry between Gatti-Casazza and Andreas Dippel, with their oddly conflicting contracts, was at its height.

Nearly a year had passed when in November, 1909, Arthur again went to see Mr. Kahn and discussed a merger of the two companies. Kahn said that one person who was a boxholder at both operas, Judge E. H. Gary, could perhaps see it through. On December 9 Mr. Kahn telephoned Arthur to say that the opposition to any merger was too great and it must be dropped for the moment, but without losing sight of the idea.

On December 15, and again on December 18, Lee Shubert of the theater-owning corporation, in the presence of his brother J. J. Shubert, made Arthur Hammerstein a proposal: the Metropolitan would "buy out" Oscar Hammerstein at his own figure. This proposal Arthur presented to his father, who rejected it with scorn and anger in his usual tempestuous way.

On January 4, 1910, the board of directors of the Metropolitan Opera issued an official statement denying all rumors of a "merger" between the two operas. They said: "No negotiations have been pending or are now pending between Mr. Hammerstein's opera company and the Metropolitan."

The signatories included W. K. Vanderbilt, Sr. (an implacable enemy of Hammerstein's, it is said because of Cavalieri's engagement at the Manhattan), and Mr. Kahn, along with seven others.

It was not long after this that the really serious negotiations got under way. As usual in all this history, Oscar Hammerstein himself did not take part, and was barely aware of what was going on. His son Arthur asked his permission to resume conversations with Mr. Kahn and then did so. The time now was February, 1910, just after the pehnomenal success of the *Elektra première*, which had thrust Hammerstein's prestige with the musical and the general public to a point higher than ever before.

The talks were long and difficult. Before they had gone far, it seemed necessary to have legal advice and, to be safe, protection. Hammerstein's interests were represented by Samuel Untermyer and the Metropolitan's by Paul Cravath; they were two of the most eminent lawyers of the day. Arthur conducted the whole negotiation on his father's behalf. On one occasion when he arrived for an appointment with Cravath, the usher, showing him into the lawyer's office, mentioned the routine warning that Mr. Cravath "can give you only five minutes of his time."

Arthur exploded: "Then I'll come back some other time—I'll need more than five minutes!" Cravath waved the usher out. "Don't disturb me while Mr. Hammerstein is here, no matter how long he stays," he ordered.

This may have been simple courtesy, or it may have signified that doing something about Hammerstein had now become a crucial matter with the Metropolitan. Arthur was not slow to discover that Mr. Cravath was in earnest. When he saw, to his own astonishment, that a satisfactory result seemed possible, he decided to exile his father to Europe until the affair was concluded. With such delicate matters in hand, he could not risk the explosion of one of Oscar's bombshells.

3. Why Did Kahn Do It?

Oscar Hammerstein went to Europe in March. It must have been bitter for him: he knew that his fate would be, at best, obliteration from the field he most esteemed. At worst it might be bankruptcy, or possibly some more painful variation of financial ruin. Even in New York his public was dwindling, and Philadelphia was a mounting disaster. He could do no more. He was reduced to obeying his son Arthur—whom he had on several occasions ordered out of his opera house: "Never come into this house again!" —and this even in smaller matters that had nothing to do with the main negotiation. Arthur told him to keep on making announcements about next season, about new singers, operas, conductors, and the like, anything to give the illusion that the Manhattan Opera intended to go on. It was important not to allow the negotiators for the Metropolitan to realize how near the brink Hammerstein actually was—or how vital their own contribution was to be for him.

One wonders if they were deceived. Otto Kahn had all the information available to a great international banking house (Kuhn, Loeb and Company). He surely had a very shrewd notion of Hammerstein's situation. To be brutally frank about it, all he had to do was to stop talking. Hammerstein would have gone bankrupt; the Manhattan could not have gone on, and the Philadelphia house would have been lost. Stotesbury had the incentive of trying to get his money back ($400,000 of it). Kahn had no such motive. His love for the Metropolitan was not at stake; the Metropolitan would have gone on just the same. Arthur Hammerstein was extremely astute and clever, but was he clever enough to pull the wool over the eyes of Kahn and Cravath?

As one ponders over this whole extraordinary transaction, one is driven back again and again to the conclusion that Kahn was, to some extent, animated by sheer generosity. It is difficult in human life to attribute such motives to any person, in particular to a great financier, and yet what else can explain it? We know that Kahn sincerely admired Hammerstein's effort. At Hammerstein's death Kahn was the first who offered to help form a memorial committee for him. His attendance at the Manhattan had been frequent enough to show what he really felt about what went on there. He had nothing to win or lose in the settlement of New York's (and America's) opera situation. He was, in the broadest sense, disinterested.

In deference to the cynicism that passes for intelligence in such matters, it is possible to examine some of the possibilities that might contradict the thesis of Kahn's generosity. For one thing, he stood to gain considerably in the respect of his fellow directors at the Metropolitan if he could eliminate Hammerstein. That is true: but he could have attained the same result by masterly inactivity. Perhaps there was some social consideration, some public acclaim, some particular aura or halo, to be won by this achievement. This, too, may be: and yet we come back to the same basic fact: that it was not necessary. He could have had it anyhow, sooner or later; Hammerstein was doomed and Kahn was destined, not only by his wealth but by his passionate, sustained interest, to dominate the Metropolitan for decades to come.

Let us suppose that there were some motives of self-interest in Kahn's case. We all know that he was denied a box at the Metropolitan for many years—a box of his own, that is, in his own name— because he was Jewish. It is conceivable that he thought he could overcome this inconvenience by doing the Metropolitan such a great service. Supposing he wished to become chairman of the board and to exercise a decisive influence upon the course of opera production in the United States: supposing even this to be altruistic, in the interest of the art itself, what then? He did all these things. He would have done them anyhow. Is it possible that his contract with Hammerstein was a means to such ends—that he sought his own aggrandizement, or his own power over opera, by the erasure of the only possible competitor?

If this were true, it would mean that he was much less astute than all the other evidence shows. That is, if Kahn actually thought it was necessary for him to do this, he must have been deficient in judgment and also very ill-informed. I have found in the press of that winter plenty of evidence that Hammerstein's financial plight was understood. It was expressed even in anonymous "letters to the editor." How could Kahn not have known?

My own view is that the motives of self-interest played a small part in the matter, where Kahn was concerned. They may have existed, but they did not determine the result. No doubt he was quite pleased to assume the attitude of St. George after the extinction of the dragon. As an extremely intelligent human being, just the same, he must have known all along that the dragon was dead before the battle began.

When the negotiation was concluded, Hammerstein was to obtain $1,250,000 in all ($400,000 of it being paid to Stotesbury). What he gave up was the right to produce opera in New York for the next ten years—that and his Philadelphia opera house, which was, in any case, a dreadful liability.

Granted that Hammerstein did not get the entire sum in cash, it is clear that the cash was paid. Whose cash? As far as the story has been made public, the sum was to have been made up by the directors of the Metropolitan. The principal in the contract was Otto Kahn on one side, represented by Stotesbury, on the other side it was Oscar Hammerstein (then in Europe), represented by Arthur.

The $1,250,000 was to be paid in stated sums at stated intervals. We never have known exactly who contributed what. My guess, for what it is worth, is that this money was paid by Otto Kahn.

The Metropolitan took over all the American rights to a string of operas, all the orchestral scores, scenery, and other properties belonging to them, and the remaining contracts with a number of the chief Hammerstein singers—Tetrazzini, Garden, Renaud, and John McCormack. It was stipulated that if Mary Garden balked at this arrangement, they would then assume the contract of Mariette Mazarin, but not otherwise. Title to the Philadelphia opera house passed, but not title to the Manhattan: the only restriction here was that it could not be used for the production of opera. Oscar Hammerstein and his son Arthur were pledged not to engage in the production of grand opera for the next ten years in New York, Philadelphia, Chicago, or Boston. Oscar Hammerstein was at this time sixty-three.

4. *Aftermath*

The unique arrangement by which the Manhattan Opera came to an end gives rise to many curious reflections. What did the singers think? We are not sure, but we know that some who were not in demand by the Metropolitan sued for breach of contract (Zenatello was one). Obviously almost everybody in New York who had any interest in opera expected something of this sort to occur; it was in the public prints, as persistent rumor, often enough. But the contract itself was a secret, and many persons whose future was determined by it never saw it. Mary Garden was to be consulted about it—the contract says so—but she has told me that she never saw the document. If so astute and centrally important a figure as Miss Garden did not see it, we may be sure it was not shown to other artists involved.

And, as far as they were concerned, it may have been a bewildering occurrence, but it did not greatly alter their lives. The Chicago-Philadelphia Opera Company, which was formed to take over a good many of these contracts, had the blessing of the Metropolitan and was in fact formed under the Kahn-Stotesbury aegis. It went on with the Hammerstein repertoire, artists, and tradition for some years until it was succeeded by the Chicago Opera Company; Campanini was persuaded to return without much difficulty; the whole Hammerstein school, if it may be called that, lasted for another fifteen or twenty years. The successor companies had their subscription performances in Philadelphia and Chicago, with (for some years) Tuesday nights at the Metropolitan in New York. Later on the Chicago Opera, the ultimate heir of the Hammerstein school, had regular seasons in New York in competition with the Metropolitan and made long tours throughout the United States. The artists who were thus transferred from Hammerstein's company had little or no reason to complain, for their fees were maintained or increased under the new arrangements, their repertoire was the same, and their public was actually wider (more truly national) than before. Only a few among the principal members of Hammerstein's company did not continue their American careers either in the Philadelphia-Chicago company or in the Metropolitan. And, of course, all the leading artists were either in demand, or actually had contracts, in various other parts of the world as well. (Garden continued to be a member of the Paris Opéra, and later on again of the Comique; Tetrazzini sang more or less everywhere for the next few years; McCormack was greater afterward than before; and lesser lights also to a lesser degree.)

But that they regretted the Manhattan Opera is strongly indicated. It had a special atmosphere, a particular element of excitement, that is not always native to opera houses. We recall James Huneker's theory that Hammerstein's actual presence on his kitchen chair in the wings at every performance had something vital to do with the electricity of the performances given. It may be so, although it would be hard to define such an influence technically. Some of the singers joined Hammerstein later in his London venture, and all retained for him a feeling of gratitude not unmixed with awe. He seems at all times to have had for singers, and with them, a communicative faculty of uncommon strength, so that he was able to do with them what few managers could. We have already seen some examples (the capture of Melba more or less against her own wishes is a case in point), but there were many more than we have room to give. If we look through the four seasons of the Manhattan Opera, we find, just as an instance of his persuasiveness, how very often he could get leading singers to perform exhausting roles on successive nights or even two on the same day. No opera singer is ever obliged by contract to work in this manner.

5. New York Wants Oscar!

The public seems to have regarded the disappearance of Hammerstein's opera as a very serious loss to New York. During the whole of this last season the press contained various suggestions— sometimes from the public, sometimes in editorial comment—

for an arrangement, any arrangement, that would keep the best of Hammerstein along with the best of the Metropolitan. The press obviously did not want him to be "bought out." He had not only made opera very lively indeed in his own house, but he had positively revolutionized the Metropolitan itself. The public liked his random boastfulness, his picturesque appearance and language, his whole aura and legend. Nobody else in New York was so invariably a "good story" or had so many "good stories" told about him. Countless persons who had never set foot in an opera house regretted the suppression, the erasure, of New York's favorite rebel, the bumptious and irrepressible, the agile Hammerstein.

There was undoubtedly one person who greeted the denouement with pure relief, and that was Arthur Hammerstein. His four-year nightmare was now to end; he could shake the opera dust from his feet; he had saved his father from ruin, kept control of the theater itself, and produced a quantity of actual hard cash which would not have seemed possible a few weeks before.

Arthur's career as representative of his father had been arduous through all this time, and it was never at any point lightened or illumined by any love of opera. During his first season he had been awash in the innumerable unfamiliar details of opera production; he familiarized himself with opera by hard work, and we have seen how he came to the fore at all the crucial moments. His last and most decisive contribution was the conduct of the conversations with Otto Kahn, from which his father had been banished throughout. (Kahn and Hammerstein never met.) Arthur's principal emotion when he perceived how far Kahn was prepared to go was, it seems, a sort of incredulous delight. The final touch in the contract, the cream of the jest from Arthur's point of view, was the clause that forbade either Oscar Hammerstein *or his son Arthur* to engage in grand opera for the next ten years. This pledge, he has said, he would have been more than happy to give for nothing; it was his dream to get out of opera (if he could do so and save his father) and stay out for the rest of his life.

To the Metropolitan Opera the contract opened up all sorts of possibilities, many of them financial. With disastrous competition removed, it was possible to concentrate authority as well as activity, to dispense with many extravagances that had been the result of competition (such as double chorus and orchestra), and to give the Gatti-Toscanini combination its real chance to function. Some of Hammerstein's singers were welcome in the company, and, in any case, the Tuesday nights at the Metropolitan for the next four years were given over to the Philadelphia-Chicago company in Hammerstein productions (Mary Garden in most of them).

The one person in the entire opera world whose reception of the news was complex and troubled was Oscar Hammerstein himself.

Let us be quite explicit: the settlement obtained was the best possible, on financial terms of great generosity, and Hammerstein knew it. He had gone to Europe in March just to give his son an opportunity to complete this negotiation away from the hazards of his own temperament. If Kahn had not come through with this or a similar settlement, Hammerstein's future would have been very black. He had lost his opera company anyhow and he knew it. He did not even have enough money for the European journey; Arthur borrowed money on his own life insurance to finance it.

But even so, even so, it was a cruel moment for him. He had dreamed of his opera company for so many long years, and had brought it into being with such unexpected brilliance, that it was a harsh and bitter thing to lose it now. The man was incapable of betraying the depth of his disappointment—it was far more congenial to him to talk bravely of future plans, to scurry about the contracts and building schemes, to boast as he had always boasted; but here and there through his frequent public statements we catch a hint of dust and ashes, a suggestion of how this "banishment" (his word) fell upon his life's ambition. For he was by now a *true* opera maniac: not for money, not for fame, not even for power, in the last analysis, but for opera itself. Many of his own contemporaries did not fully understand or accept the validity of the obsession, but all the rest of his life showed how irresistible it had become.

XXX

The London Venture

$\mathbf{A}$RTHUR HAMMERSTEIN received a certified check for $100,000 as first payment on the contract with Kahn. He left Kahn's house for the Victoria Theatre, where his brother William was waiting, and showed him the check. "He nearly fainted," Arthur said in telling the story later. They went to the Knickerbocker Hotel across the street and bought champagne "for everybody in the bar." On that night they composed a long cablegram to the Old Man in Paris, giving all the details, and they must have been many, for Arthur remembers that it cost him $700. The Old Man cabled back: "You are a good boy. Come to Paris at once."

1. To London

Arthur took the first ship to France, went to the Grand Hotel in Paris, and put the legal papers and the money in his father's lap. He quotes his father's words exactly as follows:

"This is great! On receipt of your cablegram stating you had closed the deal, I bought a piece of property on the Kingsway in London, on which to build an opera house."

Arthur's answer, also directly quoted, was: "I'll never talk to you again as long as I live!" He took the next ship back to New York.

307

It is easy enough to see how dumfounded he must have been to have the family liberation treated in such a manner. It must have sounded wrong-headed to the point of insanity. Yet it was precisely what Oscar Hammerstein had done.

This act shows, more than any of the subsequent statements, how bitter it was to the Old Man to acknowledge defeat, even for $1,250,000 in recompense. It seems an act of monomania. For if it had been impossible to compete with the Metropolitan in New York, what possibility would there be of winning against Covent Garden in London? In those days before the First World War, the Royal Opera at Covent Garden was an extremely powerful institution. It had for decades been an ally of the Metropolitan, at some periods more closely than at others. The two houses had a good many of the same artists, ran the same kind of international season, and benefited in London as in New York by the entrenched, unshakable support of high society and finance. At least in New York Hammerstein was on familiar ground. In London he would face a world entirely new and strange: stranger, beyond a doubt, than he could have supposed at that time.

He was behaving like a man who has just been rescued, by a combination of skill and luck, from certain death by drowning, and rewards his rescuer by plunging back into the water.

We can see why he burgeoned at this period in statements of plans, engagements of singers, schemes for the future. He could not and would not give up. His pride was injured, of course, but something deeper than pride was involved: a self-justification was at stake for a whole life, not just a part of it. His trip to Europe "for reasons of health" had turned into a whirlwind of activity— hearing singers, buying properties, arranging for new works. His health was somewhat impaired and he did see some doctors about it, but he took none of that so seriously as he took the inner necessity to demonstrate his continued powers as an impresario.

When he landed in New York on July 15 from the *Lusitania* he was full of these plans. He was going to reopen the Manhattan for comic opera in English, and had already engaged a number of principal singers from Europe: the first offering would be *Hans the Flute-player*, September 12. He was going to put a roof theater on the Manhattan and give legitimate plays there at the same time as comic operas in the house itself. As he was barred by contract only from opera in New York, Chicago, Philadelphia, and

Boston, he was going to form a grand-opera company on the international scale to play in the leading cities of the United States where he could still legally give opera.

His "banishment," he said, had been and always would be "a source of the deepest and most painful regret." He had been forced to accept it to avoid "absolute disaster."

"Nevertheless," he said, "no money in the world can repay me for the feelings of sorrow and regret that I have experienced at leaving a field in which I believe I won the respect and affection of the world of music and the public in general."

The sincerity of these feelings could hardly be doubted, and yet the impresario's behavior seems an almost perfect example of the effort to eat your cake and have it too. The turmoil of motives included a certain amount of sheer resentment against fate. We see this in one of his famous brief messages. When he was asked to dine with the directors of the Metropolitan he replied in one line:

"Gentlemen, I am not hungry."

2. King Oscar Is Himself Again

Arthur Hammerstein's relationship with his incomprehensible father did not remain in the state of feud set up by their Paris meeting. The Old Man seems to have been able to dominate or win over his sons whenever he tried hard enough. Arthur was at this point just about to begin his long career as a producer of operettas and musical comedies. His first venture was a memorable one: *Naughty Marietta*, by Victor Herbert, which was to set a number of records in its field. At first Oscar Hammerstein, who had paid no commission to his son on the contract with Kahn, was supposed to finance this operetta; as it turned out, he drew heavily on its profits to discharge some of his own old obligations. The settlement finally made with Arthur in 1914, in lieu of commission for the opera contract, was the lease-holding of the Republic Theatre.

Naughty Marietta rehearsed in the Manhattan, but had its opening in Syracuse and its New York triumph in an Erlanger theater. Meanwhile, Oscar Hammerstein had opened his comic-opera season on September 12, exactly as promised, with a production of *Hans the Flute-player*, by Louis Ganné. It seems to have had a crowded and high-spirited opening night, rather like an opera opening, with demonstrations of New York's good will toward the Old Man, and immediately thereafter Hammerstein sailed again for Europe to get his London venture going.

The plot of land he had acquired in the Kingsway, between Portugal and Batavia streets, was London County Council property taken over as part of a slum-clearance scheme. It was near enough to the Strand to seem appropriate, and although Londoners had not yet acquired the habit of going quite so far for their entertainment, Oscar was buoyantly sure that they soon would. The Kingsway was no more than a dirt road at the time, according to Arthur's memory of it, and it may be that Hammerstein's activity there helped it to develop into the busy thoroughfare it later became. He was back again in New York October 13, again on the *Lusitania*, and spoke freely about the London Opera House.

"The Londoners don't really believe that I'm going to do any more than talk," he said shrewdly. "They smile when I tell them I am going to give them their first real grand opera. But on October 17 the work on the building begins. The location in the Kingsway is perfect. I expect the house to be ready by November 1, 1911. I am going back to Europe in January to get my company together. I expect to find new singers for the London house just as I did for the Manhattan. I must virtually have three companies for French, German, and Italian works. For the French singers I have an arrangement with MM. Messager and Brusseau of the Paris Grand Opera to exchange artists with them.

"From this country I shall take, among others, Orville Harrold, the tenor, whom I discovered singing in vaudeville. He is to sing in Paris next June and will come to me when I need him. My singers will have yearly contracts, so that when the London season closes I shall be able to bring them over here. My arrangement with the Metropolitan bars me out of grand opera in only four cities, and that leaves me a good deal of territory."

The confident tone shows that King Oscar was himself again. It probably amused him to find that London regarded him rather quizzically. He did not fully realize, then or later, that some of the characteristics which had made him an object of familiar affection in New York would not operate in quite the same way in London. It amused him to be called "the Barnum of grand opera" and to act accordingly. He liked to call everybody "Mike," if he could, and carry his bookkeeping and his correspondence in his own head. Formality of any sort, aside from his invariably elegant clothing, was alien to his nature. His wit was frequently coarse, his language whatever came into his head; he was never a re-specter of persons. All this New York knew and loved. It was not quite the same in London, where, before 1914, a good deal more decorum was expected, especially in such a field. It would seem to one who explores this period over forty years later that Hammerstein was a shade too much himself, too characteristic, too pungent, for the London of that day. It was all right to be Ameri-can, and even rather comically American: but to be this in full consciousness of the role seemed excessive. When Hammerstein caricatured or parodied himself, as he was quite capable of doing and had often done in New York, he created an unease among Englishmen. They were never quite sure whether he was making fun of them or of himself.

Thus, in the autumn of 1910, when the excavations began on the site of the new opera house in the Kingsway, Hammerstein put up an enormous billboard almost covering the front of the property. "On this site," it declared boldly, "the London Opera House is to be erected by Oscar Hammerstein, Builder of Opera Houses." The self-advertisement startled Londoners, perhaps a little more because it took place in the realm of opera, which at that period, more than before or since, was the particular appanage of royalty, aristocracy, and oligarchy.

Hammerstein went merrily on, and before the opening of his house a year later he had accustomed Londoners to a good many of his odd ways. The very uncertainty as to whether he meant what he said or not—whether all was a pose, or only part, and what part was intended to hoax or bewilder—made the impresario a subject of conversation in ever-widening circles, so that by the time of his London Opera's first night the correspondent of the New York *Times* could cable home that he was "the most talked-of man in London."

He carried to London all his managerial habits of yore: he did a great deal of work himself, without secretaries, bookkeepers, or records, and he was surrounded by men like Lyle Andrews, the treasurer, and Jacques Coini, the stage manager, who knew his methods and would have been startled to find them changed. All this, along with the speed with which the new opera house came into being, quite dazzled the London press. For one thing, Hammerstein was always accessible to the press unless he had taken some special personal dislike to individuals in it. This was a novelty in itself. And then, too, for the delight of the newspaper writers, he expressed himself in a way that made him eminently quotable. Thus, it was to a London newspaper writer that he made one of his most pungent remarks in that first year (1911). Coming into Hammerstein's office in the still incomplete opera house, the writer said:

"Well, Mr. Hammerstein, how's the opera business?"

"Opera's no business, Mike," said Hammerstein. "It's a disease."

In his own case, certainly, his words were precisely true.

3. Sunset and Afterglow

He does not seem to have suffered from any other disease, just the same; we find him sprightly, healthy, cheerful all through these years, bubbling with optimism. In Carl Van Vechten's excellent "epitaph," as he calls it, on Hammerstein—an essay written after the Old Man's death in August, 1919—he says that the impresario had been dying from the moment he lost the Manhattan Opera. If this is true—and Mr. Van Vechten knew him well enough to say—it must have been well concealed from most of those who saw him in London.

Or, in another sense—and this seems very likely—we have in the London venture a sort of afterglow, or Indian summer, for the ebullient Oscar. The loss of the Manhattan may have been irreparable, but he did not yet feel that it was so: he had new worlds to conquer and he was, for the moment, very much in funds.

We are told that after his heavy obligations in New York had been discharged and his general credit fully restored, he had in hand better than $300,000 to spend on the London Opera House. In the mystery of his finances, of which detailed record does not exist, this seems in one way to be a great deal of money. In another it seems not enough, as he had received, on paper at least, $1,250,000 by the settlement with Kahn. There were, of course, mortgages on his opera houses in both New York and Philadelphia: the Metropolitan assumed the Philadelphia mortgage of $400,000, and the one in New York came to another $340,000. There was another matter of $39,960 which Stotesbury in Philadelphia had advanced for the last Hammerstein season there. Hammerstein said it was an outright gift and Stotesbury said it was a loan. There was a suit in court, resulting in a mistrial, and eventually the case was settled by Hammerstein's paying the costs ($4,000).

To invade London as an opera impresario on the grand scale with only $300,000 as capital may seem daring, but Hammerstein had done much the same thing before. He was entitled, in his boundless self-confidence, to feel that he could win again. We, as observers, know that he was foredoomed to failure by the very magnificence of his plans, to which no limit could ever be set. He never knew or believed, to the very end, that he could be permanently defeated. Had he not obtained one of the most promising theater sites in London for a ground-rent of only $24,000 a year for ninety-nine years? This in itself was an achievement, and there were always mortgages to be had.

So he went on in high spirits, upheld most of all, we think, by joy in what he was doing. He was hearing singers all the time, drawing up casts, picking out new operas, deciding on architectural details and stage designs and colors and fabrics. All of this gave him enormous pleasure. He continued to do it even when it had become little more than a game without a chance of fulfillment in real life. He was doing it, and still believing in it, within a few weeks of his death. In London, at any rate—and for the last time—he was doing it in deadly earnest, risking his all, as usual, and loving every moment of it.

He must have regretted the loss of Tetrazzini and Mary Garden. He never admitted it. Their contracts in America made them out of the question for him, and he was still at this time under the spell of his final quarrel with Garden: he would find other Gardens, other Tetrazzinis. His sublime belief in his own ability to conjure new and remarkable singers out of nowhere was frequently expressed just at this time: it may have covered some slight anxiety, but not much. He really did possess that ability, as he had proved: it was only in degree that he esteemed it too highly. Even a Hammerstein, that is, cannot find a Garden or a Tetrazzini every day, because they do not exist every day in every given place. His errors in singers (Maria Labia or Carmen Melis, for example, who did not live up to expectations) were easy to forget; his triumphs with other singers obliterated them.

So, for his first London season he resolutely searched for new voices, new names and faces. This was not only a necessity, because so many of the famous were under contract to Covent Garden, but it suited his way of doing things. He liked discovery and revelation: it was his form of the creative. When he discovered a pretty young American girl in Paris with a fluent coloratura voice, he persisted until he had obtained her signature to a contract for London, and here again he was right: the girl was Felice Lyne and she provided the great sensation of his opening season. He believed in Orville Harrold, who had sung in opera before, and again was proved right. Aside from a few famous artists, such as Renaud, he relied most of all on novelty: freshness of approach and the general electrical excitement of the new—the new, lavishly presented. This had been his formula before, and he could not believe that it would fail.

For the house itself he used the services of a well-known architect, Bertie Crewe, who had built a number of theaters throughout the United Kingdom, but, as usual, his own ideas predominated.

There were some respects in which even Hammerstein yielded to London. We smile to think that he put in not one but two royal entrances—the customary one for the King and Queen (that is, George V and Queen Mary) and another for Queen Alexandra, so recently widowed, whose fondness for opera was known. This was the same Hammerstein who, in his first season at the Manhattan in New York, had made no proper entrance at all for the boxholders. The grand staircase at the London Opera House was grand enough for the display of gowns and jewels, and it led down to the boxes. The white-rose-and-gold décor of the house was more or less what Hammerstein had always wanted and used, more or less what every opera house in the world does want and use.

But he also had his special novelties. He installed a "Marconi apparatus" on the roof of this theater, so that his adherents "even six hundred miles out at sea" could order their seats. The "Marconi apparatus" was then the wonder of the world (as, for my feeble comprehension, it still is). There is no record of use, but perhaps it was intended more to be mentioned than used. Similarly, the London Opera House had an artesian well of its own. There has been little complaint against London water in recent centuries, but Hammerstein was going to be sure that in his own opera house it was pure.

The seats in the house (stalls in London, orchestra seats in New York) were comfortable, by Oscar's special effort, and were raked down at the ratio of one-in-twelve, giving everybody a good view of the stage. The statement made in the London newspapers, more than once, was that this was "the most ambitious structure of its kind in the United Kingdom."

4. London Opening Night

The opening night of the London Opera House was November 13, 1911, a Monday. Two days before, King George V and Queen Mary had departed for India, for the Great Durbar in which they were to be crowned Emperor and Empress—the only British sovereigns ever to be so crowned. Hammerstein must have felt this as a blow of fate, because he had undoubtedly hoped for their presence at his opening night. He could not have known, when he made his plans and announced them a year before, that the sovereigns would be absent just at this moment. He must have witnessed their ceremonial departure through the streets of London with some dismay. The Hammerstein who had built two royal entrances to his theater was well aware that such matters were important.

Nevertheless, he had a full and even brilliant audience for his opening. He had chosen the opera *Quo Vadis?*, by Jean Nouguès, which provides an opportunity for much display on the stage— Christians thrown to the lions, excited crowds, and all that—as well as some meretricious and momentarily effective music. The opera still remains in the repertoire in Paris, but is not heard in other parts of the world because its score has failed to retain interest. Hammerstein thought it would give a splashy first night to his opera company, and he was right. Jacques Coini, the stage director, had a field day. The individual singers were, as a rule, of less importance than the chorus, ballet, and supernumeraries, not to speak of the stagehands, electricians, and others functionally vital to the spectacle.

There were, however, good singers. Maurice Renaud, just beginning to show his age—and therefore getting ripe for the Metropolitan—sang Petronius, and had the same success he had had for a good many years. The other singers were unknown to London and have since remained unknown, except for Mlle Aline Vallandri of the Opéra-Comique, who sang Eunice and made a good impression. Vallandri was a Hammerstein standby in London, and must have been an extremely reliable artist, although those who have heard her on early opera recordings will remember that her voice had a razor's edge.

The Old Man sat on his usual kitchen chair in the wings throughout the performance, smoking his cigars in violation of all rules. His daughter Stella had brought him a new stock of cigars from New York, the press declares, although we are reliably informed that he always made his own, even in London. He did not meet the notables. He met the performance.

Then there was a day of rest (Tuesday), during which Hammerstein could reflect that no opening night of opera had aroused more attention in London and throughout the world than his. He had evoked an audience of the greatest size and the most varied quality, had been praised by practically everybody, and had had the news cabled to the four ends of the earth. The King and Queen, on their way to India, if they had the advantage of a "Marconi apparatus" on their battleship, must have known that his opera house had opened. They may even have regretted that they were not there—the Bay of Biscay being what it is.

Even without royalty, the glitter of an opening night had not been denied him. The Duchess of Marlborough was there. Although her father was W. K. Vanderbilt, one of Hammerstein's most implacable opponents who was ready to go to any length to expunge him from the operatic record, the Duchess of Marlborough remained an adherent of Hammerstein's. She had gone often to his opera house when she was in New York, usually sitting in Mrs. Mackay's box, and now she had a box of her own at his opera in London. She was frequently in the audience, but most notably in his first week.

Mr. and Mrs. Whitelaw Reid had their box, too: he was the American Ambassador and lived in the old Dorchester House (now gone), and his wife was one of the greatest London hostesses. We may be forgiven for not knowing who was in whose box, but among those present, according to the record, were the Austro-

Hungarian and Portuguese Ambassadors (with the Duchess of Marlborough) and Lady Charles Beresford; Lady Cunard and Mrs. John Jacob Astor (afterward Lady Ribblesdale) in their own box, with guests; and, indiscriminately, Lord and Lady Alington, the Countess of Carnarvon, the Duchess of Rutland, the Duchess of Westminster, Lady Speyer, Lady Maud Warrender, and Prince Nicholas of Greece, the father of the present Duchess of Kent. A pretty bouquet—if space permitted, one could go on and on. The American papers of the day made much of the fact that the "American peeresses" were present, but in fact they were not, particularly: it was not a "national" occasion, except that the American Ambassador had a box and kept it throughout the season whether he used it or not. (When he lent it to others, their names were all religiously inscribed in the press.) The notable Americans were the Duchess of Marlborough, who remained faithful, and Lady Cunard, who did not. The other duchesses and notables were not born in the United States.

As far as I have been able to find out, Hammerstein had no acquaintance with these glittering personalities. It had not been his custom in New York and it did not become his custom in London—with, of course, a few notable exceptions. His place was on the stage, fiercely watching every detail of the performance and puffing such a cloud of cigar smoke that it was enough to suffocate any singer who came too close.

He was, on the whole, pleased with the results of his opening night. The press was extremely favorable, the audience enthusiastic. I think, myself, that he was not at home: that he was repeating familiar gestures—the kitchen chair, the cigar—more or less as a man does who has forgotten their meaning. I have done this before, he seems to say; and, at this long space of time, we echo, we have seen this before.

The Times says (November 14):

"Mr Hammerstein's new London Opera House opened its plate-glass doors last night and admitted a large and eager audience onto its rose-pink pile carpets. The company descended the stairs flanked with marble balustrades, to settle themselves comfortably in the ample armchairs, officially called stalls, or passed through the charming little ante-rooms into spacious boxes, or climbed other stairways into the well-planned balconies above. The welcome seemed complete. . . ."

317

The reviewer eventually got on from the house to the spectacle, and remarked that it was a bit Drury Lane, a bit Gaiety show, with "some of the semi-religious stuff of Wilson Barrett's 'The Sign of the Cross.' " After saying that the work had been successful in Paris and America (which is not quite true—*Quo Vadis?* reached production in the United States a year later), the reviewer says: "We may suppose that its strange combination of interests commended it to Mr Hammerstein when he chose it as the work with which to open his house. He cleverly added one more element of special attraction to the British mind by securing a representative of Mr. Sandow's Institute of Physical Culture to play the giant Ursus."

The Times's review says that all the excitement made it impossible to judge music or singers—the "burning of Rome" must have been show enough for all—and concludes:

"Mr. Hammerstein's speech at the end of the third act was short and to the point. 'I thank you for this flattering reception. All I wish to deserve is your respect, your friendship and your admiration.' Everyone in the house seemed ready to assure him that he already possessed all three."

5. *A Pair of American Hits*

After his day of rest (which, if we know Hammerstein, was no rest at all) he unveiled his second London production, on the Wednesday of that week (November 15).

It was *William Tell*, with Orville Harrold as the heroic Arnold. The other singers did not matter much to Hammerstein or anybody else, because in fact he based a great deal of his hope for the London enterprise on this tenor. He had undoubtedly been hypnotized, as everybody was in that era, by Caruso's power to fill any opera house at any time, and there was a general inclination to believe that if you could get hold of a rich, strong tenor voice somewhere, you could fill your theater by it. Harrold got excellent reviews and much applause, but he did not affect his audience to tears, shouts, or bewilderment, as Caruso so often did. There must be many middle-aged or even youngish persons who remember Orville Harrold, one of the most accomplished of American tenors, in his years at the Metropolitan Opera afterward. He was an extremely skillful singer whose voice was both pleasing and strong. I remember with great distinctness how he sang *Faust* at the Metropolitan, enriching it by a vocalism otherwise absent from the aging and overworked cast. (This was ten or twelve years later, but he did it extremely well.)

Orville Harrold was, however, no Caruso. The cheers for his London debut were a maximum that declined afterward, perhaps unjustly, and during his later career he was usually regarded as a tenor who sang when Caruso could not or was dead. This was one of the grossly unfair things that happened to practically every tenor in the world during the last ten years of Caruso's public life: all, even the best, were regarded as unsatisfactory substitutes. (McCormack would be the exception, but he abandoned opera at just about this time.)

The other singers did none too well. Victoria Fer, a Spanish soprano, was not much admired; José Danse, a French baritone (Opéra-Comique), was thought to be "the best since Renaud," a comment that, as Renaud was right there in the company and had sung only two nights before, was rude to both of them.

Then there was a *Norma*, not particularly remarkable except for the fact that some bits of the scenery and furniture of Rome, in *Quo Vadis?* four nights before, had now suddenly appeared in ancient Gaul.

Then, on Saturday, November 25, Hammerstein had the kind of flaring success which always gave him enormous pleasure. It came with the young American singer Felice Lyne, from Kansas City, whom he had found in Paris during the preceding summer and had used in New York in his production of *Hans the Flute-player*. She was now Gilda in *Rigoletto*, and the results with both press and public were such as London had not known since the debut of Tetrazzini.

Miss Felice Lyne did not fulfill the promise of this brilliant beginning, and to most persons today her name is unknown; yet she was an interesting phenomenon, not only as an episode in Hammerstein's life, but also in American culture. She was young and pretty and had all the technique imaginable for vocal fireworks— all but the greatest, that is. She made her London debut when she was nineteen. It was quite wonderful to see (so the critics of the day tell us) anybody so slight and appealing with a voice so fluent

319

and high: it did not seem at all absurd that she should be rolled in a sack and mishandled. She was pathetic; she was sweet; she could sing almost carelessly. Reviewing her Rosina in *Il Barbiere di Siviglia* a year later, one critic said she seemed to be singing the most difficult coloratura actually for fun, to amuse herself. This quality made an instant impression, and she stormed the citadel of London in a single night; she remained Hammerstein's most notable success during his time there.

And yet, considering how many others there have been like Miss Lyne since then, we can see that she was an exemplar of something that happens in American culture more than in others —a proficiency, perhaps, or a physical bravado, which sparkles and quickly dies because it has no base. Any operagoer can remember a number of young ladies who made the same appeal as Felice Lyne and made it just as briefly. It seems to come especially from American conditions (similar examples are few in Europe), and the reasons, which may be guessed, are not established. The main reason in my own mind is that these gifted girls with brilliant voices do not really care enough to absorb the meaning of what they do; they do it like juggling, and juggling soon palls, even on the juggler.

But it was all very good for Oscar. We learn from the New York *Times* of November 19 that he was "in a very cheerful frame of mind about the future"; this was even before Lyne's debut. He needed about $15,000 a week to pay his expenses at the London Opera House, and he had brought in $25,000 the first week. Caution must surround all his figures, and yet it does sound as if he had some basis for cheer. He thought it very unfortunate that the King and Queen had gone, but he was pleased by the response of the general public, thought the press had been appreciative, relished the attentions of the boxholders, and was proud of the performances given by his singers, orchestra, and technical staff. He was going on and on, higher and higher, further and further.

6. Peers for Oscar

There were persons in London well-disposed toward Hammerstein's venture for a variety of reasons, principally because it promised variety, change, novelty, but also because his own personality aroused interest. A certain number of these persons occupied high positions in society and finance. It was the same story all over again: Hammerstein did not know or care anything about them, but they would have helped him if they could. Several of them tried. The Dukes of Norfolk and Argyll were favorable; we have seen that the Duchess of Marlborough was an active supporter; Lord Howard de Walden, a patron of the arts in innumerable respects, was interested from the beginning. The Honorable Alfred de Rothschild, then about seventy, younger brother of Lord Rothschild, was an enthusiast both for opera and for novelty; he had conducted his own private orchestra, collected pictures and *objets d'art*, and at one period had kept a private circus at his house in the country. He was quite naturally attracted to Hammerstein's enterprise, which in a sense combined all of these interests, and even in the first season he was a source of great encouragement to the impresario. He took a box; he gave money; he asked his friends to go. Best of all, he negotiated a mortgage of $350,000 on the theater, through the Rothschild bank.

When Hammerstein's first season, running from November 13, 1911, to March 3, 1912, came to an end, a group of those who had enjoyed its flavor banded together to form the "Committee for the Welfare of the London Opera House." This was by no means a board of directors, nor did any of them exercise any powers over Hammerstein. The committee was headed by the Dukes of Norfolk and Argyll, with Lord Harewood, Lord Howard de Walden, and others of the faithful. The concession Hammerstein made for this support may have been his promise to produce an opera called *The Children of the Don*, a dramatic poem by "T. E. Ellis," who was in fact Lord Howard de Walden. The fate of this work (June 15, 1912) dominated the events of Hammerstein's second season, which ran from April 22 to July 15 and was destined to be, in spite of all his struggles, his last in grand opera.

The decline in public support was fairly steady throughout Hammerstein's first season: in the second season (spring of 1912), it became disastrous. There was an obvious reason: the season of the Royal Opera at Covent Garden had opened two days before that of the London Opera House. Covent Garden was not only traditionally and institutionally powerful, but it actually gave a better opera season with far more famous and popular singers. Hammerstein could not compete with its social or financial power, its glittering array of international celebrities on the stage, or the fact that its royal box remained well tenanted while his stood empty.

All this is quite true, and yet an inspection of the record of his two seasons in London shows that Hammerstein himself was not offering London anything like the magic innovations he had brought to New York. He may have lost a little of his old flair, but it seems more likely that the whole enterprise suffered from a feeling, conscious or unconscious, that he had done it all before to no avail, and that he was in this case reproducing actions rather than originating them.

His repertoire for the first season was not so adventurous as it might have been, perhaps because he could not find singers prepared to adventure. In the first part, after *Quo Vadis?*, he produced *William Tell, Norma, Rigoletto, Faust,* and *Lucia.* On December 15 came *Hérodiade,* with Lina Cavalieri, Mme Marguerite d'Alvarez, and Renaud. They were not particularly well received; even M. Renaud was thought "too noble" for Herod. After a Christmas interval, the operas were *Les Contes d'Hoffman, Le Jongleur de Notre Dame, Louise, La Traviata,* and *Il Barbiere di Siviglia,* with repetitions of all of them. Sunday-evening concerts filled out his season.

This was, with two or three exceptions, a repertoire very familiar to London operagoers, some of it too familiar. Even those works which had not been heard in London before, such as *Quo Vadis?* and the two Massenet operas, lacked musical or dramatic interest for this public. Without Mary Garden, *Le Jongleur de Notre Dame* was robbed of almost everything that had made it successful in America, and the same was true to a great degree of *Louise.* (Victoria Fer sang the first, Mlle Vallandri the second.)

Hammerstein attempted to oppose the declining tide of public interest by two devices, both expensive. He embarked on a new style of advertising with quotations from reviews, heavily emphasized type for some singers, and other typographical devices making all his announcements longer and splashier than before. Then, on February 5 he cut his prices sharply to half a guinea instead of a guinea for orchestra stalls ($2.50 instead of $5.00). Nothing helped.

He should have known by experience that the "Garden operas," as they were called—those which were the personal creations of

Mary Garden—seldom did well without her in any theater, except in Paris. "Garden operas" with Geraldine Farrar or other singers failed also at the Metropolitan. And most of the other works on his list depended, as they depend today, upon superlative performances, which, for one reason or another, he was unable to provide.

The exception noted before was Felice Lyne, who did have, in *Rigoletto*, one of those successful debuts which are the dream of every young singer. When she sang it with Orville Harrold and Maurice Renaud, the house was filled. She could not, however, repeat the success with *Lucia*, for which she was perhaps too young, and her dominion over the public showed a decline from then on. Even this singer, the most appealing in the company, was destined to have a quarrel with Hammerstein and to cease singing before the spring-and-summer season ended.

And his passionate admiration for Mme Marguerite d'Alvarez was not particularly helpful, in that it led him to make her more important than Lina Cavalieri in the advertising for *Hérodiade*. True, D'Alvarez was singing the title role, but the center of the drama was Salome, and Cavalieri objected with vehemence.

All this, the savage brutality of the box-office graph (always downward, never up), the quarreling singers and angry conductors, the beautiful opera house almost going to waste, must have been complicated for Hammerstein by his vain pursuit of Mme d'Alvarez—vain, that is, as far as is known. She departed from his company after the first season, and when the house reopened for the spring and summer, the leading contralto parts were sung by Augusta Doria.

7. Perhaps Chaliapin . . . ?

It was probably some time during this winter, when even the undaunted Oscar saw the handwriting on the wall for his London Opera House, that he made a journey to Paris. His errand was to persuade Chaliapin to come to London and sing in his company. An impresario of a slightly later period, Max Rabinoff, met him en route, and Rabinoff recalls that Hammerstein showed him a bank balance in pounds sterling amounting to about $12.50.

It shows dizzying self-confidence to be offering Chaliapin a contract with a total cash balance behind it of $12.50. It is equally startling to see how quickly Hammerstein had spent a fortune. This was a bare two years after the Metropolitan had paid him the famous million and a quarter, the million in cash, to get him out of opera in New York.

It should also be noted that Hammerstein's unfailing acumen still had not failed him. Chaliapin declined his offer, but he did go to London not long afterward, to the Royal Opera at Covent Garden, where his success was one of the most remarkable in the annals of the theater. If he had been persuaded to join Hammerstein instead, the end of the London venture might have been otherwise.

XXXI

Last Fling

THE SPRING season in London, Hammerstein's last fling at opera, although we may be sure he did not so regard it, began April 22, 1912, with a performance of *Roméo et Juliette* (Felice Lyne and Orville Harrold, conducted by Fritz Ernaldy). The *Titanic* disaster had occurred just six days before and occupied public attention for several weeks while the inquiry proceeded. Covent Garden had opened two days before and was a constant and brilliantly successful rival throughout.

1. Troubles Gather

Hammerstein had sprinkled English singers through his casts this time, and his chorus and orchestra had always been largely English, like a good many of his stage and theater staff. He was now to essay an English opera, *The Children of the Don*, and felt himself therefore in a better position to command English support. The error has been made by other managers before and since.

For this swan song he retained, from the previous productions, *The Tales of Hoffmann* (but without Renaud or Cavalieri), *Rigoletto, Faust, Barber*, and *William Tell*. *Tell* got only two hearings, but *The Tales of Hoffmann* ran through the whole season. The additions to the repertoire were: *Mignon, La Favorita, Il Trovatore, Don Quichotte, Les Cloches de Corneville* (played under that title), and *The Children of the Don*.

Of the new singers, only Lafont in *Don Quichotte* and Gennaro de Tura in *Il Trovatore* caused any particular excitement in press or public. Augusta Doria, who had the important contralto parts in *Favorita* and *Trovatore*, did not do well. The new conductors, Ernaldy and Gaetano Merola, were well received, Merola in particular. He had been assistant to Campanini and was to end a long career forty years later (1953) by death on the podium while conducting the San Francisco Symphony Orchestra.

But in this final season there exhales from all the evidence, as there did from the final year at the Manhattan, a sense of gathering disaster. Nothing went exactly right. There was not even a resplendent exception like the *Elektra* of Hammerstein's last year in New York opera. *Don Quichotte* probably was the best received of the novelties, actually bringing cheers at the end of the last act, perhaps because this act has the best music in the score. Yet even this work, in spite of its novelty in London, in spite of its "wonderful stage pictures" and fine performances, its warm reviews and first-night cheers, brought in nothing at the box office to justify its great cost. Hammerstein gave it eight performances, and is on record as saying that the *première* itself brought in only £85, which by the eighth performance had dwindled to £51 for the entire house (this undoubtedly means exclusive of the subscriptions, as his box-office figures always did).

Felice Lyne quarreled with Hammerstein in mid-season, and her roles were usually sung by Victoria Fer afterward. As the story goes, Miss Lyne was kept waiting for a rehearsal by the absence of the conductor, went looking for him, and found him in the Old Man's office. The conductor explained that he had been summoned by Hammerstein. Miss Lyne slapped Hammerstein's face and departed; her contract was fulfilled by the required payments, but she could not sing in any other opera house until it was completed.

There is no question that Hammerstein was growing more and more short-tempered, nervous, and anxious. It is difficult to imagine now what a London season of those days, before the First World War, was like—how many things were going on at once, how stupendous was the prestige of Covent Garden, how rooted in conservatism and habit were the British upper classes. His first season had been, in the London language of the day, "out of season," which means that he did not suffer from the heavy competition of innumerable large parties, court ceremonies, Covent Garden opera, and other events that occurred only in the spring and summer. A court ball in June might coincide with two or three recitals of the first importance (Casals or Paderewski, for instance), while forty or fifty theaters were going full tilt and Destinn and Caruso were singing *Madama Butterfly* at Covent Garden. This was the most ferocious competition an opera manager new to London could possibly encounter, and the chances are that Hammerstein did not know how ferocious it could be until it happened. In all probability, he did not take into account the fact that "the London season," because of its brevity, was far more crowded with events of interest than similar "seasons" elsewhere.

2. The Royal Visit

Nor could Hammerstein have foreseen the supreme importance of the Court. When he realized it, he made attempts, as his friends did, to get the King and Queen into his theater. He succeeded only once. It was a matinee performance arranged for one of Queen Mary's favorite charities.

The famous story that then arose, and was told throughout London and elsewhere, was that Hammerstein greeted His Majesty with: "Pleased to meet you, King."

What actually happened was that Hammerstein awaited the King at the ordinary entrance of the theater, where it had been indicated that Their Majesties preferred to enter. The royal entrance, never used, had an effigy of Hammerstein himself over the doorway: this might have had something to do with it. Lyle Andrews, his treasurer, stood beside him holding his hat. The staff had been afraid, it seems, that the Old Man would forget to remove the famous Parisian-style topper, as he wore it through almost all his waking hours wherever he was.

They had forgotten the cigar, however. This remained firmly anchored in Oscar's face when the King and Queen punctually appeared before him. He stretched out his hand and said: "How are you, King? I'm glad to see you."

This does not seem to have disturbed King George; perhaps he had expected it. He took Hammerstein's hand and said: "I'm delighted to meet you, Mr. Hammerstein. I admire your theater very much." A similar exchange took place with Queen Mary.

It is said that Hammerstein never saw anything funny in this episode, including his failure to remove the cigar from his mouth. If so, it is but one more example of his quite native and deep-seated refusal to accept the customs of the country.

And, of course, such a refusal meant more in 1912 by far than it would mean today. London before the First World War was apparently a different world from the London of any subsequent period. One survivor from those days said to me, years later: "Oh, if you didn't know London before 1914, you can't know London at all." It was a time of the most tremendous wealth and power, when the forms of an old, deeply respected monarchy had remained unaltered for generations; the aristocracy had revolved about this monarchy for a long time, but especially again since the death of Queen Victoria, whose secluded life was succeeded by the brilliance of society under King Edward VII. The Edwardian day was now also over, but its tone remained until it was killed by the war. Hammerstein's reception of the King could have made no difference at all to the King, but it probably caused a considerable flurry among the very persons upon whom any opera house would be obliged to rely for patronage.

It was, however, Hammerstein's way, and no other way would have been natural to him. For him to wait in the ordinary manner to be presented, and then to make a bow, and wait until the King had spoken to him first—all of which he had undoubtedly been instructed to do, and more besides—would have been to him like wearing a strait-jacket. After all, wasn't it his theater? Hadn't he built it himself? Was he not the great Oscar Hammerstein? Why should he bow to a king?

All this was in the character of the man, but one wonders about the cigar. Was that not in some way an unnecessary defiance— the extra touch, the little too much? This excess, too, was in his nature, but his habit of underlining his nature, exploiting or exhibiting it, gives a shade of deliberation to every such act.

The story traveled swiftly over London and was repeated in

New York. The Committee for the Welfare of the London Opera House probably did not enjoy it very much.

3. *An Opera by a Noble Patron*

During these months in London Hammerstein was becoming increasingly impatient. His English opera, *The Children of the Don*, had a singular ability to upset him. We may see in this his lifelong aversion to producing anything for others, his refusal to have a "board of directors," his dislike for wealthy patrons, and perhaps also some echoes of his own series of failures as a composer. The story is that at one performance of this work, probably the *première*, Lady Cunard occupied a box with the King of Portugal and a party. Lady Cunard was famous in London for her habit of talking through music. In spite of decades of conspicuous devotion to opera, she did abstract her attention from the stage a good deal for the greater interest of her own remarks. Similar incidents occurred ten and even twenty years later, but without Hammerstein's Draconian solution. He grew steadily more irritable and angry as he heard the chatter and laughter from the box, just above where he sat in the wings. No doubt something of the same kind had happened before, and by this time he knew that his days in London were numbered anyhow. He sent for an attendant and gave positive orders for a message to Lady Cunard and her party: "Mr. Hammerstein requests you to leave his theater at once." They did so, of course, and never returned.

The Children of the Don could only have been produced because its librettist was a very rich man who might yet save the London Opera. Lord Howard de Walden had written a long dramatic poem on ancient Welsh or British mythology, in extremely high-flown language, during the course of which hardly any action took place on the stage. This was set to music by Josef Holbrooke, a composer of the ripest post-Wagnerian music employing a vast orchestra that enabled him to revel in "every conceivable complexity," in the words of *The Times*.

The opera was prepared with great care, had ample rehearsal, was staged by Coini and conducted by Artur Nikisch, one of the reigning conductors of the time. Its first performance took place

June 15, and *The Times* on the following day said: "This production has probably been the most severe blow which the cause of struggling English opera has sustained for many years."

The review continues later:

"There is nothing even to stimulate an enquiry as to what it is all about. The words are declaimed in such a way that one often catches quite unimportant details with unforgettable distinctness, while the real turning points of the story are allowed to drift past smothered in orchestration or so badly accented as to be inaudible. More than once Math, the Druid priest, insisted upon the family relationship between himself and Gwydion in the words, 'You are my sister's son,' a point which did not matter much to anybody else, yet essential things . . . could only be discovered by reading the book."

When there were calls for the author and composer at the end of this performance, Mr. Coini came forward and announced that they had left the building. Then, said *The Times*, "the audience hastened to follow their admirable example."

This work had already thrown Hammerstein into a bad temper during rehearsal, and its reception by press and public must have been irksome to him above all because he agreed with them. It was at one of these performances, or perhaps at the equally unpopular *Don Quichotte*, that he was asked about "business" and replied:

"Fine, oh, fine! All day long there has been before the box office a continuous line of one!"

The sheer annoyance he felt for *The Children of the Don* led him, with better reason than he had on other occasions, to destroy what was undoubtedly his last chance of substantial support. Lord Howard was rich enough to underwrite another season, and he had many friends. All he wanted, it seems, was one more performance of his opera, which had had four. He approached Hammerstein in the lobby of the opera house and asked how much an additional performance of *The Children of the Don* would cost. Hammerstein snapped at him: "Four thousand pounds!" And without further conversation he turned his back on the startled Maecenas and made his furious way to his own office.

Hammerstein's staff attempted to smooth things over, but there was nothing further to be done. There was even a second quarrel about the scenery of Lord Howard's opera, which apparently the author had paid for but which Hammerstein considered his own property. Oscar got the scenery, which did him no good at all in a New York warehouse, but he never saw Lord Howard again.

4. *Once More Arthur Picks Up the Pieces*

The London season ended on July 15 with a "grand gala" in which various members of the company appeared in their chosen showpieces. The chief applause seems to have gone to Victoria Fer for a brilliant performance of the Mad Scene from Ambroise Thomas's *Hamlet*, which had not been given during the season; the rest of the scenes and excerpts were from the repertoire. In the middle of the evening Hammerstein made his statement.

It is a statement of which we may doubt the full sincerity, as there are plenty of indications that he knew his London career was over. He told the public that he had lost £45,000 in seven months in the effort to give them opera. He said he had known when he started that he would have to present his productions to a public which was operatically uneducated, although musically deserving of the best he could give. He was alone in his enterprise, without associates or backing. He had a largely British organization, with the exception of a few principal artists, and he did not want to disband it. To turn his opera house into a music hall would be a crime, and to a man with his love for his profession, withdrawal was an absolute horror. Therefore he would reopen his theater for opera again next November, and end "when you don't come again."

This statement, so like others he had made in Philadelphia and New York, represented an amalgam of fact, opinion, and hope. The idea of reopening in November was sheer hope, if that. His view of the British public was opinion. His statement of loss was fact.

At this very time Mr. Alfred Rothschild, or his family's bank, was beginning to be restive about the mortgage on the London Opera House. And at the same period Hammerstein had struck up an acquaintance with the South African millionaire Solly Joel, who showed some interest in acquiring the property. We do not know the precise sequence of these events, but it is probable that Hammerstein was preparing a departure, meanwhile hoping that something quite unexpected would enable him to resume production in the following November.

Whatever hope he had—perhaps in Rothschild, perhaps in some other source of beneficence—was disappointed. He cabled his son Arthur to come to London at once. Arthur had taken no part in the London venture, but he obeyed the summons and had the whole enterprise thrust into his hands for liquidation. It was up to him to dispose of the theater, pay off the mortgage and other debts, and clean the slate again if possible. Oscar returned to America as soon as he had deposited this responsibility upon his son. His loss in London was about a million dollars in all, including mortgage and indebtedness, and the tangle of affairs must have been—in view of his methods of business and his lack of records—something more difficult to cut through than all the preceding tangles. However, it was done in the summer of 1912, and "Hammerstein's London Opera House" ceased to be.

If we should ask ourselves why his London career was so brief and disastrous, a sort of telescoped version of his four years in opera in New York, we are forced not only to all those external explanations which have already been given, but also to one central fact: his opera was actually not good enough. Lavish production and skillful stage direction could not take the place of actual musical and dramatic values. There were no masterpieces in the whole repertoire except, perhaps, from Rossini and Verdi. Such works were then completely out of fashion except when given with star-laden casts for vocal display. There was no *Pelléas*, no *Elektra*, there were no singers of the international first rank. He had built a splendid theater, as on previous occasions, and had had nothing to put into it which could justify the effort. His scenery, costumes, and stage direction far surpassed the standards of Covent Garden, but it has been proved innumerable times that *mise en scène* alone never attracts any public to the opera. Thus, even if he had understood England, even if he had known the full rigors of what it meant to oppose Covent Garden, his effort would have come to the same end.

He was an obstinate man in his middle sixties, so inured to this constant struggle that he could not abandon it without also abandoning life. He returned to America with every intention of trying again, in one way or another, in spite of the ban put upon any such attempt by his contract with the Metropolitan. Now the wish was more than ever removed from fulfillment. It remained the irresistible wish to the end.

333

XXXII

The Closing Years

THE BATTLE was to be engaged again. This we might have known from Hammerstein's whole past. He spent some months in relative quiet, working on a new invention for utilizing the stems of tobacco in the making of cigars. His mind was nevertheless busy with various schemes for the production of opera in the United States in some way permitted under his contract with the Metropolitan.

1. One More Opera House

At first he returned to his oft-repeated notion of opera houses in Cleveland, St. Louis, or other cities from which his Metropolitan contract did not ban him. He ran hard up against the fact that such a plan would demand great sums of money and that he had none. He had none at all: his children, agreed that the revenue of the Victoria had been milked quite enough in the past for operatic purposes, had so resolutely tied it up with banks and trust funds that to obtain anything at all from it he had to go through a labyrinth of legalities.

But the Manhattan Opera House was still his, and the leasehold of the Republic Theatre had not yet been transferred to Arthur. His reputation for magic had not deserted him, and he could always conjure up money in one way or another when he had scarcely a dollar in his own pocket.

He returned to living in his rooms over the Victoria Theatre, working on his tobacco invention, making and discarding plans. In the end he determined to challenge the ban on his activity: he would build a magnificent new opera house, ignore the Metropolitan, and go ahead with opera in English. He had been advised by no less a person than Paul Cravath, legal respresentative of the Metropolitan, that opera in English did not come under the prohibition in the agreement.

The building of the Lexington Opera House was a harebrained affair, but to Oscar the architect and acoustical engineer—amateur but successful in both respects—it was a final triumph. When he started out on this theater he had small encouragement from his children or anybody else. He had the inevitable difficulties in raising money, and at one critical moment during the process he signed away the one sure source of revenue for the entire family.

The way of it was this: a "vaudeville war" was in the making between new and old interests. Hammerstein had benefited once before from such a situation, and had extracted from it a form of treaty with the great vaudeville-theater magnates by which the territory from Thirty-fourth to Ninety-sixth streets on the west side of Manhattan Island was his alone. Since then, Martin Beck, at the head of the Orpheum Circuit which stretched across the nation but had no house in New York, had built the Palace Theatre. The rival Keith Circuit, which was paramount in the eastern states, obtained control of this theater, but found itself unable to book its programs properly in view of the previous contract with Hammerstein. Under the circumstances, Keith found it necessary to buy Hammerstein out, and with his Lexington Opera House bogged down in financial troubles before it was even completed, Hammerstein agreed. He was paid $250,000.

But the end of the vaudeville franchise in midtown New York meant the end of the Victoria Theatre. For more than a decade it had ruled alone, the queen of variety in the heart of the city. And for more than a decade it had fed Oscar's dream of opera unstintingly, as well as paying the family's grocery bills. It had already begun to suffer from the growing popularity of films. Now, with the sale of the franchise, it found itself eclipsed by an opulent new neighbor, and its days were numbered.

335

When he signed the death knell of his great variety house Hammerstein was thinking of the Lexington alone, even though he continued to live in his old rooms at the Victoria and do all his work there. He had announced the opening of the Lexington Opera for November 10, 1913, with his usual assurance, but he could not even begin to break ground for the structure until its tenants, the New York Nursery, vacated the premises. In his public pronouncements he said he would have not only an opera house, but also a school to train singers in the singing of English. He declared (and few would contradict him even now) that one reason why English was not an opera language was that singers were never trained to sing it properly; this he would remedy.

"My new house," he said, "will be large enough to seat about three thousand people, and it will be a house for all. There will be no exorbitant prices. I will charge only what I have to. I'm not trying to make money. I'm trying to found an institution dedicated to the service of opera in English."

That the enigmatical Old Man had his mind on something beyond opera in English is obvious: no doubt this was the line to which he would retreat if legally obliged to do so, but at this very time his son Arthur, who was in Europe, was making approaches in Hammerstein's name to a long list of artists whose knowledge of English must have been, to say the least, remote. They included a few who never did go to America, such as Marthe Chenal from Paris and Gemma Bellincioni from Milan, and some like the Spaniard Maria Barrientos, who went to the Metropolitan three years later. There was also a negotiation with Nellie Melba, who had certainly never sung any of her repertoire in English and was a little beyond the age to learn it all anew. From this alone one can see that Hammerstein's real plan was to defy the Metropolitan again on the international scale and on more or less equal terms, as before.

The Metropolitan brought an injunction to put a stop to all this and was upheld by the courts; Hammerstein appealed, of course, and on April 17, 1914, the Appellate Division of the Supreme Court of New York handed down a unanimous decision that put an end to his plans. Until the ten-year contract with the Metropolitan had expired, neither he nor his son Arthur was to engage in the production of opera in New York, in English or in any other language.

The Closing Years

The Lexington Opera House opened on August 22, 1914, as a theater for "motion pictures on a magnificent scale, with organ and chorus music as a feature," under the management of Arthur Hammerstein. The theater was said to have cost $1,225,000 in all, with its equipment and decorations. According to those who later sang there, it was an acoustical marvel. Hammerstein never did give opera there, but others did: Campanini and the Chicago Opera Company gave several seasons in the house, with conspicuous success. It was in the Lexington that Amelita Galli-Curci made her phenomenal debut in New York (1918), creating mob scenes and police interventions like those which had occurred for Tetrazzini just ten years before. The Chicago Opera season at the Lexington opened January 23, 1918, with Mary Garden in *Monna Vanna*, Campanini conducting, and must have given the Old Man the wry satisfaction of having his theater, his company, and his whole achievement thrown into the face of the Metropolitan, contract or no contract.

2. Tragedy in the Family

The spring and summer of 1914 were bitter to Hammerstein for more than professional reasons. Three of his sons died in succession: Abe, Willie, and Harry. He had never been what is called a "family man," and his children hardly knew him until they were adults; he had lived alone by choice and depended upon them, after they were grown, when and as he needed them. His relations with Abe and Harry had been something less than cordial. Indeed, his specific talent for quarreling seems to have been exercised even more with his own children than with strangers. And yet the death of a son, any one of these three, affected him deeply.

How much more, therefore, the death of Willie! It was Willie Hammerstein who had—with Arthur—made his whole opera career possible. Willie, a genius in vaudeville, had made the Victoria Theatre a species of gold mine upon which the whole family could depend, and to which the Old Man turned again and again in time of need. There is no possibility of finding out, or even of guessing, how much of the profits from the Victoria were thrown away on grand opera. It is generally said—as it is in *Show Biz*, by Abel Green and Joe Laurie, Jr., a breezy but authoritative work —that the Victoria earned more than $20,000,000 during its lifetime of seventeen years, and that the net profit was above $5,000,000. Willie Hammerstein, so quiet and thoughtful, apparently so unlike his father, was ingenious beyond any showman except his father in thinking up new attractions, tricks, and publicity stunts; under his hand the Victoria was unique in the country.

But beyond this aspect of Willie as the foundation of his own flamboyant career in opera, Hammerstein had for him a regard that he probably fully realized only in the hour of loss. He saw Willie every day when he was in New York, as his workshop and his home were in the Victoria; Oscar would not use any other quarters. Arthur came and went; Arthur had once made a very good start for himself in the contracting business, until his father sent for him again; and now, since the row over the building of the London Opera, Arthur was well launched on another career as producer of operettas and musical comedies. But Willie was always there, and had been since the days of the Harlem Opera House. His death, which came quite suddenly as a result of Bright's disease, unnerved Hammerstein as hardly anything had been able to do in his long, agitated life.

One day soon after Willie's death a reporter encountered Oscar in the lobby of the Victoria, making his way up to his rooms. He said:

"You know, there never was anyone like Willie. Thirty-seven years I have been in the theatrical business, mostly, of course, connected with music, but Willie knew vaudeville. He knew more about it than any of the others. It was his life; the Victoria Theatre with its sensational acts, its novelties—they were all Willie's. He always thought of something new, of some new trick to play on the public. They liked him and the house better for it.

"In my life I have experienced every great joy, every triumph, every success, every honor that can be won by a man singlehanded; but I have also experienced every sorrow, every disappointment, every grief and every tragedy. But this——"

He went on upstairs.

Willie was only forty-one when he died. He had lived, aside from his theater, a quiet and rather domestic life and was from most points of view as unlike his father as could be imagined. His first marriage, to Alice Nimmo, who died in 1910, was followed by a second marriage to her sister Anna a year later. His sons Oscar II and Reginald were the children of the first marriage. It is beyond doubt that he cherished for his father the same emotions of mingled devotion, fear, and admiration which characterized Arthur. Between them, Arthur and Willie had tried to curb Oscar's extravagance, supply his needs, and help to fulfill his unceasing ambition. It seems to me obvious that both regarded him as a very great man indeed, as many others did, and for this reason were willing to endure and even to support that lifelong obsession which they could not understand.

The Victoria Theatre survived Willie Hammerstein by a year. Hammerstein put Arthur in charge of it, but Arthur was busy with his own productions and had to delegate the authority. The Palace Theatre near by was coming into its own as the capitol of vaudeville; film theaters were rising on all sides; the Victoria was finished. Hammerstein continued to live and work there, struggling with some new inventions in cigar-making which would, he believed, help to finance the opera company he intended to create as soon as his contract with the Metropolitan had elapsed.

There now descended upon him the illness from which he never fully recovered. A septic infection developed in his left foot which necessitated an operation on March 11, 1915. Within two weeks he was back at the Victoria again, hobbling along on crutches. He was furious at this disability, changed the crutches for a cane as soon as he could, and set himself to inventing a sun-machine (a sort of violet-ray lamp), which, he claimed, "cured" his foot in a few weeks. The sore reopened two years later and never healed; although it did not actually cause his death—which, for the sake of diagnosis, was attributed to diabetes—it darkened all his last days and lowered his spirits as nothing else could.

One of the strange things about this complex and contradictory man—so fine in some ways and so blatant in others—is his medical history. He detested doctors and seems to have had no real illnesses throughout his life until he was sixty-seven years old. Once, as we know, he fainted in the street and was compelled to take a rest in a hospital, simply from exhaustion. Once he fainted on the stairs at the Manhattan Opera and sustained some contusions and abrasions from the fall. These are the only instances on record when his energetic physical organism succumbed. And, as is well known, fainting is often a purely nervous or psychological effect of unknown causation. These instances—two fainting fits, one enforced rest—were widely separated in point of time, years between them. Is it possible that he never was ill in all this time? If so, it must have been because of his indomitable spirit, and his history would thus furnish an excellent argument for those who, like Hammerstein, have no faith in medicine or doctors.

3. Deepening Twilight

In this same year he lost both the Lexington Opera House and the Victoria Theatre—the first for a reported price of $820,000, although it had cost more than a million. The Victoria was transferred to a company that wished to tear it down and rebuild in the form of a super-palace for super-films. Oscar seems to have fought to the end to keep from signing the papers that lost him the Victoria, and even after he had done so—even while the wreckers were at work on the building—he retained his office there, his "machine-shop" as he called it.

It was in this darkening period that he was visited one day by Max Rabinoff, who was at that time managing the Boston-Pavlova Opera Company. This combined the ballet of Anna Pavlova with an international opera troupe containing many of Hammerstein's former songbirds; Felice Lyne was one, Zenatello another.

Hammerstein eyed his younger friend severely and asked if he intended to continue as a producer of opera. Rabinoff replied with enthusiasm that he certainly was.

Hammerstein said: "Mike, I like you, and I'm going to give you a piece of advice. You keep on giving opera and in a few years your foot will be as bad as mine."

The liquidation of the two theaters brought enough cash, after the payment of obligations, to give Hammerstein some respite—which, of course, he did not want, but which his son Arthur, who negotiated the sales, thought he should be guaranteed. He acquired a house at Atlantic Highlands, in New Jersey. Here he was interviewed in the summer of 1915 by Karl K. Kitchin for the Hearst papers.

The Closing Years

"I'm taking my first vacation in forty years and I'm not enjoying it," Hammerstein said. "You see, I never learned to loaf. If I had, this enforced idleness would not be so hard to endure. For forty years I worked from eight o'clock in the morning until after midnight. I realize now that I should have learned to play as well.

"Nature has made many mistakes, but I think her greatest mistake was in failing to equip us with a switch by which we could turn off our thoughts. We can say 'I don't want to see,' shut our eyes and we don't see. We can say 'I don't want to hear,' stop our ears and we don't hear. But we can't say 'I don't want to think' and stop thinking.

"And that is one reason why I'm not enjoying my vacation. I can't stop thinking."

Kitchin describes the hearty voice and manner, contradicted by the "tell-tale crutches" lying beside the chair. When the Old Man removed his hat—"not the famous one, but a black Fedora"—the interviewer could see that his sparse hair was now snow-white. They were sitting on the porch of the house at Atlantic Highlands, and Hammerstein waved at the view.

"It is beautiful, isn't it?" he asked. "I suppose I ought to be happy here, but I'm not. I'd rather be back on Broadway in my machine-shop at the Victoria. Vacations don't suit me. . . . I never learned how to relax. Now, when it is too late, I realize my mistake."

The interviewer said he had always supposed Mr. Hammerstein to get his play and pleasure out of his work. The impresario agreed and said that when he was tired out from a long day at the opera house he used to go home to his rooms in the Victoria and work for hours with machines. He thought so much work had been, just the same, a cumulative burden, and mused over it a bit: "And for what?" he asked. Then, straightening up, he declared:

"This I do know. I have found my greatest happiness in my work. The so-called pleasures of life do not bring real happiness. A man must find his happiness in his work—in accomplishing things. So, after all, I guess we'd better not worry about what it is all for."

4. A Late Marriage

Hammerstein's last marriage, to Emma Swift, took place in January, 1915. She was beautiful—on this all witnesses agree—and kind; he fell in love with her with all the vehement concentration of a man of sixty-eight clutching at life as it departs. She was a great deal younger, and no doubt her motives in marrying were not of the same category as his.

They had met on a ship, with an introduction from a newspaper reporter, and Hammerstein knew scarcely anything about her when they married. It was only after his illness began that she grew impatient with him and, according to one observer of those days, downright brutal. Her age is uncertain, but must have been at least thirty-five years less than his, and for a young woman of her beauty and her taste for life there must have been a grievous devolution in the events of the next few years. She wanted, as we understand, the great world; she had married the great Hammerstein for that as much as for anything else. He was famous and she evidently thought he was also very rich; he was going to produce opera, build theaters, work marvels; and instead of all the glitter of the life thus presented to her avid imagination, she found herself in a very few months transformed into the nurse and companion of a dying man. There is much evidence that she resented this bitterly, as a shabby trick of fate, and her discontent in the last years was wreaked on him as much as on those who attempted to come near him.

They lived at Atlantic Highlands, and Hammerstein's enforced idleness undoubtedly did no good to his temper. His son Arthur tells of bringing Rudolf Friml to the house once in the summer of 1917 to play the piano for the Old Man. Friml was then composing musical comedies and operettas that were usually produced by Arthur. Hammerstein was delighted at first, and went to the piano himself after a while to play some of his own music. When he had done, Friml succeeded him at the piano and played the same pieces, only giving them enough musicianship and pianistic skill to make them sound better than they were. The Old Man grasped his cane and helped himself up from his chair; then he shook his cane at Friml and said: "Rudolph, get away from that piano! You're ruining my music!"

There was one occasion when Hammerstein appeared in public as a musician during these years, and we may be sure it gave him enormous pleasure. It was an evening organized at the Hippodrome, on March 26, 1916, for and by a considerable number of American composers, who conducted their own works. The Hippodrome, Thompson and Dundy's vast auditorium dating from the time of Hammerstein's own Manhattan Opera House, was then at the height of its popularity for spectacles, concerts, and even opera. When Hammerstein hobbled across the stage, there was a storm of applause and the whole audience stood up. John Philip Sousa, introducing him, said he had "done more for music than any other man in America," and at another point called him "the Columbus of music." Oscar then advanced to the orchestra and conducted his own "Louise Waltz," dedicated to Mary Garden.

His health seemed to get better in 1918 and early 1919, and he came to New York more often. Since the Victoria was gone, he had to have another office. He found one first in Forty-second Street and afterward, for a somewhat longer period, in Thirty-eighth Street. In each case he had his cigar-making machinery installed in the floor above his office, and of course his office also always contained sleeping accommodation. He was never really well at this time, and his limp indicated the presence of incessant pain, but those who saw him in the last year found his spirits rising again, his style of conversation much as before.

There are a dozen variations of his recurrent statements—printed quite widely at the time—of what he was going to do when his contract with the Metropolitan was terminated. He was hesitating between "ten-dollar opera and ten-cent opera," a choice that would have had a great effect on the blank contracts which strewed his rooms. He spoke also of giving opera "all the year round," and such was his persuasive magic that those who heard him say so believed him. Perhaps he believed in it himself. He had in mind the usual great international repertoire, but he also had one opera from Czechoslovakia and one that was in Yiddish. And sometimes, perhaps, he talked for the sake of talking.

Still, the time was drawing near when he would be free to give opera again if he wished, and most of the interested public now began to regard his plans as likely to materialize.

It was in 1918, after the Chicago Opera opened its season in his Lexington Theatre, that Mary Garden came to see him in his office. This was known at once—nothing Garden did in those days was unknown—and gave added weight to the stories of his return to opera. For him it must have been a strange meeting, as Garden had played so decisive a part in his life and then had vanished from it. She had never ceased to regret him, and never has since then (she has told me so). She was at that time in a position of the most blazing celebrity throughout the country: these were the years when she was quite commonly called "Our Mary" in the press everywhere. She had been famous in Paris before she came to Hammerstein ten years before; she had grown even more famous to the country at large after she left him, through long tours and the accumulation of time. At this stage of her career she could not move without being questioned by reporters. They asked her whether her visit to Hammerstein meant that she was going to sing for him again when he returned to opera.

"If Mr. Hammerstein ever wants me to sing for him again," she said, "I will be glad to do it for nothing."

5. End of the Magnificent Oscar

In July, 1919, Harry Rosenberg, Hammerstein's brother-in-law, was driving over from Long Branch, where he lived, to see the Old Man at Atlantic Highlands. Passing the railway station on his way to the house, he glanced across at it and was startled to see the unmistakable top hat, the Hammerstein silk hat of song and story, lying upside down beside a bench on the station platform. He stopped his car and went to investigate. He found Hammerstein lying unconscious where he had fallen, behind the bench.

Rosenberg got him into the car and drove straight to the Lenox Hill Hospital in New York. When Arthur, his only surviving son, got to the hospital, Hammerstein was conscious and told him what had happened. After a dispute of some kind with Emma, acrimonious as they all were, the lady had taken a pail of cold water and thrown it over him as he lay in bed. He got up and dressed at once, and with the aid of a cane was able to hobble down to the railroad station. The effort was too much for him and he collapsed. At this moment he gave orders that Emma was not to be admitted to his room, but by the next day she had made her way in (as he told Arthur also) and was there most of the time for the next two weeks.

On August 1, 1919, a Saturday, at about half past seven in the evening, Hammerstein died. He had been in a coma for days. Both Arthur and Emma were in the room when he died; Rose and Stella arrived soon afterward.

His death produced a spate of obituary and elegiac writing in the newspapers. The sober paragraphs of the *Times* appeared, as was rare indeed then, on its front page. Among other things it was said:

"His death removes from the public eye one of the most interesting personalities the melting pot of America has produced. Manifestations of his many-sided genius were so varied that had he shunned the spotlight of publicity, a claim even Mr. Hammerstein in his most modest moment would not have made, it would have sought him out. For his was one of those seemingly charmed lives in which the most insignificant episode reflected some ray of unusual interest."

This and most of the other newspapers, reviewing his life, spoke of his "delicious accent," his charm and wit, his story-making quality. A note of genuine regret pervaded them all.

Carl Van Vechten wrote an essay on Hammerstein not long afterward which he called "an epitaph." He, too, spoke of the accent, the stories, the wit, and the indomitable character. He recalled a good many of the significant moments of that long career and of his own acquaintance, as a music reporter, with the impresario during his opera days and afterward. The essay begins:

"Some years ago, passing by the northwest corner of Forty-second Street and Seventh Avenue, I observed a short stubby figure of a man with a thin greyish Mephistophelean and slightly rakish beard lounging under the lintel of one of the doorways of the old Victoria Theatre. He wore a morning-coat and grey trousers and large soft-leather shoes. His toes were turned out at a wide angle. His linen was immaculate. On his head reposed a very French top-hat and in his mouth, which frequently assumed a quizzical expression, was a large black cigar. The eccentricity of the figure was apparent at first glance, but magnetism and a certain Napoleonic magnificence raced in as second impressions. It was my first week in New York and I was curious: I asked another newspaper man for a label.

" 'That,' replied my friend in his most satirical manner, 'that is Oscar Hammerstein.' "

After reminiscences covering the years, Van Vechten's epitaph concluded:

"It was not in Oscar Hammerstein, I think, to inspire affection. His way was too big, his egoism too colossal, his genius too evident. These qualities made men stand a little away from him. A few, indeed, disliked him; a few, alas, derided him. To some, even, who did not know him, he was a trifle ridiculous. He was never ridiculous, however, to those who knew him; his dignity was too perfect; he was even, in a sense, magnificent! He could and did command admiration, admiration for the things he accomplished, more than that, admiration for the way he failed.

"He was not, as a matter of fact, what is called a good loser. He groaned and moaned over loss, but in a few days the board was erased and with a clean piece of chalk he was drawing a new diagram, making a new plan. I admired him; more than that, I liked him. He was a figure, he lived his own life; he fashioned it sometimes with difficulty but he always carved it out. He was an artist; he was a genius. I have met few men who have seemed to me as great. Some day, I hope, his statue will stand in Times Square. He would like that."

At eleven on the morning of August 4 Hammerstein's funeral service was held in Temple Emanuel with Rabbi Joseph Silverman officiating. It was a brief service, consisting of a scripture reading, a short prayer, two songs sung by John McCormack, and a eulogy. The temple was filled to capacity with people from everywhere in the world of New York. The honorary pallbearers were the principal theater owners and managers of the day—Belasco, George Cohan, the two Shuberts, Mr. Brady, Mr. Woods, and Mr. Gest—along with Hammerstein's faithful treasurer, Lyle Andrews, and his brother-in-law Harry Rosenberg.

John McCormack now, like so many of the singers Hammerstein had brought to America, was, although still very young, a national institution as well as the possessor of a voice unlike any other. Its moonlit quality remained and still remains in the memories of all who ever heard it. He was representing those, and they were many, who owed their fame and fortune in this new world to Hammerstein. Most of them were in Europe or elsewhere, not in New York, at this time of year. John sang for all of them. I find it both characteristic and appropriate that what he chose to sing in the temple for the Old Man was "The Lost Chord."

INDEX

Index

Index

Calvé, Emma, 66, 85, 123, 160, 164, 173-176, 179, 186, 214, 239, 240
Camille, 59
Campanari, Leandro, 159, 219
Campanini, Cleofonte, 89, 130, 132, 135, 139, 144ff, 157ff, 170, 171, 177, 192, 199, 201, 208, 213, 216ff, 240, 259ff, 273, 277-280, 303, 326, 337
Campanini, Italo, 72, 132
Carasa (tenor), 282
Carmen, 46, 51, 58, 59, 71, 85, 136, 137, 138, 159, 160-161, 172, 173, 174, 175, 191, 212, 218, 223, 224, 235, 239, 261, 267, 293
Carmencita, La, 77
Carnarvon, Countess of, 317
Carnegie Hall, New York, 68
Carré, Albert, 193, 199, 202, 203, 206
Carter, Mrs. Leslie, 60, 90, 108
Caruso, Enrico, 10, 125, 126, 131, 136ff, 156, 157, 166ff, 178, 228, 231, 232, 240ff, 258, 261, 272, 275, 280, 290, 294, 318, 319, 327
Casals, Pablo, 327
Casino Theatre, New York, 63, 64
Cavalieri, Lina, 157, 167, 196, 206, 207, 266-267, 281-282, 287, 288, 292, 293, 299, 322, 323
Cavalleria Rusticana, 60, 62-66, 85, 124, 172, 174, 175, 192, 293; reviews, 64-65
Cayvan, Georgia, 45
Cellier, Alfred, 72
Chaliapin, Feodor, 178, 196, 206, 207, 233, 241, 323, 324
Chanler, Robert Astor, 281
Chapman, Captain, 93

Chaplin, Charles, 113
Chenal, Marthe, 336
Cherry Sisters, 92, 97
Chevalier, Albert, 77
Chicago: Auditorium Theatre, 56, 123, 129; Opera Company, 303, 337, 344; World's Fair, 93
Chickering Hall, New York, 68-69
Children of the Don, The, 321, 325, 329; review, 330
Church Clubs, Federation of, 188
Circuit Court, United States, 153
Cisneros, Eleanora de, 131, 138, 142, 161, 167, 216, 218, 224
Clarke, Payson, 64, 65, 71
Clayton, Bessie, 120
Clément, Edmond, 288
Cleveland, Grover, 68
Clive, Carver B., 96
Cloches de Corneville, Les, 286, 326
Coghlan, Rose, 59, 60
Cohan, George M., 346
Coini, Jacques, 133, 266, 311, 315, 329, 330
Collini (singer), 58
Colombini (tenorino), 260
Columbus Theatre, New York, 55, 57-60, 73, 111
Concert Hall, Olympia Theatre, 84, 85, 90, 94
Connors, Chuck, 95
Conried, Heinrich, 39, 124-127, 133, 135, 140, 141, 151, 154, 157, 166ff, 177ff, 192, 196, 206, 213, 230, 231, 241, 268
Conried Light Opera Company, 57

Index

Index

Index

Index

Index

356

Index

Index

Index

Index

Index

Index

Index

ABOUT THE AUTHOR

LONG BEFORE *he became one of the world's most brilliant foreign correspondents, Vincent Sheean started his lifelong career as an opera* aficionado. *While an undergraduate at the University of Chicago, he began ushering for the great performances presented under the leadership of Mary Garden, then the director of the company. It was a company composed largely of singers originally imported by Oscar Hammerstein, the subject of this book. Thus, even as a very young man, Mr. Sheean was unconsciously preparing to write the biography of America's most colorful impresario.*

The love affair between Sheean and grand opera has been common knowledge among his friends ever since. His penchant for being at the right time in the right place as foreign correspondent has been equally common knowledge among the general public—how he was in Vienna when Hitler moved in, in Paris when it fell, in England at the time of the Blitz, at Wake Island before the Japanese attacked, in the garden prayer meeting when Gandhi was assassinated. He has been equally Johnny-on-the-spot with musical events, especially operatic ones, and he counts among his closest friends many of the stars who inhabit the lists of company members in the leading opera houses of the world.

Mr. Sheean is the author of many books, the best known of which, perhaps, is Personal History, *an autobiographical account of his experiences as a foreign correspondent. He is at present engaged in writing his musical reminiscences, which will be a personal history of his experiences with music and musicians.*